ASSESSMENT PACK
with Audio CD and Test Generating CD-ROM

4

FOCUS
ON
GRAMMAR
AN INTEGRATED SKILLS APPROACH

THIRD EDITION

JOAN JAMIESON
CAROL A. CHAPELLE

WITH
LESLIE GRANT
BETHANY GRAY
XIANGYING JIANG
HSIN-MIN LIU
KEVIN ZIMMERMAN

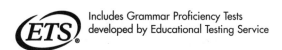

Includes Grammar Proficiency Tests developed by Educational Testing Service

PEARSON
Longman

Focus on Grammar 4: An Integrated Skills Course
Assessment Pack

Pearson Education, 10 Bank Street, White Plains, NY 10606

Staff credits: The people who made up the *Focus on Grammar 4: An Integrated Skills Course, Assessment Pack* team, representing editorial, production, design, and manufacturing, are listed below:

Rhea Banker
Nancy Blodgett
Elisabeth Carlson
Christine Edmonds
Margot Gramer
Stacey Hunter
Laura Le Dréan
Wendy Long
Michael Mone
Linda Moser
Julie Schmidt

ISBN: 0-13-193139-3

Printed in the United States of America
5 6 7 8 9 10—BAH—10 09

Contents

Introduction

The *Focus on Grammar 4 Assessment Pack* includes the following assessment tools to help you determine students' grammar proficiency level and monitor their progress and achievement in the *Focus on Grammar* course.

In addition to the tools listed below, a separately packaged *Focus on Grammar Placement Test* (ISBN 0-13-199437-9) is also available. To obtain a copy of the *Placement Test,* contact your local Longman ELT specialist.

FOG Student Book Assessment Tools

- Part Diagnostic and Achievement Tests
- Unit Achievement Tests
- Audio CD with the listening portions of the Diagnostic and Achievement Tests

Supplementary Assessment Tools

- Two ETS Grammar Proficiency Tests (Levels 4 and 5)
- Test Generating CD-ROM

You can find detailed descriptions of each type of assessment tool, as well as instructions on administering and scoring the tests, in the "General Information" sections that precede the test forms.

About the Authors

Joan Jamieson, Project Director, is a Professor in the Applied Linguistics program in the English Department at Northern Arizona University. She received her Ph.D. from the University of Illinois at Urbana-Champaign. Dr. Jamieson is the author of several publications on English as a Second Language assessment and computer-assisted language learning. She has collaborated with Pearson Longman and Carol Chapelle in the past on several projects, including *Longman English Assessment* and the testing program for *Longman English Interactive*.

Carol A. Chapelle, Project Director, is a Professor of TESL/Applied Linguistics at Iowa State University. She received her Ph.D. from the University of Illinois at Urbana-Champaign. She is the author of *Computer applications in second language acquisition: Foundations for teaching, testing and research* (Cambridge University Press, 2001), *English language learning and technology: Lectures on teaching and research in the age of information and communication technology.* (John Benjamins Publishing, 2003), and *ESOL tests and testing: A resource for teachers and program administrators* (TESOL Publications, 2005). Dr. Chapelle was until recently the editor of *TESOL Quarterly.* She has collaborated with Joan Jamieson and Pearson Longman in the past on several projects, including *Longman English Assessment* and the testing program for *Longman English Interactive.*

Project Staff

The following people worked on the development of the tests under the guidance of Joan Jamieson and Carol Chapelle:

Leslie Grant, Ph.D., Northern Arizona University

Bethany Gray, MA-TESL student, Iowa State University

Xiangying Jiang, Ph.D. student, Northern Arizona University

Hsin-min Liu, MA-TESL, Iowa State University

Kevin Zimmerman, MA-TESL, Brigham Young University

and

Liza Armstrong, MA-TESL, Northern Arizona University

Maja Grgurovic, Ph.D. student, Iowa State University

James McCormick, Ph.D., Michigan State University

Erin Kate Murphy, MA-TESL, Northern Arizona University

Pamela Pearson, MA-TESL student, Iowa State University

Lia Plakans, Ph.D. student, University of Iowa

Kornwipa Poonpon, Ph.D. student, Northern Arizona University

Kerri Quinn, MA-TESL, Northern Arizona University

Betsy Tremmel, MA student, Iowa State University

Part Diagnostic Tests, Unit Achievement Tests, and Part Achievement Tests

General Information

Overview

The *Focus on Grammar* Part Diagnostic, Unit Achievement, and Part Achievement Tests have set a new standard in ELT grammar teaching and testing. Developed under the direction of applied linguists Joan Jamieson and Carol A. Chapelle, these tests

- are manageable in length and easy to administer and score;
- accurately reflect the material presented in the Grammar in Context, Grammar Charts and Notes, and Focused Practice sections of the course;
- offer a sufficient number of items to assess students' knowledge of each grammar point;
- include a wide variety of item types;
- provide a powerful remediation tool.

About the Test Development

These tests have been carefully developed so that the weighting and distribution of test items mirror those of the Student Book content. For example, if 40 percent of the items in a unit practice the simple present and 60 percent of the items practice the present progressive, then the Unit Achievement Test maintains the same balance. The Part Diagnostic and Achievement Tests additionally reflect the distribution of items across the units in a part. For example, if one unit in a part has 110 practice items, and the second unit in the part has 53 practice items, then the Part Diagnostic and Achievement Tests maintain the same balance.

Using the Tests for Remediation Purposes

Codes provided in the Answer Key help you determine what grammar points students might be having difficulty with. In the Unit Achievement tests, each answer has a code that refers to one or more of the Grammar Notes or to the Grammar Chart. In the Part Diagnostic and Part Achievement tests, each answer has a code that refers to the unit where the item was presented. By referring to these codes, both you and the student can try to pinpoint grammar points that are causing confusion or proving to be difficult.

EXAMPLE:

Item 5 in Exercise 2 of the Unit 14 Achievement Test has the code N5 . This means that the item is testing the grammar point associated with Grammar Note 5 in the Student Book: "*When* and *where* can also be used to begin adjective clauses. *Where* refers to a place. *When* or *that* refers to a time. Note that you can leave out *when* and *that* in identifying adjective clauses." If a student answered this item incorrectly, that student may need more help with this grammar point.

NOTE: If a test item has two codes separated by a comma (for example, N1, N2 or U1, U2), that item is testing two grammar points or two units.

Test Purpose and Design

The **Part Diagnostic Tests** help you determine how well students know the material they are about to study in the next part of the Student Book. Since the material they are about to study is usually new, students often score low on these tests.

Each Part Diagnostic Test takes 50 minutes and includes about 60 items. The test begins with a listening exercise, includes several contextualized grammar exercises, and ends with an editing exercise.

The **Unit Achievement Tests** help you assess students' knowledge of the specific grammatical topics presented in the unit. If students have mastered the material presented in the unit, they should answer most of the questions correctly. The codes provided in the Answer Key help you determine what grammar topics students may need to review.

Each Unit Achievement Test takes 30 minutes and includes about 30 items. The test begins with a listening exercise, includes two to three contextualized grammar exercises, and ends with an editing exercise.

The **Part Achievement Tests** help you determine how well students have mastered the material they have studied in that part of the student book. If students have mastered the material presented in the part, they should answer most of the questions correctly. The codes provided in the Answer Key help you determine what units students may need to review.

Each Part Achievement Test is identical in structure to the Part Diagnostic Test for the part, including the same number of items and testing the same grammar points with equal balance and weighting. By comparing a student's results on the Part Diagnostic Test and on the Part Achievement Test, you can determine how much students have learned.

Administering the Tests

Before administering a test:

- Make photocopies of the test form.
- Set up your CD player in the testing room and check the volume.
- Check the track list on the inside back cover for which track you will need to play.

The listening section in the Part Diagnostic, Unit Achievement, and Part Achievement Tests is the first section of the test so that it may be administered to all students at the same time without interfering with the other parts of the test. When students are ready to begin the test, play the audio CD and have students listen and answer the questions. You should play each track two times.

After students have completed the listening section, stop the CD and ask students to work on the remaining sections of the test.

Scoring the Tests

To determine a student's score on the tests, add up the number of questions the student answered correctly, using the Answer Key on pages 253–290. You may also wish to subtract the number incorrect from the total number of items. The total number of items for each test is shown on the first page of the test.

To determine the percentage score, first divide the number correct by the total number of items; then, multiply that proportion by 100. (Use the total number of items on the test, not the number of items that a student answered.)

EXAMPLE:

The Part VI Achievement Test includes 60 items.
A student answered 47 items correctly.

$47 \div 60 = .78 \rightarrow .78 \times 100 = 78$

The student's percentage score is 78%.

A scoring box is provided on the first page of each test to record the student's score.

PART I Diagnostic Test

70 Items
Score: _____

1 | LISTENING: AN AWARD-WINNING NEWS CORRESPONDENT

A. 🎧 *Listen to this radio station announcement about an accomplished journalist. Complete the announcement by writing the words that you hear. You will hear the recording two times.*

Radio News International proudly _____*announces*_____ the addition of its newest
0.

correspondent, Wesley Hammond. Mr. Hammond _____ his journalism degree
1.

from Wimbley College and began his journalism career in Los Angeles in 1979. He

_____ briefly as a local sports announcer there before he started reporting news
2.

internationally with Urban News Systems in 1982. In 1985, he _____ an award for
3.

the stories he _____ the previous year about teachers who _____ a
4.   5.

difference in Rio de Janeiro schools. He was working in China when the Tiananmen Square

protests _____ place in 1989. In 1990, he was honored with the Arnold Gutman
6.

award for the stories he _____ about this event.
7.

Mr. Hammond _____ to Radio News International as a guest correspondent
8.

throughout his career, but he now _____ us as a permanent senior correspondent.
9.

This week he has been covering the elections in India, and he will return to our studios on

Monday.

Mr. Hammond is currently finishing a book called *From Where I* _____. In
10.

his book, he shares some of the stories that have made him one of the most recognized names

in broadcast journalism. He lives in New York and has one daughter, Samantha, who

_____ currently _____ in a Broadway production.
11.

B. *Reread the announcement. Then read each statement and circle* **T** *(true) or* **F** *(false).*

(T) **F**   0. Mr. Hammond graduated from college before becoming a journalist.

T **F**   1. He was living in China in 1989.

T **F**   2. He has won two awards.

T **F**   3. Mr. Hammond has always worked for a newspaper.

T **F**   4. He covered the election in India last year.

T **F**   5. He is writing a book.

T **F**   6. His book is about the stories he plans to write.

T **F**   7. Mr. Hammond worked in New York in 1989.

T **F**   8. His daughter is also a journalist.

---

2 | A GROWING FAMILY

Read this passage about a family. Complete the passage with the correct verb forms. Write the letter of the best answer on each line.

It was 2001, and I _____*a*_____ (a. had been living b. were living c. am living d. live) here in Alaska for
  0.

a year. I met my wife, Carol, while I _____ (a. was working b. work c. have worked d. am working) at
  1.

a restaurant. A friend of ours _____ (a. was introducing b. introduced c. had been introducing
  2.

d. introduces) us. When I met Carol, I _____ (a. had known b. know c. was knowing d. knew) that I
  3.

liked her a lot. We started dating. We often _____ (a. went b. gone c. are going d. were going) on
  4.

long walks and talked. Eventually, I _____ (a. had been buying b. was buying c. bought d. buy) her
  5.

an engagement ring. We _____ (a. dated b. had been dating c. are dating d. have been dating) for
  6.

three years when I asked her to marry me. By the time we got married, we _____ (a. had made
  7.

b. make c. are making d. have been making) lots of plans for our life together.

After the wedding, we _____ (a. are deciding b. decide c. had been deciding d. decided) to move
  8.

to a bigger apartment. Our son, Eric, was born a year after we _____ (a. move b. had moved
  9.

c. were moving d. had been moving). We _____ (a. are living b. live c. had been living d. have been living)
  10.

in the apartment for about a year and a half when I began to look for another job.

Name _____ Date _____

Now I _____ (a. start b. have started c. had started d. was starting) a new job at a bank. I
    11.

_____ (a. earn b. had earned c. earned d. earning) more money than I did at the restaurant. Carol
  12.

_____ (a. had stayed b. was staying c. stays d. had been staying) at home with Eric. Now Eric
  13.

_____ (a. had been starting b. has started c. had started d. was starting) to walk, and he _____
  14.   **15.**

(a. had been talking b. was talking c. has talking d. is talking) a little bit. We _____ (a. had read b. were
                                                                                        16.

reading c. read d. had been reading) books to him every night.

Recently we _____ (a. talks b. have talking c. talking d. have been talking) about having another
                17.

baby. We _____ (a. are planning b. have planning c. had been planned d. plans) to buy a house next
          18.

year because we'll definitely need a bigger place for our growing family.

3 | A SMART DECISION

*Read this conversation about Tina and her decision to sell her car. Complete the
conversation by writing the simple present, simple past, present progressive, present
perfect, present perfect progressive, past progressive, past perfect, or past perfect
progressive form of each verb. Some items may have more than one possible answer.*

AMY: Tina! _____*Do*_____ you _____*want*_____ a ride?
                                  0. (want)

TINA: Oh sure! Thanks. I _____ just _____ to run to the store.
                                                    1. (go)

AMY: I'm heading that way, too. _____ you _____ a car?
                                                        2. (not have)

TINA: No. I _____ a couple of years ago that I _____ too much to
              3. (decide)   **4. (pay)**

keep it. My car _____ some problems, and I _____ into debt,
                  5. (have)   **6. (get)**

so I _____ it. I _____ since then, and I _____ a
      7. (sell)   **8. (walk)**   **9. (save)**

lot of money. Plus, I think I've become healthier since I _____ walking.
                                                              10. (start)

AMY: I'll bet. But how _____ you _____ to places that are too far
                                                    11. (get)

to walk to?

TINA: I ride my bike or _____ the bus.
                          12. (take)

AMY: It sounds like selling your car was a smart decision.

TINA: Well, for me it really was.

4 | WANTED: DRUMMER

*Read this interview with a possible drummer for Tim's band. Complete the interview by
writing the simple present, simple past, present progressive, present perfect, present perfect
progressive, past progressive, past perfect, or past perfect progressive form of each verb.
Some items may have more than one possible answer.*

TIM: ____*Have*____ you ever ____*been*____ in a band before?
0. (be)

BRIAN: I _____ in a couple rock bands. I _____ for three years
1. (be)   2. (play)

with a band called Stereoscope. We _____ an album just after I
3. (record)

_____ the drummer. The last band I was in was called Groove-a-phone. We
4. (become)

_____ the United States and Canada twice, but we _____
5. (tour)   6. (not make)

any money. I left when I found out that our manager _____ from us.
7. (steal)

TIM: Why _____ you _____ to play with us?
8. (want)

BRIAN: Well, I came to your concert last night after I _____ your ad for a
9. (see)

drummer in the paper. I liked what I heard, and to tell you the truth, I

_____ work.
10. (need)

TIM: Well, we _____ quite a bit, and we _____ a little money.
11. (work)   12. (make)

Have a seat at the drums. Let's play something together and see how you do.

5 | EDITING: NEW BAND

*Read this magazine article about the rock band Exile. There are 10 mistakes in the verbs.
The first mistake is already corrected. Find and correct 9 more. (Note: There can be more
than one way to correct a mistake.)*

A fresh sound is in the air, and it's ~~come~~ *coming* from Arizona. The first album from the Phoenix-

based band Exile has hitted radios and stores. The band's singer, Tim Reeves, is quickly become a

superstar. Like most local bands, Exile had struggling since its members started playing together

seven years ago. However, that all changing after Reeves had bring some fresh talent to his group

last year. Reeves reorganize his band, which included bringing on a sensational new drummer,

Brian Fathera. Success came when a representative of Electra Records had be visiting Phoenix

and attends an Exile concert. Before the band members left the building that night, they had sign

a contract to record with Electra, and the rest is music to our ears.

Unit 1 Achievement Test

30 Items
Score: _____

PART I

---

1 | LISTENING: THE POWER OF NAMES

A. 🎧 *Listen to this review of Dr. Paul Sellers's book* The Power of Names. *Complete the review by writing the words that you hear. You will hear the recording two times.*

Madison. Paula. Sarah. Each of these names _____*creates*_____ an impression and carries

0.

certain cultural meanings, according to social scientist Dr. Paul Sellers, author of the book *The*

Power of Names. Sellers _____ that our names influence not only how others feel

1.

about us, but how we feel about ourselves. He claims that names shape our careers, personalities,

and relationships. For example, when most people hear the name Madison, they

_____ of a woman who is hardworking and professional, most likely a

2.

businesswoman. The name Paula, on the other hand, sometimes _____ to mind a

3.

woman who is always taking charge and _____ "no" for an answer. Finally, people

4.

often imagine a woman named Sarah to be nice, sweet, and youthful. In addition to providing

people's impressions of thousands of names, Sellers _____ dozens of studies that

5.

look at how names impact our lives. The author _____ the politics and cultures

6.

that have influenced naming America's babies over the past two hundred years.

B. *Reread the book review. Find seven simple present verbs and one present progressive verb. Write them in the table below. (Note: Only use verbs that are given in the passage. Do not use any verbs that you wrote.) An example is given.*

SIMPLE PRESENT	PRESENT PROGRESSIVE
0. *carries*	8. _____
1. _____	
2. _____	
3. _____	
4. _____	
5. _____	
6. _____	
7. _____	

2 | A FUTURE AUTHOR

Read this conversation about a science book for kids. Complete the conversation by writing the simple present or present progressive form of each verb.

CARLA: Miguel, did you know that Dan _____*is writing*_____ a book?
0. (write)

MIGUEL: No, I didn't know that! What's it about, Dan?

DAN: Oh, it's a science book for kids. I've collected unusual scientific facts for a long time, so

I _____ them all in a book.
1. (put)

CARLA: Tell him the one about termites.

MIGUEL: Termites?

DAN: You know, the little insects. Anyway, all the termites in the world _____
2. (weigh)

10 times more than all the humans.

MIGUEL: Wow! That's amazing! How _____ scientists _____ things
3. (figure out)

like that?

DAN: Well, I'm not really sure, but I think that they study some termites and then

_____ a scientific guess about all of them.
4. (make)

CARLA: Interesting, Dan. What other facts _____ you _____?
5. (know)

DAN: Well, our bodies create and _____ 15 million blood cells per second. Oh,
6. (destroy)

and bats always _____ left when flying out of a cave.
7. (turn)

MIGUEL: That _____ like it'll be a fun book. Are you close to finishing it?
8. (sound)

DAN: I don't know. I could finish it now, but I _____ to it. Anyway, I
9. (always / add)

_____ it for money, just for fun.
10. (not write)

---

3 | EDITING: E-MAIL TO MONSON BOOK PUBLISHERS

Read this e-mail from Dan to a book publisher. There are seven mistakes in the use of simple present and present progressive. The first mistake is already corrected. Find and correct six more. (Note: There can be more than one way to correct a mistake.)

To Whom It May Concern:

         am writing
    I ~~write~~ this letter to introduce you to a book I have written, *Fun Facts of Science*. The book is

for children ages 8 to 12 and is including color photographs. Parents and teachers often complain

that their children are not interested in science, and I am thinking this book can help motivate

these children. As a teacher myself, I always collects ideas to make science interesting. I printed a

few copies of the book from my computer, and I am currently give them to small groups of

children to read. These children say that they find the book very interesting. I am believing such a

book could be a valuable reference in homes and school libraries. I looks forward to hearing

from you.

Sincerely,

Daniel Stoletta

Unit 2 Achievement Test

1 | LISTENING: MATCHMAKER

A. 🎧 *Listen to this radio interview with the creator of a dating and matchmaking service. Complete the interview by writing the words that you hear. You will hear the recording two times.*

DONNA: Welcome to *Love Affair*. I'm your host, Donna Wright. Today on our show we're

talking to Nancy Powers, who _____founded_____ the highly successful dating and
0.

matchmaking service MatchRight. Nancy, welcome to the show.

NANCY: Thank you, Donna.

DONNA: Nancy, why _____ you _____ MatchRight?
                                                           1.

NANCY: Well, Donna, I get that question a lot. Some people think I started MatchRight because

I _____ for my true love, but actually I set up the company after I was
2.

already married. I just love being a matchmaker. In fact, in college I introduced three of

my best friends to the men who became their husbands. Matchmaking just comes

naturally to me.

DONNA: I understand that you consider a person's dating history to be very important when

making a match. Why's that?

NANCY: I look for patterns that either help or hurt a person in finding a good match. For

example, one woman walked into my office after she broke up with her boyfriend. I

found out that when they were dating, she was working 60 hours a week, which

_____ much time for her relationship. While we _____
                    3.   4.

together over the next couple of weeks, she realized that if she wanted to have a healthy

relationship, she would need to slow down a bit.

DONNA: You're listening to *Love Affair* with our guest Nancy Powers of MatchRight. We'll be

right back.

*B. Reread the radio interview. Then read each statement and circle **T** (true) or **F** (false).*

T (**F**) 0. Nancy began MatchRight when she was looking for love.

T **F** 1. Nancy started matchmaking after college.

T **F** 2. Nancy's best friends in college became her husbands.

T **F** 3. She helped a woman who broke up with her boyfriend.

T **F** 4. The woman started working 60 hours a week after she broke up with her boyfriend.

T **F** 5. The woman discovered that she needed to change.

2 | NEW MATCHRIGHT CLIENT

Read this interview with a new MatchRight client. Complete the interview with the correct verb forms. Write the letter of the best answer on each line.

NANCY: I see that you ___*a*___ (a. finished b. finish c. finishes d. was finishing) your paperwork.
          0.

Now I'd like to ask you a few questions to get to know you better and to find out the

kind of person you're looking for. Tell me about your previous relationships.

PIETRO: OK. Let's see, when I was in college, I _____ (a. dated b. dating c. date d. were dating) a
                                                    1.

girl named Jana for about six months or so. I liked her because she was really smart and

funny, but then I _____ (a. am moving b. moved c. was moving d. move) to Louisiana for
                    2.

work. I _____ (a. was dating b. date c. am dating d. dates) a girl there named Heather, but
          3.

we had different goals in life, so we stopped dating. And most recently, I was seeing a

girl named Becky when I _____ (a. was having b. have c. had d. am having) to move
                          4.

again. She was making a lot of money at her job when I _____ (a. leave b. leaving
                                                          5.

c. left d. was leave), so she decided to stay.

NANCY: It sounds like you don't have any trouble finding people to date. Why _____ (a. did
                                                                          6.

you decide b. do you decide c. are you deciding d. were you deciding) to come here?

PIETRO: Well, even while I was dating these women, I _____ (a. don't feel b. didn't feel c. was
    7.
feeling d. am feeling) like we were the best match. With Becky, for instance, I felt like she

lived to work while I _____ (a. am work b. works c. working d. worked) to live. Even
    8.

when she _____ (a. can work b. work c. didn't working d. wasn't working), she was still
    9.

thinking about work, you know? So I'd just like to find somebody who values the same

things I do.

NANCY: I understand, and I can help.

---

3 | BAD DATE

*Read this paragraph from Pietro's journal about a horrible first date. Complete the
paragraph by writing the simple past or past progressive form of each verb. Some items
may have more than one right answer.*

I just _____had_____ a horrible date! Her name was Marilyn, and I met her through
          0. (have)
MatchRight. When I arrived to pick her up, she _____ in front of the television,
                                                    1. (sit)
and she _____ on the phone! She had completely forgotten about our date! She
          2. (talk)
went to get dressed, and I _____ for an entire hour! I almost fell asleep while she
                              3. (wait)
was getting ready. Well, finally we left for the restaurant. On the way there, I was trying to talk

while she _____ with the windows, locks, and radio! When we finally got to the
            4. (play)
restaurant, an employee _____ the doors, closing for the night. When I
                              5. (lock)
_____ a different restaurant, she _____, "Don't worry, I always
    6. (suggest)   7. (say)
bring food with me." And she pulled a sandwich out of her bag and _____ to eat
                                                                          8. (start)
it! That was the last time she'll ever see me!

4 | EDITING: GOOD NEWS

Read Pietro's e-mail to Nancy Powers at MatchRight. There are five mistakes in the use of simple past and past progressive. The first mistake is already corrected. Find and correct four more. (Note: There can be more than one way to correct a mistake.)

Hi Nancy,

I'm writing to let you know that Melissa and I just celebrated seven months of dating, and

she is so perfect for me. Thank you for matching us up!

Last night, I ~~propose~~ *proposed* to Melissa, and she says yes! My hand was shaking while I holding out

the ring, and Melissa was cry. We were both very emotional! When I woke up this morning, I

decide to tell you the good news first. We are two very happy people because of you.

Thank you,

Pietro

Unit 3 Achievement Test

1	**LISTENING: ITALIAN COOK**

A. 🎧 *Listen to this conversation with an Italian cook. Complete the conversation by writing the words that you hear. You will hear the recording two times.*

ANNA: Wow! I _____'ve_____ always _____loved_____ Italian food, but I
                                                    0.

_____ lasagna as delicious as this before! Where _____ you
        1.

_____ to cook so well?
        2.

ELIO: I grew up in an Italian family, and I _____ all my life.
                                                              3.

ANNA: _____ you _____ in Italy when you were a child?
                                            4.

ELIO: Yes, I did. I lived there for twenty-five years and studied at a cooking school. I moved

here last year, and I _____ at a couple of Italian restaurants in town since
                              5.

then.

ANNA: No wonder you're such a good cook! _____ you _____
                                                                              6.

about opening your own restaurant?

ELIO: I've considered it, of course, and I really want to, but I haven't saved enough money yet.

B. *Reread the conversation. Then read each statement and circle* **T** *(true) or* **F** *(false).*

Ⓣ **F** 0. Anna loved Italian food in the past, and she still loves it.

T **F** 1. Elio used to cook, but he doesn't anymore.

T **F** 2. Elio is living in Italy.

T **F** 3. Elio studied in Italy.

T **F** 4. Elio worked at Italian restaurants.

T **F** 5. Elio is saving some money to open a restaurant.

2 | IRENE BARROW—AN ARTIST

*Read this magazine interview with Irene Barrow, a well-known artist. Then read each statement and circle **T** (true) or **F** (false).*

INTERVIEWER: Irene, you have become quite successful as an artist. You are an expert potter, so you create things like vases, cups, and pots from clay. Tell us, have you been working with clay for a long time?

IRENE: Yes, I have. I began working with clay when I was five years old, and I have been creating dinnerware, pots, and vases ever since. I studied pottery in Italy for two years, and my work has appeared in numerous galleries around the world. In fact, my work toured France, Hong Kong, and New York earlier this year.

INTERVIEWER: I didn't realize this before, but you are one of the most productive potters working today. What have you been working on this month?

IRENE: This month alone, I produced and sold nearly 200 pieces. I've also been working on a photo book of my work over the past few months. I bought a professional camera and lighting equipment six months ago, and I've been taking tons of photos of my work. I am a little surprised to say that I love taking photos! In fact, I've probably taken about 60 rolls of film. I took three rolls of film just this morning. Taking these photos has given me a new way to look at my work.

(T) F   0. Barrow worked with pottery in the past, and she is still working with pottery.

T F   1. Barrow's work has been to France, Hong Kong, and New York.

T F   2. Barrow will probably produce 200 more pieces this month.

T F   3. Barrow hasn't sold any work for several months.

T F   4. Barrow owns a professional camera.

T F   5. Barrow has taken many pictures of her work and will continue to do so.

T F   6. Barrow says she will probably take more pictures this morning.

T F   7. Barrow has gained a new understanding of her work recently.

T F   8. Barrow has been taking pictures longer than she has been making pottery.

3 | CAR LOVER

Read this paragraph about Collin Ferkett's business. Complete the paragraph by writing the simple past, present perfect, or present perfect progressive form of each verb. Some items may have more than one right answer.

Collin Ferkett of Detroit ___has been working___ on cars since he was little. He
                                          0. (work)

_____ in Detroit all his life, and he _____ around 30,000 cars.
      1. (live)   **2. (fix)**

Twenty years ago, Collin _____ his own mechanic shop. "I _____
                            3. (open)   **4. (see)**

just about every kind of car they make," he says. He _____ his shop four years
                                                5. (expand)

ago, and he _____ great business ever since.
         6. (do)

4 | EDITING: POSTCARD FROM ISTANBUL

Read this postcard from Istanbul. There are six mistakes in the use of the simple past, present perfect, and present perfect progressive. The first mistake is already corrected. Find and correct five more. (Note: There can be more than one way to correct a mistake.)

Hi Roger,

       been sightseeing

   I've ~~sightseed~~ in Istanbul for the past week, and it was wonderful! On Saturday, I have visited

the Hagia Sofia. Then on Monday, I've been spending about three hours at the Rumeli Fortress.

The food here is amazing! I ate *dolma* almost every day since I arrived. I don't find a flying

carpet for you yet, but I'm still looking!

Linda

Unit 4 Achievement Test

1 | LISTENING: GARDENING FOR LIFE

A. 🎧 *Listen to this interview with author/TV show host Amy Wang. Complete the interview by writing the words that you hear. You will hear the recording two times.*

INTERVIEWER: We return now to our interview with Amy Wang, author of *Gardening for Life,*

and host of the popular television program by the same name. Amy, before our

break you ___*had mentioned*___ that you moved to Chicago in 2002.
                    0.

_____ you ever _____ to Chicago before that?
                                              1.

AMY: Actually, I _____ once to visit the Chicago Botanical Gardens—
                         2.

a beautiful place! But I moved here much later—after I had finished my book.

INTERVIEWER: And what finally brought you here to live?

AMY: Well, my book _____ already _____ really well when
                                                          3.

I was invited to be the host of *Gardening for Life*. I _____ never

_____ to work in television before then, but I've been on the show
        4.

for a year now, and I love it!

INTERVIEWER: So how did you get into gardening? I mean, _____ you

_____ as a gardener before writing the book?
        5.

AMY: Yes, I had. I was working in a greenhouse for a long time before I started writing. I

had often thought about sharing my gardening ideas. So I decided to write a book.

B. Reread the interview. Then read each statement and circle **T** *(true) or* **F** *(false).*

T (**F**) 0. Amy moved to Chicago before 2002.

T **F** 1. First Amy moved to Chicago, and then she visited the Chicago Botanical Gardens.

T **F** 2. First Amy finished writing her book, and then she was invited to host a TV show.

T **F** 3. Amy always wanted to work in television.

T **F** 4. First Amy thought of ways to share her ideas about gardening with people, and then she began writing a book.

---

2 | NEW JOB

Read a paragraph from Jyoti's diary. Complete the paragraph by writing the past perfect or past perfect progressive form of each verb. Do NOT use simple past. Some items may have more than one right answer.

I can't believe I got the job! I ___*had been looking*___ through the classified section of the
                                     0. look

newspaper for weeks before I finally saw the ad for an office manager at a department store. I

_____ in that store before, and I really liked it. When I showed up for the
     1. (shop)

interview, there were four other people who _____ before me. One of them told
                                              2. (arrived)

me that at least five other people _____ already _____ interviews
                                                                      3. (have)

and left. Then it was my turn. The interviewer asked me about my office management

experience. I explained that even though I _____ never _____ an
                                                                   4. (manage)

office before, I was familiar with the responsibilities because I _____ at my dad's
                                                                  5. (worked)

office for several years. It turns out the interviewer went to high school with my dad, so we had a

great conversation. I was nervous at the beginning of the interview, but by the end, I

_____ completely _____. I _____ that good about an
                                6. (relax)   **7. (not feel)**

interview for as long as I could remember. Maybe the old saying is true: It's not *what* you know,

but *who* you know.

3 | A MUSIC CAREER

*Read the timeline about Nala Mwabi's life. Complete the sentences by writing the past perfect forms of the verbs in the timeline. Use **already** or **not yet**.*

is born in Jamaica	starts band	releases first album	gets married	wins Grammy Award	album goes platinum	stars in movie	has first child	buys record label
1962	1982	1989	1993	1995	1998	2000	2002	2004

0. In 1961, he _____*had not yet been*_____ born.

1. It was 1981. He _____ a band.

2. It was 1988. Mwabi _____ his first album.

3. In 1994, he _____ married.

4. By 1998, he _____ a Grammy Award.

5. In 1997, his album _____ platinum.

6. It was 2001. Mwabi _____ in a movie.

7. By 2003, Mwabi _____ his first child.

8. In 2003, Mwabi _____ his record label.

4 | EDITING: A COMEDIAN'S START

Read this article about the start of one comedian's career. There are seven mistakes in the use of the past perfect and the past perfect progressive. The first mistake is already corrected. Find and correct six more. (Note: There can be more than one way to correct a mistake.)

In 2004, moviegoers first enjoyed the unique humor of actor Steven Wall in the comedy hit *Farmland*. They were amazed to learn that Wall actually *had* been a high school math teacher before his first film role. His students already knew that he was a funny teacher, but they hadn't imagine him as the next big name in comedy.

Wall was born in Ontario, Canada, in 1974. His father was a mathematician, and by the time Wall was 10, his father taught Wall most major mathematical formulas. But Wall never really liked math, even though he was good at it; he liked to make people laugh! At age 25, Wall began to write comedy and to appear in Ontario comedy clubs (by then, he had already been teach for three years). In 2003, Wall starred in a local television commercial, which made him hugely popular in Ontario. Before the commercial, Wall had struggling to start his comedy career. A movie producer saw the commercial and knew immediately that he found the star for *Farmland*. At that time, Wall's hopes had finally been being realized.

PART I Achievement Test

> 70 Items
> Score: _____

1 | LISTENING: A NEW EDITOR IN CHIEF

A. 🎧 *Listen to this introduction of a new editor in chief to employees of Empire Publishers. Complete the introduction by writing the words that you hear. You will hear the recording two times.*

Empire Publishers proudly ____*welcomes*____ its newest editor in chief Ramona Gibbons.
　　　　　　　　　　　　　　　0.

Ms. Gibbons grew up in Baltimore and _____ her editing career there in 1981.
　　　　　　　　　　　　　　　　　　　　1.

After she had written as a leisure columnist at the *Baltimore Daily* for a few years, she moved to

Los Angeles in 1984. In 1985, she _____ popularity from a series of articles she
　　　　　　　　　　　　　　　　　2.

_____ earlier about gifted children and how L.A. schools _____
　　3.　　　　　　　　　　　　　　　　　　　　　　　　　　　　**4.**

them.

She was working in Berlin when the Wall _____ in 1989. In fact, she had been
　　　　　　　　　　　　　　　　　　　5.

living there for five years, so she _____ about the event from direct experience. In
　　　　　　　　　　　　　　　6.

1990, she was honored with the Gretta Eisner award for articles she _____ the
　　　　　　　　　　　　　　　　　　　　　　　　　　　　　　　7.

previous year about the fall of the Iron Curtain.

Ms. Gibbons had been serving as president of the Editing Standards Association for three

years when she agreed to join Empire Publishers. She strives for excellence in editing and has

been writing essays on the topics of standards and quality for the past 10 years. She has edited

22 books.

Ms. Gibbons _____ currently _____ in England, and she
　　　　　　　　　　　　　　　　　　　　　　　8.

_____ to work from home. She _____ one son, Anthony, who also
　　9.　　　　　　　　　　　　　　　　　**10.**

_____ in publishing. Together, they are working on a book. Please join me now in
　　11.

welcoming Ramona Gibbons.

*B. Reread the introduction. Then read each statement and circle **T** (true) or **F** (false).*

(T) F   0. Ms. Gibbons lived in Baltimore before 1981.

T   F   1. At first, Ms. Gibbons wrote about leisure.

T   F   2. She won an award for her series on an educational problem.

T   F   3. First she moved to Berlin, then the Wall fell.

T   F   4. She became the president of the Editing Standards Association before working at Empire Publishers.

T   F   5. This year she will begin editing books.

T   F   6. She lives in the United States.

T   F   7. She recently started writing about quality.

T   F   8. She is currently writing a book.

2 | A GROWING FAMILY

Read this passage about a growing family. Complete the passage with the correct verb forms. Write the letter of the best answer on each line.

It was 2001, and I ____*a*____ (a. had been working b. work c. am working d. had working) in New
0.

York City for a few years. I met my husband, Shigeo, while he _____ (a. studies b. was studying
1.

c. is studying d. had studied) medicine at Columbia University. A friend _____ (a. was suggesting
2.

b. suggested c. suggests d. has suggested) we go out, so we did. When I _____ (a. had been meeting
3.

b. have met c. was meeting d. met) Shigeo, I liked him instantly. First we were friends, then we began

dating. We _____ (a. took b. are taking c. had taken d. take) road trips together and had great
4.

conversations. We _____ (a. had been seeing b. have been seeing c. saw d. have seen) each other for
5.

a year when he asked me to marry him. He _____ (a. had been proposing b. has proposed
6.

c. proposed d. was proposing) during one of our trips. By the time we got married, Shigeo _____
7.

(a. is completing b. has been completing c. completes d. had completed) medical school. He _____ (a. is
8.

getting b. has gotten c. got d. gets) a job at a hospital in California in 2003. Our daughter, Ericka,

was born a few months after he _____ (a. has started b. had started c. starts d. was starting) the job.
9.

We _____ (a. had been living b. was living c. lives d. lived) in California for about two years when
10.

our son, Austin, was born.

Now I _____ (a. begin b. was beginning c. had begun d. have begun) a daycare business in our
        11.

home. I _____ (a. had been enjoying b. enjoyed c. enjoy d. had enjoyed) working from home. I also
        12.

_____ (a. had written b. was writing c. write d. wrote) poetry when I have time. Now Austin
    13.

_____ (a. has begun b. had begun c. begins d. began) to walk, and Ericka _____ (a. had been
    14.   15.

singing b. had sung c. is singing d. was singing) a lot. Shigeo and I _____ (a. took b. take c. had taken
                                                                              16.

d. taken) the children to the park every Saturday. We _____ (a. is hoping b. hope c. have hoped
                                                            17.

d. had hoped) to buy a bigger house next year because we _____ (a. thought b. had been thinking
                                                                18.

c. thinks d. have been thinking) about having another baby!

3 | MOTORCYCLE BLUES

*Read this conversation about John's motorcycle. Complete the conversation by writing the
simple present, simple past, present progressive, present perfect, present perfect
progressive, past progressive, past perfect, or past perfect progressive form of each verb.
Some items may have more than one right answer.*

ALEX: John! _____ *Do* _____ you _____ *want* _____ a ride?
                                                    0. (want)

JOHN: Oh sure! Thanks. I _____ just _____ to class.
                                                          1. (walk)

ALEX: I'm heading that way too. _____ you usually _____ a
                                                              2. (not ride)

motorcycle?

JOHN: I do, but it's in the shop right now. I _____ it in yesterday. It
                                                  3. (take)

_____ some weird noises. It _____ down last month, and I
    4. (made)   **5. (break)**

_____ to find the money to fix it. I almost _____ to sell it at
    6. (struggle)   **7. (decide)**

that point. Since then I _____ whether or not to sell the bike because I
                              8. (debate)

_____ any money since I got it. Plus, I _____ to fix it myself,
    9. (not save)   **10. (try)**

but I just wasted a lot of time.

ALEX: Sorry to hear that. I _____ a bicycle you can use if you
                                    11. (have)

_____ it.
    12. (want)

JOHN: Thanks. Maybe I'll borrow it for a while.

4 | WANTED: GUITARIST

Read this interview with a possible band member for the pop group Spinal Column.
Complete the interview by writing the simple present, simple past, present progressive,
present perfect, present perfect progressive, past perfect, or past perfect progressive form of
each verb. Some items may have more than one right answer.

TINA: _____ *Have* _____ you ever _____ *been* _____ in a band before?
                                        0. (be)

JEN: I _____ in a couple of pop bands. First, I _____ form a
             1. (play)   **2. (help)**

band called Gypsy Girls four years ago. We _____ touring after we
                                          3. (start)

_____ an album. The last band I was in was called Swirl System, and we
4. (release)

_____ and played in Europe twice, but we _____ many
5. (travel)   **6. (not sell)**

albums. I left when I found out that our manager _____ our money for a
                                              7. (take)

long time.

TINA: Why _____ you _____ to play with us?
                                 8. (want)

JEN: I _____ your band's ad in the paper, and I saw your concert last night. I
           9. (read)

_____ what I heard.
10. (like)

TINA: Well, we _____ an experienced guitarist, and we _____
            11. (need)   **12. (do)**

several shows a week. Let's hear you play something and see how you sound.

5 | EDITING: OVERNIGHT SUCCESS

Read this magazine article about the pop group Spinal Column. There are ten mistakes in the verbs. The first mistake is already corrected. Find and correct nine more. (Note: There can be more than one way to correct a mistake.)

    The first album by the band Spinal Column has been ~~rise~~ *rising* to the top of the charts. Their funky sound had broken the rules of contemporary pop music, and their distinctive style is quickly makes Spinal Column a household name. The new album is going on sale last month, and it had selling poorly in the first two weeks until the band appeared on *The Nightly Show*. Their appearance had been changed the course of the band's success. It happen quickly: A talent scout from *The Nightly Show* had be shopping downtown when he hears music from the new album coming from one of the shops. Before the end of the day, he had book Spinal Column for their appearance on the show.

PART II Diagnostic Test

60 Items
Score: _____

A. 🎧 *Listen to the description of daily life in the future. Complete the description by writing the words that you hear. You will hear the recording two times.*

Technology is improving all the time and changing our lives as a result. In the future,

_____*how will you be communicating*_____ ? How _____ and
　　　　　　　　　　0.　　　　　　　　　　　　　　　　　　　　　　　　　**1.**

work? How _____ society change as a result?
　　　　　　　　　　　2.

A typical day in the future will go something like this: While you're sleeping, you

_____ through a miniature computer in your brain. You'll put
　　　　　　　3.

on clothes that _____ by your robot. You'll ride to work in a
　　　　　　　　　　　　　4.

flying car. But you _____; the car will drive itself. When you
　　　　　　　　　　　　5.

come home, you'll eat a delicious meal that will have already been prepared for you.

By the time you celebrate your 120th birthday, you will be living with about 10 billion people

on the Earth, but you _____ cleaner air your whole life. You
　　　　　　　　　　　　　　6.

_____ 80 percent less stress during your life than people do
　　　　　　7.

today, and you won't have gotten sick once. You _____ lonely
　　　　　　　　　　　　　　　　　　　　　8.

with all the technological improvements in communication. You will have learned 600 percent

more than people do today. You _____ many foods that you
　　　　　　　　　　　　9.

can't even imagine today. You will even have visited Mars on vacation. These are just some of the

ways technology _____ the future. This is only half of what is
　　　　　　　10.

possible!

B. *Reread the description of daily life in the future. Find five future verbs and four future perfect verbs. Write them in the table below. (Note: Only use verbs that are given in the passage. Do not use any verbs that you wrote.) An example is given.*

FUTURE VERBS	FUTURE PERFECT VERBS
0. *will work*	6. _____
1. _____	7. _____
2. _____	8. _____
3. _____	9. _____
4. _____	
5. _____	

2 | NEW TECHNOLOGY MUSEUM

Read the museum director's speech to a volunteer group about a new museum. Complete the passage with the correct verb forms. Write the letter of the best answer on the line.

The new International Technology Museum ___c___ (a. opening b. will opens c. will be opening
0.

d. is going open) in October. By the opening date, our volunteers _____ (a. will have working b. will
1.

have worked c. will work d. are going to be working) over 200 hours to complete the building of the

museum. When we _____ (a. are going to finish b. will finish c. are finishing d. finish), we _____
2.   3.

(a. will have saved b. are going to save c. will have been saving d. will save) $45,000 because of your help. I

have never seen so much volunteer support! I certainly _____ (a. am going to be forgetting b. will
4.

not have forgotten c. will never forget d. will have forgotten) it. I _____ (a. will be flying b. will flying
5.

c. am going to have been flying d. will have been flying) to Asia next week to help bring many exhibits to

their new home here. When the museum doors _____ (a. will open b. will be open c. open d. will be
6.

opening), we _____ (a. will get b. will have been getting c. are getting d. will have gotten) exhibits from
7.

nearly 150 different countries. Join us on opening day—we _____ (a. will have had b. will be
8.

having c. are going have d. have) a huge celebration with food, drinks, and live music.

3 | CLASS PRESENTATION

*Read this conversation between Ming and Carl about their class project. Complete the
conversation by writing the correct future, future progressive, or future perfect form of each
verb. Use contractions where possible. Some items may have more than one right answer.*

MING: Carl, today's Monday, and our book report and presentation are due on Thursday.

That day _____*will be*_____ here before we know it! Let's plan what we
                0. (be)

_____.
    1. (do)

CARL: I think I _____ the book we need from the library later today. By tonight, I
              2. (check out)

_____ the first half, and by tomorrow afternoon I _____ a
    3. (read)   **4. (write)**

summary of those chapters.

MING: Great! Meanwhile, I _____ reviews about the book on the Internet, and I
                    5. (look for)

_____ some of the main points. Tomorrow, I _____
    6. (summarize)   **7. (give)**

you what I've written and start reading the second half of the book. When we

_____ on Wednesday, I _____ it. Then on Wednesday night,
    8. (meet)   **9. (finish)**

let's promise that we _____ our presentation a couple of times.
                        10. (practice)

CARL: I'm glad that we _____ before our presentation! We'll be prepared!
                    11. (practice)

4 | TODAY

Read Michael's schedule for the day. Complete the sentences by writing the future, future progressive, future perfect, or future perfect progressive forms of the verbs in the schedule. Use contractions when possible. Some items may have more than one possible answer.

  8:00 have breakfast
  9:00 walk the dog
  9:30 mow the lawn
10:00 do laundry
12:00 make lunch
  1:00 go shopping for food
  2:00 wash the car
  3:00 pick up the kids
  3:30 read the newspaper
  5:00 make dinner
  6:00 eat dinner
  7:00 watch a movie

0. By the time Michael walks the dog, he _____*'ll have had*_____ breakfast.

1. By 10:00, he _____ the dog.

2. At 9:30, he _____ the lawn.

3. By 11:00, he _____ laundry for an hour.

4. At 12:00, he _____ lunch.

5. By 1:45, he _____ for food.

6. At 2:00, he _____ the car.

7. By 2:30, he _____ the car for half an hour.

8. By the time he picks up the kids, he _____ the car.

9. By 3:45, he _____ the paper for a while.

10. At 4:00, he _____ the kids.

11. At 6:00, he _____ dinner.

12. By the time he begins watching the movie, he _____ dinner.

5 | EDITING: END-OF-SEMESTER EVENT

Read this e-mail to students about an end-of-semester event on a college campus. There are 11 mistakes in the use of the future, future progressive, future perfect, or future perfect progressive. The first mistake is already corrected. Find and correct 10 more. (Note: There is often more than one way to correct a mistake.)

          visit

Comedian will ~~visits~~ campus!

  By the end of the semester, you will have study too much and laughs too little. Comedian Jeff

Foster had helped bring fun back into your life. Foster will have gave a free show this coming

Saturday at 6:00. After his comedy show, he'll speaking about the benefits of humor. The first 50

people to arrive received free tickets to City Comedy Club. Everyone will be having a chance to

win tickets to Foster's television show. We have given away free hotdogs. Foster's performance

will be begin the end-of-semester activities on campus. By the end of the week, we have been

having four other comedy performances, and you will have had an opportunity to relax.

Unit 5 Achievement Test

| 30 Items |
| Score: _____ |

1 | LISTENING: A FUTURE NEWSCAST

∩ *Listen to a future newscast about a trip to Mars. Complete the newscast by writing the words that you hear. You will hear the recording two times.*

The Mars Vacation Group _____*will launch*_____ its first commercial flight to Mars next week.
                                              0.

Eight civilian, non-military passengers will be on the spaceship. The group _____
                                                                                                          1.

60 million kilometers in 208 days. When the flight _____, some people
                                                                          2.

_____ an extended hiking and camping trip and _____ about the
            3.   **4.**

Red Planet firsthand. While this group is exploring, other travelers _____ different
                                                                                                    5.

activities that the Mars Vacation Group _____. These include a variety of classes
                                                                6.

such as Gardening on Mars and Mars in Literature. The whole group _____ a
                                                                                                  7.

total of six months on Mars before returning home. Crew members have promised that they

_____ us digital photos throughout the trip.
            8.

2 | SPACE CARS

Read this future newspaper article about space cars. Complete the passage with the correct verb forms. Write the letter of the best answer on each line.

Cosmo Cruisers of Los Angeles, a new space car company, ___*c*___ (a. open b. is open c. opens
                                                              0.

d. will to open) its doors for business next Saturday. The company _____ (a. will being b. will be
                                                                            1.

c. is being d. is going to) the first of its kind. Five other car dealers _____ (a. will be going to sell
                                                                          2.

b. sell c. are selling d. will be selling) space cars by the end of the month. Mayor Dixon

_____ (a. will be attending b. will attending c. attends d. will be going to attend) the grand opening and
    3.

_____ (a. participates b. participating c. will participates d. going to participate) in a ribbon-cutting
    4.

ceremony when the new business _____ (a. opens b. is going to be opening c. will open d. will be
                                     5.

opening) its doors at 5 A.M. He believes the space cars _____ (a. change b. are changing
                                                           6.

c. are going to change d. will be going to change) travel forever. The company's founder, Tim Berg,

says he thinks sales _____ (a. are b. are being c. will be d. are going to being) heavy for the first
                        7.

few months. Among his largest clients will be the Los Angeles police department, who

_____ (a. will use b. uses c. is using d. will be use) the space cars to monitor ground and air vehicle
    8.

traffic soon. Meanwhile, the Federal Aviation Commission _____ (a. is going to be finalize
                                                             9.

b. will finalizes c. is going to finalizing d. will finalize) regulations for the new cars this Friday.

3 | COMET X

Read this conversation between a reporter and a scientist about a comet. Complete the conversation by writing the future, future progressive, or short answer form of each word. Use contractions where possible. Some items may have more than one right answer.

REPORTER: The rumors are that a new comet _____ *will be passing* _____ close
0. (pass)

to Earth next week. Dr. O'Hara, what's your opinion?

_____ we _____
1. (be)

safe?

DR. O'HARA: Yes, I think that we _____ fine. In fact, the
2. (be)

comet _____ very close. Our scientists
3. (not come)

_____ it closely through a telescope in our
4. (watch)

observatory as it's passing by.

REPORTER: _____ you
5. (invite)

_____ reporters to watch too?

DR. O'HARA: No, unfortunately, we _____. The observatory
6. (not)

where we have our telescope is too small.

REPORTER: People also say that the new comet _____ faster
7. (move)

at this time next week. Are you sure it isn't going to be dangerous?

DR. O'HARA: Yes, there's really nothing to worry about. However, we

_____ information on the comet's path and
8. (measure)

speed the entire time it's near Earth.

4 | EDITING: COMET X MESSAGE BOARD

Read Joe's message on the Comet X message board. There are six mistakes in the use of future tenses. The first mistake is already corrected. Find and correct five more. (Note: There can be more than one way to correct a mistake.)

will be traveling

I ~~travel~~ to Auckland next week, and I am concerned about the comet passing so close to

Earth. I wonder if it will being safe to travel when the comet passes by. How close it is going to

get to Earth? With our current technology, are we going be able to get an exact measurement?

Where we will be safest? I check the message board later this week for any warnings or advice.

Joe

Unit 6 Achievement Test

30 Items
Score: _____

1 | LISTENING: A NEWS REPORT

🎧 *Listen to the news report about Ted Johnson, who is breaking world records. Complete the news report by writing the words that you hear. You will hear the recording two times.*

PATTY: We're returning now to live coverage of Ted Johnson, who is trying to break two world

records at the same time.

DOUG: That's right, Patty. Ted has been walking for about a day and a half. Two days from now,

when he arrives in Chicago, Ted _____*will have traveled*_____ nearly 200 miles—or 322

0.

kilometers. He _____ for 82 hours straight, breaking the

1.

previous world record by 10 hours. Twenty-four hours into his walk, he began singing,

and in two days, he _____ for 58 hours, breaking that record by

2.

18 hours. Another amazing fact, Patty, is that he _____ about

3.

3,520,000 steps by the time he finishes. Doctors, of course, will be watching him

carefully, since he _____ about 20,000 calories during his

4.

adventure. He _____ for about three and a half days. In

5.

addition, he _____ the song he is singing about 1,560 times.

6.

PATTY: Doug, have you had a chance to speak with Ted?

DOUG: Yes, just a few minutes ago Ted sang to me that, by next year, he hopes he

_____ two more records, for a total of four world records. But,

7.

he said he still _____ enough to satisfy himself. He believes that

8.

by the time he is 30, he _____ 10 world records for a variety of

9.

activities. How much satisfaction _____ by then? We can only

10.

imagine.

2 | BIG DREAMS

A. *Read these monthly goals for Sam, a computer salesman. Use the words in parentheses and the information in the chart to complete the sentences about what Sam will have done or won't have done if he achieves his goals.*

JANUARY–FEBRUARY	MARCH–APRIL	MAY–JUNE	JULY–AUGUST	SEPTEMBER–OCTOBER	NOVEMBER–DECEMBER
Make 200 contacts Sell 500 computers	Buy a new sports car Begin losing weight Go to the dentist	Read a book a week Open computer store Start advertising	Start training for marathon Sell 1,000 computers	Buy my first house Ask Wendy to marry me	Get married!

0. (make 200 contacts) By the end of February, _____ *he will have made 200 contacts* _____ .

1. (sell 1,000 computers) _____ before the beginning

of July.

2. (buy a sports car) By the end of April, _____ .

3. (go to the dentist) By the beginning of May, _____ .

4. (open a computer store) _____ before May

or June.

5. (buy first house) By the end of October, _____ .

B. *Reread Sam's goals. Imagine that he will achieve all of his goals. Then read each statement and circle **T** (true) or **F** (false).*

(T) F   0. By February 28, he will have made 200 contacts.

T F   1. He won't have lost weight by March 1.

T F   2. He will not have read a book a week by April 1.

T F   3. He will have gone to the dentist by February 4.

T F   4. He will not have started advertising for his computer store by September.

T F   5. He will have started training for the marathon by June.

T F   6. He will have married Wendy by the end of the year.

3 | EDITING: A NEW CAREER

Read this description of one man's career. There are 10 mistakes in the use of the future perfect and the future perfect progressive. The first mistake is already corrected. Find and correct nine more.

       By August, I will have ^been^ working as a janitor for five years. I'll have been earned the same amount of money each year, and I won't saved very much. I'll been living in the same apartment for five years, too. So I've decided to become a mechanic instead! By the time spring will arrive, I will have decide where to apply, and I will have applies to different auto shops. By summer, I have gotten job offers, and I will have been starting my new career. But before doing anything, I have to ask myself, will I made a change for the better?

PART II Achievement Test

60 Items
Score: _____

1 | LISTENING: DATING IN THE FUTURE

A. 🎧 *Listen to the description of dating in the future. Complete the description by writing the words that you hear. You will hear the recording two times.*

Are you single and trying to date the old-fashioned way? In the next 100 years, how

_____*will people be dating*_____? How _____ their
          0.   **1.**

spouses? What kind of dates will they go on? How is society

_____ as a result?
       2.

Imagine that you're dating in the future. Your search will go something like this: You'll

register with a website where people can read about you and your interests. When you come

home each day, you _____ e-mails from people who are
                             3.

interested in dating you. You'll choose the ones who interest you, and you'll have online "dates"

with them. It's possible that you _____ many people at the
                                  4.

same time.

By the time you finally meet your true love, you _____
                                                5.

about five hours a week getting to know people, but you

_____ face to face with any of them. You'll have saved
       6.

lots of money because you will never have gone out to a restaurant. You

_____ 80 percent less stress about dating than you do today,
       7.

and if things don't work out with someone, you _____ as
                                      8.

rejected. You _____ bored because you will have met 300
                     9.

percent more people than you do today. You _____ many
                                      10.

conversations with people. You will even have visited exotic places like Hawaii on virtual

vacations with your dates. In short, you _____ many more
                                  11.

dating opportunities than you have today. Will such virtual romances result in fewer divorces?

Only time will tell.

B. Reread the description of dating in the future. Find four future verbs and four future perfect verbs. Write them in the table below. (Note: Only use verbs that are given in the passage. Do not use any verbs that you wrote.) An example is given.

FUTURE VERBS	FUTURE PERFECT VERBS
0. _will go on_	5. _____
1. _____	6. _____
2. _____	7. _____
3. _____	8. _____
4. _____	

2 | A NEW SCHOOL

Read this letter about a new school from the principal to volunteers in the community. Complete the passage with the correct verb forms. Write the letter of the best answer on each line.

The new Williamson School ____c____ (a. opening b. will opens c. will be opening d. is going open) in
0.

August. Many thanks to the community volunteers who _____ (a. will have been helped b. will
1.

have helped c. are going to have been helped d. are going to be) complete the building of the school.

When we _____ (a. are going to finish b. will finish c. are finishing d. finish), we _____ (a. will have
2.   3.

saved b. will have been saving c. are going to have been saving d. will save) $20,000 because of your help. I

have never experienced so much community involvement! I know I _____ (a. am not going to
4.

have forgotten b. will never forget c. will never have forgotten d. am never going to be forgetting) your help in

this project. I _____ (a. will be receiving b. will receiving c. receive d. am going be receiving) new
5.

computers and other school supplies next week. By the time the school doors _____ (a. will
6.

open b. are going to open c. open d. will be opening), we _____ (a. are going to be gotten b. are going to
7.

have been getting c. get d. will have gotten) new playground equipment as well. Join us on the first day

of school, as we _____ (a. will have been having b. will be having c. are going have d have) free
8.

breakfast and live music. Certainly, you _____ (a. will have earned b. will be earning c. earn d. will
9.

have been earned) a party by then.

3 | BUSINESS PRESENTATION

Read this conversation between Jeff and Angie about their business presentation.
Complete the conversation. Write the correct future, future progressive, or future perfect
form of each verb in parentheses. Use contractions where possible. Some items may have
more than one right answer.

ANGIE: Let's see, today is Monday, and our presentation for the new client

_____ *will need* _____ to be ready by Friday. Let's plan what we
   0. (need)

_____ .
   1. (do)

JEFF: I think I _____ the first report later today. By tonight,
   2. (read)

I _____ it, and by tomorrow afternoon I
   3. (finish)

_____ a summary.
   4. (write)

ANGIE: Great! I _____ our partners to find out about their
   5. (call)

sales, and I _____ the main points by tomorrow
   6. (summarize)

afternoon. Then I _____ you what I've written and
   7. (give)

start reading the second report. When we _____
   8. (meet)

on Wednesday, I _____ it. When
   9. (complete)

_____ we _____ our
   10. (practice)

presentation?

JEFF: How about Wednesday night? It's good that we _____
   11. (have)

time to practice before our presentation! We'll be prepared.

---

4 | TOMORROW

Read Mahmoud's plan for the day. Complete the sentences by writing the future, future progressive, future perfect, or future perfect progressive forms of the verbs in the schedule. Use contractions when possible. Some items may have more than one possible answer.

8:00 have breakfast
9:00 work at the office
9:30 meet with Gerald
10:00 shop for office supplies
12:00 have lunch
1:00 write report
2:00 talk to advertisers
3:00 meet with investor
3:30 pay office bills
5:00 go home
6:00 eat dinner
7:00 leave for theater

0. By the time Mahmoud leaves for work, he _____*'ll have had*_____

breakfast.

1. At 9:15, he _____ at the office.

2. At 9:40, he _____ with Gerald for only 10 minutes.

3. By 10:30, he _____ for office supplies for 30 minutes.

4. At 12:00, he _____ lunch.

5. At 1:05, he _____ his report.

6. At 2:00, he _____ to advertisers.

7. By 2:30, he _____ to advertisers for a half hour.

8. By the time he meets with the investor, he _____ to the

advertisers.

9. At 3:35, he _____ office bills.

10. At 5:00, he _____ home.

11. By the time he leaves for the theater, he _____ dinner.

5 | EDITING: EMPLOYEE APPRECIATION DAY

Read this e-mail to employees about employee appreciation day. There are 11 mistakes in the use of the future progressive, future perfect, or future perfect progressive. The first mistake is already corrected. Find and correct 10 more. (Note: There is often more than one way to correct a mistake.)

                   celebrate

The company will ~~celebrates~~ employee appreciation day this Friday!

By the end of the week, you will have work too much and relaxed too little. Meditation expert James Clark had helped to bring balance back into your life. Clark will be lead a free meditation workshop this coming Friday at 4:00 P.M. Before teaching us how to meditate, he'll speaking about the benefits of relaxation. The first 10 people to arrive to the workshop had received free tickets to a health spa. All employees will be having a chance to win a certificate for a free massage. After Clark's workshop, we began the employee office party at 7:30. By then we will have been sit for hours, so be prepared to dance. We will offering free sushi, and a band will have played as well. Join us!

PART III Diagnostic Test

1 | LISTENING: DINNER WITH FRIENDS

🎧 *Listen to a conversation between Jonathan and his friend, Sara. Circle the letter of the best answer. You will hear the recording two times.*

0. What does Jonathan mean when he says, "This is a great Japanese restaurant, isn't it?"
   a. He'd like to know if Sara likes his choice of restaurant.
   b. He is making comments about the quality of the restaurant, and he expects Sara to agree.
   c. He doesn't know how Sara feels about the restaurant, and he doesn't care either.

1. Sara really likes the food at this Japanese restaurant. How about Jonathan?
   a. He doesn't say if he likes the food.
   b. He doesn't like the food.
   c. He likes the food too.

2. Do Jonathan and Sara eat at this restaurant occasionally?
   a. Yes, they do.
   b. No, they don't.
   c. This is their first time at the restaurant.

3. Does Jonathan know Sara's been to Japan?
   a. No, he doesn't, and he expects Sara to tell him.
   b. Yes, he does.
   c. No, he doesn't, but he doesn't expect Sara to say anything.

4. What does Jonathan mean when he says, "Learning Japanese is quite a challenge, isn't it?"
   a. I don't think it's a challenge.
   b. Isn't it a challenge?
   c. I already know it's a challenge.

5. Do Jonathan and Sara like jazz?
   a. No, they don't.
   b. Yes, they do.
   c. Only Jonathan likes it.

6. Are they going to the movies after dinner?
   a. Yes, they probably are.
   b. Sara wants to go, but Jonathan doesn't.
   c. No, they probably aren't.

7. Does Sara think they should be able to find something to do?
   a. No, she doesn't.
   b. No, she wants to eat.
   c. Yes, she does.

2 | BEST FRIENDS

A. *Read the story and conversation. Then answer the questions below.*

Two friends, Mary and Kate, met in England when they were kids. When the girls turned 10 years old, Kate's family moved to France, but Mary's didn't. They lived in separate countries for 15 years before they saw each other again. During those years, Kate wrote to Mary once a year, but Mary didn't write back. She preferred to call on Kate's birthday. They finally met when Kate decided to invite Mary to Paris for an exhibition of her artwork. They discovered many surprising similarities in their lives. Mary had studied art for years and had had her first exhibition when she turned 18. So had Kate. Mary had once had a Spanish boyfriend. So had Kate. Mary had never worn glasses, and neither had Kate. However, there were important differences. Mary was shy and moody, but Kate wasn't. Kate didn't like to travel, but Mary did.

B. *Now read part of the conversation that Mary and Kate had when they met in Paris.*

KATE: You look so happy! You can't believe we're finally together again, can you?

MARY: No, I can't! It's incredible. Anyway . . . you're still studying art, aren't you?

KATE: Yeah, I'm studying painting in a small art school run by the famous painter Marc Lesser.

MARY: It's right in downtown Paris, isn't it?

KATE: You're right, it is. How did you know? Have you been to that area?

MARY: Yes, once. I worked on a mural with Marc three years ago when I was a student at an art school near his studio. We were lucky to be able to work with him.

KATE: That's amazing! But aren't you still studying art?

MARY: No, not anymore. But I miss being a student. How do you like studying with Marc?

KATE: I love it. He's really great, isn't he? And of course painting is my life. I wouldn't trade it for anything. You wouldn't either, would you?

MARY: No, I wouldn't!

C. *Read the story and conversation from Exercise 2 again. Then read each statement and circle* **T** *(true) or* **F** *(false).*

(T) F   0. Only Mary stayed in England after she was 10.

T F   1. Mary wrote letters to Kate.

T F   2. Only Kate studied art.

T F   3. Kate is not shy or moody.

T F   4. Mary and Kate had art exhibitions when they were 18.

T F   5. Only Mary had a Spanish boyfriend.

T F   6. Kate has worn glasses.

T F   7. At the beginning of the conversation, Mary doesn't think Kate is a student.

T F   8. Kate thinks Marc Lesser is a good teacher.

T F   9. Mary is surprised that the art school is downtown.

T F   10. Kate thinks that Mary is still a student.

D. *Reread the conversation. Find two negative tags and two affirmative tags. Write them in the table below. An example is given.*

NEGATIVE TAGS	AFFIRMATIVE TAGS
0. *aren't you*	3. _____
1. _____	4. _____
2. _____	

3 | MEETING A FRIEND

Read the story about two friends. Complete the passage with the correct words. Write the letter of the best answer on each line.

Sometimes things that you can never explain just happen for no reason! In high school, I was

in Mrs. Wood's grammar class. ____*a*____ (a. So b. Neither c. Too d. Either) was a new student named
0.

Maria. On the first day of class, Mrs. Wood kept switching our names. Our classmates did

_____ (a. so b. neither c. too d. either). I kept correcting them, and _____ (a. so b. neither c. too
1.   2.

d. either) did Maria. Because of this, we became close friends. We did everything together. I was on

the soccer team, and so _____ (a. were b. got c. was d. did) Maria. I took French, and Maria did
3.

_____ (a. too b. so c. neither d. either). However, we never liked the same music or movies. I

4.

liked pop music, but Maria _____ (a. doesn't b. did c. won't d. didn't). Maria always went to

5.

science fiction movies, _____ (a. and b. but c. or d. that) I didn't. Just the other day, I asked

6.

Maria about Mrs. Wood's grammar class. She doesn't remember the class, but I _____

7.

(a. don't b. know c. too d. do). We are so different! It's amazing that we're such good friends!

---

4 | DOING WELL

*Read this conversation between two acquaintances. Complete the conversation by writing
the correct form of the tag question or negative question.*

RUTH: You've lived in Orlando for years, _____*haven't you*_____ ?

0.

MIKE: Yes. I came here one summer to work at an amusement park and never left.

RUTH: No kidding! I also started out working in an amusement park.

MIKE: Really? I can't believe we both did that!

RUTH: Neither _____. When you came, you didn't know anyone here,

1.

_____ ?

2.

MIKE: No. But it's easy to meet people here, _____?

3.

RUTH: That's true. So where are you working now? I'm managing a water park.

MIKE: Oh, yeah? I'm managing a comedy club.

RUTH: Well, our jobs are pretty different. Your job is probably busiest at night, but mine

_____. The park is busy during the day. You're also probably busy all year

4.

round, but _____ not. Summer is our busiest season.

5.

MIKE: Our jobs aren't that different, _____? We're both in the "fun" business!

6.

Don't you love watching people have a good time?

RUTH: Yes, _____. It makes my job even better.

7.

MIKE: We've really done well here, _____? Don't you sometimes wonder how it

8.

all worked out so well?

RUTH: Yes, I _____. We've both had some amazing luck and good fortune.

9.

5 | CATHY AND NATALIE

Read this information about Cathy and Natalie. Complete the sentences by writing additions of similarity or contrast using **so, too, neither, not either,** *and* **but**.

	CATHY	NATALIE
Country of birth	Australia	Canada
Age	29	22
Weight	110 lbs.	120 lbs.
Hair color	Brunette	Brunette
Eye color	Brown	Brown
Hobbies	Reading	Reading
Education	Oxford University	High school graduate
Job	Actress	Secretary
Languages spoken	English, Japanese	English, French

0. Cathy is Australian, _____ but Natalie isn't _____.

1. Cathy is 29, _____.

2. Natalie weighs 120 lbs., _____.

3. Natalie loves reading, _____.

4. Natalie doesn't have blonde hair, _____.

5. Cathy hasn't attended acting school, _____.

6. Cathy attended university, _____.

7. Natalie has brown eyes, _____.

8. Cathy is an actress, _____.

9. Natalie speaks French, _____.

6 | LIFE OF A STAR

Read the information about actor Clive Simons. Imagine you are going to interview him and you are not sure of the information in parentheses. Write negative yes / no questions to check that information.

0. Clive Simons: singer, actor, (songwriter?)
1. lives in Los Angeles (live in California since graduating from high school?)
2. born in Ames, a city in Iowa (grew up in Iowa?)
3. records and listens to music in his home (has always loved R&B?)
4. worked for DreamField Studio, but they didn't want to release his albums (work was too extreme for them?)
5. acted in *Goodnight New York* and *Adventureland*—both were big successes (liked *Adventureland* better?)
6. enjoys singing, but will work on more movies and TV series (just started his own company?)
7. future plans (opening an organic French restaurant?)

0. *Aren't you a song writer?* _____

1. _____

2. _____

3. _____

4. _____

5. _____

6. _____

7. _____

7 | EDITING: SANDY'S DATE

Read Sandy's diary entry about a first date. There are eight mistakes in the use of negative yes / no questions, tag questions, and sentence additions. The first mistake is already corrected. Find and correct seven more.

Dear Diary,

This evening I went on my first date with David. What a funny, handsome guy!

It's funny how you sometimes "click" with someone, ~~is~~ *isn't* it? For the most part, I feel I really

clicked with David. We have so much in common! For example, he likes classical music and so

am I. I love old movies, and he is too. Both of us read every day, but I don't read fiction, and

either does he. But although we are similar in many ways, in other ways we are. David likes fast

food, but I am. (Isn't he realize how bad fast food is for him?) He doesn't work out regularly, but

I work out every day. All in all, I feel pretty good about the date. I hope we go out again. I guess

time will tell, will it?

Unit 7 Achievement Test

1 | LISTENING: NEW FRIENDS

🎧 *Listen to a conversation between David and someone he just met at a conference in Toronto. Circle the letter of the best answer. You will hear the recording two times.*

0. Does David know the woman works for Globe Enterprises before asking her?
   a. No, he doesn't, but he doesn't expect an answer.
   b. Yes, he does, and he expects her to confirm the information.
   c. No, he doesn't, and he expects an answer.

1. Does David know Globe Enterprises is headquartered in San Francisco?
   a. Yes, he does, but he doesn't expect the woman to agree.
   b. No, he doesn't, and he expects an answer.
   c. Yes, he does. He asks her to confirm what he knows.

2. Does David know it doesn't snow in San Francisco?
   a. No, he doesn't, and he expects an answer.
   b. Yes, he does, and he expects the woman to agree.
   c. No, he doesn't, but he doesn't expect an answer.

3. Does the woman know about the winter weather in Toronto?
   a. Yes, she does, and she expects David to agree.
   b. No, she doesn't, so she asks David.
   c. No, she doesn't, but she expects David to agree.

4. Does the woman think that David likes the winter?
   a. Yes, she does, and she's commenting on it.
   b. No, she doesn't, and she expects David to agree that he doesn't.
   c. Yes, she does, and she doesn't expect an answer.

2 | CITY LIVING

A reporter and Jack are talking about living in the city. Match the statements with the tags.

Statement	Tag
_d_ 0. You haven't lived here very long,	a. haven't you?
____ 1. No, but most cities are the same,	b. can't they?
____ 2. But it's especially great living in this city,	c. isn't it?
____ 3. Most of the residents don't want to leave,	d. ~~have you?~~
____ 4. You've visited other cities,	e. aren't they?
____ 5. Yes, and cities can be overwhelming,	f. do they?
____ 6. Cities have their own personalities,	g. doesn't it?
____ 7. San Francisco does for sure,	h. don't they?
	i. can they?

3 | A TV INTERVIEW

Read this conversation between a host and a celebrity. Complete the conversation by writing the correct form of the tag question or negative question.

HOST: You've been living in Seattle for some time, ___*haven't you*___ ?
                                                        0.

KAUFMAN: Yeah, I moved here from New York City 10 years ago. I love it here.

HOST: Most actors want to live in New York. _____ plan to stay in New York
                                                      1.
to work in the theater?

KAUFMAN: Yes. I thought I'd stay in New York forever. But life does surprise us,

_____ ?
      2.

HOST: True. You've found success with the new TV series, _____ ? I hear that
                                                                3.
it was ranked the top show this season.

KAUFMAN: Well, I hope that's true. But those rankings change quickly, _____ ?
                                                                            4.

HOST: Yes, _____ . But don't you also have a blockbuster movie coming out
           5.
next summer?

KAUFMAN: _____. It's called *Summer on Ice*. That's a catchy name,
                  6.

      _____?
                  7.

  HOST: Yes, it is. Well, we'll all be watching your TV show and looking forward to the

movie.

---

4 | LIFE OF A STAR

*Read the information about writer Jean Murphy. Imagine you are going to interview her
and you are not sure of the information in parentheses. Write negative* yes / no *questions
to check that information.*

0. Jean Murphy: writer (screenwriter?)

1. born in Reno, a city in Nevada (grew up in Reno?)

2. wrote short stories as a teenager (has always loved short stories?)

3. worked for *Writers Weekly* magazine, but they didn't want to publish her stories (topics in the
stories were too controversial?)

4. wrote book and screenplay *On the Edge*—both were big success (Jean liked the book better?)

5. enjoys writing novels but will work on some more screenplay projects (just opened her own
writing school?)

0. *Aren't you a screenwriter?* _____

1. _____

2. _____

3. _____

4. _____

5. _____

5 | EDITING: BANK ROBBERY

Read this script for a TV drama. There are eight mistakes in the use of negative yes / no *questions and tag questions. The first mistake is already corrected. Find and correct seven more.*

NICK: You stole the money from the bank, ~~haven't~~ *didn't* you?

LEE: I don't think banks miss money. They have enough, don't that?

NICK: If it's not yours, you can't take it. Doesn't you know right from wrong?

LEE: Yes, I don't. But I need the money and they will never notice, will they?

NICK: Of course they will. In fact, the missing money has already been reported on TV. Doesn't you think you should turn yourself in?

LEE: No. But I'm leaving town tonight. I just need you to tell the police you haven't seen me.

NICK: I can't do that. I can't afford to get in trouble with the police. You know that, do you?

LEE: Yes, I guess that's true. You can't even help me hide, can you?

NICK: Yes, I can. There is no way for me to help you hide. Don't I understand?

Unit 8 Achievement Test

| 1 | **LISTENING: NEW FRIENDS** |

🎧 *Listen to a conversation between Jason and his friend Diana. Circle the letter of the best answer. You will hear the recording two times.*

0. Jason loves shopping, movies, and good food. How about Diana?
   a. She likes shopping and good food, but she doesn't like movies.
   b. She does too.
   c. She doesn't like any of those.

1. Sometimes Diana shops online. How about Jason?
   a. He never shops online.
   b. He sometimes shops online too.
   c. He doesn't say anything about online shopping.

2. Do they like to read?
   a. Only Diana likes to read.
   b. Only Jason likes to read.
   c. Yes, they both like to read.

3. Do they like to read biographies?
   a. Yes, they do.
   b. No, they don't.
   c. Only Diana does, but Jason doesn't.

4. Do they watch sports on TV?
   a. No, they don't.
   b. Yes, they do.
   c. Only Jason does.

5. Do they play sports?
   a. Only Diana does.
   b. Only Jason does.
   c. No, they don't.

2 | A TRUE STORY

Read the story. Then answer the questions below.

Vladimer and Erik, twin brothers, were born in Russia and adopted by different families when they were very young. Erik's family lived in the United States, but Vladimer's family didn't. Erik never knew he had a brother, but Vladimer did. In fact, Vladimer asked the adoption agency to contact Erik. When the two finally met, they discovered some surprising similarities and differences between them. Vladimer had worked as a travel agent and as a restaurant manager. So had Erik. Vladimer had a big black dog. So did Erik. Vladimer had never been married, and neither had Erik. Vladimer liked hiking, dancing, and Italian food. Erik did too. However, Vladimer was outgoing and expressive, but Erik wasn't. Erik traveled a lot, but Vladimer didn't.

*Reread the story. Then read each statement and circle **T** (true) or **F** (false).*

T **(F)** 0. Both brothers stayed in Russia.

T **F** 1. One brother knew he had a twin.

T **F** 2. Erik was not outgoing or expressive.

T **F** 3. Only Vladimer was married.

T **F** 4. They both worked as travel agents.

T **F** 5. Erik had a big black dog.

T **F** 6. Only Vladimer liked hiking.

T **F** 7. Erik and Vladimer traveled a lot.

T **F** 8. The brothers met, but didn't find any similarities between them.

3 | THERE'S MY DINNER!

*Read this conversation at a fast food restaurant. Complete the conversation by writing the correct forms of additions with **so, too, neither, not either** and **but** in the blanks.*

JASON: I'm so happy we finally got here.

DIANA: So _____*am I*_____. I didn't think we'd make it.
         0.

JASON: Me _____. I've always wanted to have burgers here.
              1.

DIANA: I can't believe how similar we are.

JASON: Neither _____. It's like seeing myself in the mirror.
                2.

DIANA: Except, of course, when it comes to lettuce. I don't like lettuce on my burger.

JASON: But _____. You don't like lettuce in your salad either.
            3.

DIANA: But _____. You like lettuce in just about everything, don't you?
    4.

JASON: Yes, I do! I wonder if there's anyone else who likes lettuce as much as I do.

DIANA: So _____!
    5.

---

4 | PARK AND KUMAR

Read this information about Park and Kumar. Complete the sentences by writing additions of similarity or contrast using **so, too, neither, not either,** *and* **but**.

	PARK	**KUMAR**
Ethnicity	Korean	Indian
Age	26	27
Height	5'8"	6'1"
Weight	160 lbs.	170 lbs.
Hair color	Dark	Dark
Eye color	Brown	Brown
Hobbies	Video games	Video games
Favorite food	Burgers	Burgers
Education	College graduate	College graduate
Job	Investment banker	None

0. Park is Korean, _____*but Kumar isn't*_____ .

1. Kumar doesn't have green eyes, _____ .

2. Park likes to eat burgers, _____ .

3. Kumar weighs 170 lbs., _____ .

4. Kumar is 6'1", _____ .

5. Kumar loves video games, _____ .

6. Kumar doesn't have blonde hair, _____ .

7. Park hasn't attended graduate school, _____ .

8. Park is 26, _____ .

5 | EDITING: BEST FRIENDS

*Read this student's composition. There are five mistakes in the use of sentence additions.
The first mistake is already corrected. Find and correct four more. (Note: There can be more
than one way to correct a mistake.)*

My Best Friend Lindsay

Lindsay is younger than I ~~is~~ *am*. However, we look alike. I have curly blonde hair and dark blue

eyes, and so have she. We share some of the same interests too. I love to talk and hang out with

friends, and she does too. Both of us play piano, but I can't play guitar, and either can she. There

are also some differences between my friend Lindsay and me. For example, she likes eating

Chinese food, but I don't. She doesn't want to be a movie star, but I don't. I am creative, but she

not. Our appearance makes us seem similar, but once you get to know us, we seem quite

different.

PART III Achievement Test

| 1 | LISTENING: DINNER WITH FRIENDS |

🎧 *Listen to a conversation between Ross and his friend Carol. Circle the letter of the best answer. You will hear the recording two times.*

0. What does Ross mean when he says, "This is a great Indian restaurant, isn't it?"
   a. He'd like to know if Carol likes his choice of restaurant.
   b. He is making a comment about the quality of the restaurant, and he expects Carol to agree.
   c. He doesn't know how Carol feels about the restaurant, and he doesn't care either.

1. Carol really likes the service and food at the restaurant. How about Ross?
   a. He only likes the food but not the service.
   b. He doesn't like the service or the food.
   c. He likes the service and the food.

2. Does Carol like the way the waitresses dress at the restaurant?
   a. No, she doesn't.
   b. Yes, she does.
   c. She doesn't say anything about it.

3. Does Ross know Carol's been to India?
   a. No, he doesn't, and he expects Carol to tell him.
   b. No, he doesn't, but he doesn't expect Carol to say anything.
   c. Yes, he does.

4. What does Ross mean when he says, "Living abroad is quite an experience, isn't it?"
   a. I don't think it's quite an experience.
   b. Isn't that quite an experience?
   c. I already know it's quite an experience.

5. Do Carol and Ross like rock music?
   a. No, they don't.
   b. Yes, they do.
   c. Only Ross likes it.

6. Are they going to a concert after dinner?
   a. Yes, they probably are.
   b. No, they probably aren't.
   c. Carol wants to go, but Ross doesn't.

7. How does Carol feel when she stays home?
   a. She feels like she's missing out on something.
   b. She feels like she can relax.
   c. She feels happy.

2 | MEETING FRIENDS

Read the story about pianists Sunan and Kevin.

Sunan and Kevin recently met at an amateur piano competition. Sunan was competing, and so was Kevin. In a conversation, they found out that there were quite a few similarities and differences between them. For example, they both were born in Thailand. However, Sunan stayed in Thailand, but Kevin's family didn't. They moved to England. The musicians grew up in different cultures, speaking different languages. Sunan spoke two languages, Thai and English, but Kevin didn't. He only spoke English. Sunan had studied piano since he was four and had his first public performance at the age of ten. So had Kevin. Sunan had also learned to play the violin, and so had Kevin. Sunan had never worn contact lenses, and neither had Kevin. Sunan liked car racing, reading, and boxing. Kevin did too. However, Sunan was tall, but Kevin wasn't. Also, Kevin didn't like to chat very much, but Sunan did.

Now read part of the conversation Sunan and Kevin had when they met at the competition.

SUNAN: Performing is scary, isn't it?

KEVIN: Yes, it certainly is!

SUNAN: It doesn't matter how often I perform—I always get nervous. You always get nervous too, don't you?

KEVIN: Yes, I do. So . . . are you still studying piano?

SUNAN: Uh-huh. In fact, I'm a student at Juilliard!

KEVIN: You aren't talking about the one in New York City, are you?

SUNAN: Yes, I am. Why?

KEVIN: Because I just graduated from there last spring. How come I've never met you?

SUNAN: Actually, I just got accepted and will start school this fall.

KEVIN: No wonder. You already studied music in Thailand, didn't you?

SUNAN: Yes, I did, but I bet Juilliard will be different. You can't do any better than Juilliard, can you?

KEVIN: That's what they say.

A. *Reread the story and conversation. Then read each statement and circle* **T** *(true)*
or **F** *(false).*

T (**F**) 0. Only Sunan plays the piano.

T   **F**   1. Both musicians grew up in Thailand.

T   **F**   2. Kevin's family moved to England.

T   **F**   3. They both speak several languages.

T   **F**   4. Kevin is not tall.

T   **F**   5. They both had a public performance at age 10.

T   **F**   6. Only Kevin plays the violin.

T   **F**   7. Neither musician has worn contact lenses.

T   **F**   8. Sunan and Kevin like reading.

T   **F**   9. Kevin doesn't think performing is scary.

T   **F**   10. Kevin has heard of Juilliard.

T   **F**   11. Kevin thinks Sunan has already gone to music school.

B. *Reread the conversation. Find two negative tags and two affirmative tags. Write them in*
the table below. An example is given.

NEGATIVE TAGS	AFFIRMATIVE TAGS
0. *isn't it* _____	3. _____
1. _____	4. _____
2. _____	

---

3 | PIANO SISTERS

Read the story about two sisters. Complete the passage with the correct words. Write the
letter of the best answer on each line.

When I was 10, I started taking piano lessons. _____*a*_____ (**a. So b. Too c. Neither d. Either**) did my
                                                        0.

sister. I took lessons from Ms. Davis, but my sister _____ (**a. wasn't b. didn't c. did d. doesn't**).
                                                                    1.

Her teacher was Ms. Lowman. Her teacher had been a professional concert pianist, and mine

had _____ (**a. too b. so c. either d. neither**). She learned to play all of the scales, and _____
      2.   **3.**

(**a. too b. either c. neither d. so**) did I. My sister didn't miss a single lesson, and neither did I. My

sister practiced every day, but I _____ (**a. wasn't b. didn't c. did d. doesn't**). I only practiced twice
                                              4.

a week when my mother made me. After five years of lessons, my sister was an excellent piano

player, but I _____ (**a. wasn't b. didn't c. did d. doesn't**). Sometimes hard work pays off!
                5.

4 | FRIENDS ARE TALKING

Read this conversation between two friends. Complete the conversation by writing the correct form of the tag question or negative question.

JASON: You've lived in San Diego for years, _____*haven't you*_____?
0.

JOEY: Yes . . . since I came here to work on my first job. It's been a while.

JASON: When you arrived, you didn't know anyone here, _____?
1.

JOEY: No. It was pretty brave of me to leave all my friends, _____?
2.

JASON: Yes. But things have worked out pretty well, _____? You make a decent
3.

living, and the most important thing is that you enjoy your job. I'm so happy for you.

JOEY: There were times when I didn't think I would make it. You know that feeling,

_____?
4.

JASON: Yeah. I also had a hard time when I first came here. I don't like looking back at those

early days.

JOEY: Neither _____. It's kind of painful. But now I have the future to look
5.

forward to. My business is growing every quarter.

JASON: Yes, mine is _____. Don't you look forward to getting those financial
6.

reports?

JOEY: Yes, _____. Especially right now when business is good.
7.

JASON: Yeah, it's been a good year, _____?
8.

JOEY: It certainly has. I hope it continues for the next decade, don't you?

JASON: Yes, I _____.
9.

5 | BROOKE AND LORENA

Read this information about Brooke and Lorena. Complete the sentences by writing additions of similarity or contrast using **so**, **too**, **neither**, **not either**, *and* **but**.

	BROOKE	LORENA
Country of birth	USA	UK
Age	35	33
Weight	130 lbs.	140 lbs.
Hair color	Blonde	Blonde
Eye color	Blue	Blue
Hobbies	Cooking	Cooking
Education	College graduate	PhD candidate
Job	Restaurant manager	Teacher
Languages spoken	English and Spanish	English and German

0. Brooke is American, _____ but Lorena isn't _____.

1. Brooke is 35, _____.

2. Lorena weighs 140 lbs., _____.

3. Lorena loves cooking, _____.

4. Lorena doesn't have dark hair, _____.

5. Lorena is earning her PhD, _____.

6. Brooke has never learned to speak Chinese, _____.

7. Lorena has blue eyes, _____.

8. Brooke is a restaurant manager, _____.

9. Lorena speaks two languages, _____.

6 | LIFE OF A DOCTOR

Read the information about Ashley Morgan, a doctor. Imagine you are going to interview her and you are not sure of the information in parentheses. Write negative yes / no questions to check that information.

0. Ashley Morgan: doctor (doctor in family medicine?)

1. name (named after a famous poet?)

2. born in Winona, a city in Minnesota (grew up in Minnesota?)

3. started becoming interested in science at age 10 (has always loved science?)

4. interested in many areas of medicine (first interest was children's medicine?)

5. worked in a family clinic and in an emergency room (disliked working in an emergency room?)

6. enjoys children's medicine, but will practice more family medicine (just opened her own office?)

7. future plans (planning to publish a book on family medicine?)

0.   *Aren't you a doctor in family medicine?* _____

1. _____

2. _____

3. _____

4. _____

5. _____

6. _____

7. _____

7 | EDITING: MIMI'S FRIEND

Read Mimi's diary. There are nine mistakes in the use of negative yes / no *questions, tag questions, and sentence additions. The first mistake is already corrected. Find and correct eight more. (Note: There can be more than one way to correct a mistake.)*

Dear Diary,

    Sometimes I forget about people from my past. That probably happens to everyone, ~~does~~ *doesn't* it? I don't want to forget people—especially my friend Debbie. She is just a year older than I am, and we look a lot alike. People sometimes confuse us, but our boyfriends doesn't. I have straight, brown hair and light blue eyes, and so have she. We share some of the same interests too. I love dancing and musicals, and she did too. Both of us cook every day, but I don't cook meat, and either does she. Although there are a lot of similarities between us, there are also some differences. That's not too surprising, isn't it? For example, she likes shopping, but I do. I like to talk on the phone, but she did. Luckily, we both love writing e-mails. That'll make it easy for us to keep in touch, and I won't forget her, won't I?

PART IV Diagnostic Test

60 Items
Score: _____

1 | LISTENING: A CAREER IN FITNESS

🎧 *Listen to the interview between a* Fitness *magazine reporter and Brian, who is helping his father get in shape. Complete the interview by writing the words that you hear. Use words from the box. You will hear the recording two times.*

adding	get	let	spending	to help	work out
decide	helping	opening	~~starting~~	to meet	

REPORTER: Tell us about your start as a fitness trainer.

BRIAN: _____*Starting*_____ a career in fitness is not an easy task. I began with a plan of
            0.

_____ my own fitness training center. My father sold some of his land
     1.

_____ me financially. One month later he asked me to help him
     2.

_____. He was my first long-term client. So I created a specialized
     3.

program _____ my father's needs. I started out slowly; then I added
           4.

extra time and weights to my father's exercise routine. _____ time and
                                5.

weights gradually helped my father's body _____ used to the exercises.
                                   6.

I _____ my father _____ when to work out, but I tell
      7.   8.

him to try to do something every day. Now, he loves it.

2 | FITNESS TRAINING

Read Brian's dad's article about his fitness training in the same magazine. Complete the passage with the correct verb forms. Write the letter of the best answer on each line.

I really like the training program that my son designed ____a____ (a. to make b. makes
0.

c. making d. make) me _____ (a. staying b. stay c. to stay d. stays) healthy and fit. He made me
1.

_____ (a. following b. followed c. follow d. follows) his training program together with a nutrition
2.

program. All the exercises are tough, but I still look forward to _____ (a. goes b. gone c. going
3.

d. went) to the gym. I would never work out so much if I didn't have a trainer _____ (a. to help
4.

b. helped c. helps d. to helping) me _____ (a. doing b. does c. to doing d. do) it. To start the nutrition
5.

program, my son had me _____ (a. to limit b. limit c. to limiting d. limited) my food choices first,
6.

and then gradually I added some back. Good food makes your body and mind _____
7.

(a. become b. becomes c. becoming d. to become) healthy. I have lost 23 pounds and 24 inches. I believe

everyone can manage _____ (a. maintains b. to maintain c. maintained d. maintenance) a healthy
8.

body weight through daily exercise and good eating habits. You just have to make it _____
9.

(a. happening b. happens c. to happening d. happen).

3 | TEEN ZONE

Read this article on being a teenager. Complete the article by writing the gerund or infinitive forms of the verbs in parentheses. Some items may have more than one right answer.

Oh, those "good old days." Sometimes, I want _____to be_____ a teenager again! I still
0. (be)

remember _____ movies like *The Breakfast Club* and _____ on the
1. (watch)   2. (talk)

phone for hours. I didn't work in my teens. I had many years ahead of me for

_____. My friends were different. It surprised me _____ that they
3. (work)   4. (learn)

wanted _____ older, and they wanted _____ more responsibility. I
5. (be)   6. (have)

never did!

Well, those great times are gone. Ever since my twentieth birthday many years ago, I have

been working full time _____ my bills and _____ care of my family.
             7. (pay)   **8. (take)**

_____ older has had some good points, however. I have learned
9. (Get)

_____ to other people and _____ ideas and opinions that are
10. (listen)   **11. (respect)**

different from mine.

4 | AN AMBITION

*Read this student's report on an interview with a child. Complete the report by writing the
gerund or infinitive forms of the verbs in parentheses. Some items may have more than one
right answer.*

Good morning, everyone. Today, I want _____*to present*_____ the information I got from
                                     0. (present)

_____ an eight-year-old boy named Patrick about his ambitions. Patrick told me
1. (interview)

that when he grows up, he wants to be a chocolate engineer. He would prefer

_____ every day working with chocolate. _____ new recipes for
2. (spend)   **3. (invent)**

chocolate is his dream job, and _____ the new recipes would be the best part of
                                  4. (taste)

that job. He also dreams of _____ candy production. He really wants
                            5. (supervise)

_____ his own chocolate, which would help him _____ very
6. (make)   **7. (become)**

popular. He'd let children _____ their own recipes in his shop. He hopes he could
                           8. (create)

have them _____ the packages themselves, and he would invite them
                 9. (design)

_____ their names on their chocolate. These might sound like unrealistic goals to
10. (print)

you, but Patrick believes his inspiration and determination will help him _____ his
                                          11. (achieve)

dreams.

5 | AN ADVERTISEMENT

A. Read the advertisement for Family Fun Walks. Complete the advertisement by writing the gerund or infinitive forms of the verbs in parentheses.

AAPP FAMILY FUN WALKS

We invite you to _____*to light up*_____ your family life with us.
0. (light up)

Join us in _____ the Urban Trail through a Family Fun Walk.
1. (explore)

Consider _____ for fitness, _____ nature,
2. (walk)   3. (share)

and socializing with other nature lovers.

Fun for all fitness levels!

We recommend _____ friends, kids, and pets!
4. (bring)

Sunday, September 17, 8:00–9:00 A.M. Meet at Park High School

Walk volunteers are needed _____ us coordinate regular walks.
5. (help)

Choose any time _____ —morning, noon, or after work.
6. (join)

If you're interested in _____ or if you want _____ in
7. (volunteer)   8. (participate)

the walk, please call Health Services at 767-3157.

B. Complete the following sentences about the advertisement. Use the correct forms of the verbs in parentheses.

1. One advantage of the Family Fun Walk is getting _____ other people.
(meet)

2. Volunteers can help participants _____ the paths to walk on.
(find)

3. The walk will let people of all fitness levels _____.
(participate)

6 | EDITING: LEARNING TO DANCE

Read the letter to the editors of a school newspaper. There are 11 mistakes in the use of gerunds and infinitives. The first mistake is already corrected. Find and correct 10 more.

To the Editors,

     Yesterday, my roommate persuaded me ~~joining~~ *to join* a dancing club. I didn't really want going because I thought a dancing club would make you doing only aerobic dance. I am not good at hear rhythm. However, be at the club changed my mind. I learned other forms of dancing that I didn't know before. Many people, like me, think they can't dance because they have poor coordination, but anyone can dance. The main purpose is to enjoy moving to music, so to dancing is suitable for people of all ages. As with most activities, it's a matter of start gently and to build up to the right level of activity. So I invite you all finding some time enjoy yourselves by to dance.

Unit 9 Achievement Test

1 | LISTENING: FOOD MATTERS

🎧 *Listen to a conversation between two friends about grocery shopping. Complete the conversation by writing the words that you hear. Use words from the box. You will hear the recording two times.*

buying	eating	sharing	to come	to go
cooking	getting	~~to buy~~	to find	to shop

LISA: Hi, Jane. Where are you going?

JANE: To the store. I need _____*to buy*_____ some groceries.
                          0.

LISA: Oh! I usually eat in the cafeteria. But next semester, I'll be in an apartment, so I'll need

_____ to the grocery store. Where do you usually go _____?
          1.   **2.**

JANE: There's a supermarket near my house that I like. It's a great place for

_____ fresh fruit and vegetables, and they have an ethnic foods section if
          3.

you need _____ something special.
                4.

LISA: Sounds great. Do you share the food expenses with your roommates?

JANE: Yes. We've found that by _____ the expenses, we can save a lot. We each
                                        5.

pay $15 or $20 for groceries and take turns shopping.

LISA: That's a good idea.

JANE: Oh, I wanted to remind you _____ to our dinner party tomorrow night.
                                           6.

LISA: I'll be there. Do you need some help with the cooking?

JANE: Actually, we're asking everyone to pay $10 for the food. We're planning on

_____ the meal together.
          7.

LISA: Oh, no problem. Sounds fun. See you tomorrow.

JANE: See you. Bye.

2 | TO PLAN OR NOT TO PLAN

Read this short questionnaire about planning habits. Complete the questionnaire by writing the gerund or infinitive forms of the verbs in parentheses. Some items may have more than one right answer.

Question 1: When you go on vacation, what do you prefer _____*to do*_____ ?
0. (do)

    a. You plan every detail in advance.

    b. You look at a few options in advance but make final decisions when you're there.

    c. You don't plan anything in advance. You prefer to make all decisions when you're there.

Question 2: What statement best describes how you do your regular grocery shopping?

    a. You make a detailed list of everything you need _____ .
1. (buy)

    b. You make a rough list for yourself.

    c. You decide what to buy without a list.

Question 3: You've bought unassembled furniture. How do you start _____ it?
2. (build)

    a. You read through the instructions carefully first and then follow them step by step.

    b. You leap in and build it. _____ to the instructions only happens when you
3. (refer)

    get stuck.

    c. You build it without using the instructions.

Answer key:

    If most of your answers are "**a**"s, you are a planner. You love _____ everything
4. (organize)

you do in your life.

    If most of your answers are "**b**"s, sometimes you choose _____ , and
5. (plan)

occasionally you don't plan things in advance.

    If most of your answers are "**c**"s, you aren't really interested in _____ all the
6. (arrange)

details of your life.

3 | A PERSUASIVE TEACHER

Read these sentences about a student's work with a professor. Complete the sentences using the words in parentheses. Use the simple present or simple past tense for the first verb.

0. My professor, Dr. Chandler, _____*wants me to work*_____ harder.
   (want / me / work)

1. Every day, she _____ questions or problems that come up
   (urge / me / write down)

   when I read articles.

2. Dr. Chandler _____ a project with her this semester.
   (persuade / me / do)

3. I _____ with her several times a month.
   (look forward to / talk)

4. Dr. Chandler also _____ me with the project.
   (ask / my friend George / help)

5. George and I _____ that we work together.
   (be happy about / her / suggest)

4 | A FOOD FAIR

Read the e-mail message below. Complete the e-mail message by writing the gerund or infinitive forms of the verbs.

Hi Robin,

Sorry I missed your call last night. I didn't want to go out, but my girlfriend persuaded me

_____*to go*_____ to the annual food fair at her university. When I got there, I was very
0. (go)

surprised because I didn't expect _____ so many different kinds of food, but then I
1. (see)

realized it was an international food fair. I visited food stands from many different countries. The

students at each stand were very good at _____ the table and the food. My
2. (decorate)

girlfriend and I enjoyed _____ the different foods so much that we couldn't stop
3. (taste)

_____. We agreed _____ to the food fair again next year.
4. (eat)   **5. (go)**

See you later,

Martin

5 | EDITING: STAYING IN PLACE, STAYING FIT

Read these tips on how to stay fit in your home. There are eight mistakes in the use of gerunds and infinitives. The first mistake is already corrected. Find and correct seven more.

You don't need ~~leaving~~ *to leave* the house to stay fit. With a bit of thought, everyday tasks can keep you trim. Here's our list of the top four tips for stay fit in your own home.

Tip 1: To dry off after a hot shower is a great time doing some simple shoulder stretches. Begin by to hold the towel. Then, still holding the towel with both hands, place one hand behind your back and the other above your head. With the top arm, pull upwards so your other arm ends up between your shoulder blades. Hold for 10–15 seconds and then change arms.

Tip 2: If you're a tall person, you probably know that bending down to do the dishes isn't good for your back. Instead, simply stand with your legs wide apart to lowering your body and arms. This position keeps your back straighter. Unfortunately, it means you won't have an excuse to keep you from wash dishes!

Tip 3: Forget the gym. If you want strong leg muscles, then all you need are some stairs. Simply climb the stairs 10 times a day to work the muscles. After three weeks, you should start to notice a difference.

Tip 4: Keep to do your exercises. If you want to stay fit, don't give up.

Unit 10 Achievement Test

30 Items
Score: _____

1 LISTENING: A DOCUMENTARY

🎧 *Listen to a conversation between two students. Complete the conversation by writing the words that you hear. Use words from the box. You will hear the recording two times.*

makes me feel	made us watch	~~help us learn~~
let students learn	get me to think	let me know
makes you get	let me read	making us learn
letting us search for	lets us choose	help you get

FRANK: So, how was the movie?

DEBBI: I really liked it.

FRANK: What was it about?

DEBBI: It was a documentary film about endangered wildlife for my environmental biology class.

Professor Thompson wants to _____*help us learn*_____ as much as possible about
0.

the subject.

FRANK: So, what were you supposed to get out of it?

DEBBI: Um . . . mostly background information. In this class, we have to do a presentation, but

he _____ a kind of endangered species to report about. The film
1.

gave us some background for the presentation.

FRANK: Cool. What kind of animals are you interested in?

DEBBI: I'm not sure yet. _____ some more, and then I'll decide. The
2.

professor's _____ information for two more weeks before we
3.

have to decide on our endangered animal.

FRANK: Oh, you have plenty of time.

DEBBI: Well, not really . . . I've got a lot of work in my other classes.

FRANK: Yeah, me too.

DEBBI: But I'm not too worried because he the movie first. Having some background

information better before starting my project.

FRANK: Yeah, the movie can _____ a rough idea before you start.
 6.

DEBBI: Right. I'm a visual person, so films really _____ more clearly.
 7.

FRANK: _____ how it goes, OK?
 8.

DEBBI: I will.

---

2 | AT THE ZOO

Read the conversation between two friends about a job at the zoo. Complete the conversation with the correct verb forms. Write the letter of the best answer on each line.

TRAN: Hi, Linda. Hey, where were you at lunch? I thought we were going to meet.

LINDA: Sorry, Tran. I had to work at the zoo. I didn't really want to, but my boss

_____*a*_____ (a. had b. get c. let d. helped) me work because he was short-handed.
 0.

TRAN: He shouldn't have _____ (a. let b. made c. get d. helped) you go to work. Does he know
 1.

that you work part time?

LINDA: Yes, he does. But he really needed someone to work. You know, my boss

_____ (a. helped b. let c. had d. made) me to get the job, so I had to go.
 2.

TRAN: I think it would be fun to work at the zoo. I remember when my family and I went to the

zoo. My sister wanted to ride a camel. But my dad said she was too little so he didn't

_____ (a. got b. made c. had d. let) her do that. And she started crying. Then when we
 3.

went to see the bears, they weren't there. A zookeeper _____ (a. get b. made c. let
 4.

d. help) them go into their cave so he could clean the cage. Then we went to see the

monkeys. It's interesting to see the way they take care of their babies. I like the way the

mothers always _____ (a. lets b. has c. let d. making) their babies hang onto their necks.
 5.

LINDA: I think the zoo is one of those places where it's more fun to visit than to work.

3 | AT AN ANIMAL CLINIC

Read this story about a terrible assistant at an animal clinic. Complete the sentences using the words in parentheses.

0. Dr. Banda's assistant, Marjorie, wrote a report on Mrs. Mira's cat. But she forgot

   to include some information about the cat's lab test results. So Dr. Banda

   _____*had her revise*_____ the report.
   (have / her / revise)

1. But Marjorie didn't know how to write about the lab test results, so she needed more help. Dr.

   Banda _____ the test results.
   (help / her / describe)

2. Then Marjorie said that she was not good at typing. So Dr. Banda

   _____ it.
   (get / another assistant / type)

3. Later that day, Mrs. Mira came to pick up her cat. Marjorie

   _____ while she finished a phone call with her friend.
   (have / her / wait)

4. When the report was finally ready, Mrs. Mira didn't understand it. Neither did Marjorie, so

   she _____ it to her.
   (have / Dr. Banda / explain)

5. When Mrs. Mira was about to leave the clinic, she realized that her cat's name tag was lost.

   Marjorie would not _____ it, and Dr. Banda had to fire her.
   (help / her / find)

4 | CAMPUS CONVERSATIONS

*Read the conversations between Bonnie and Joe. Complete the conversations with **make**, **have**, **let**, **help**, or **get** and the correct form of the verb in parentheses.*

0. BONNIE: How did you get that poster of the zebra baby? I've heard that it's very popular.

   JOE: I just went to the zoo and asked a worker to _____ *help me find* _____

   (me / find)

   it.

1. BONNIE: Do you know where the Pet Festival is going to be held this year?

   JOE: Probably on campus. I know that the Festival committee will

   _____ the event.

   (our university / arrange)

2. BONNIE: I didn't go to the Festival meeting this morning. Did you do much?

   JOE: Yes, the president _____ a brochure.

   (us / prepare)

3. BONNIE: Do you know that there'll be a cat show in the Civic Center this weekend?

   JOE: Yes, I heard that. I'd like to enter. I should _____

   (my sister / groom)

   my cat before the competition.

4. BONNIE: That's a good idea. I'd like to enter my cat too, but he's at my friend Tom's house

   because my apartment doesn't allow pets.

   JOE: You should _____ your cat for you.

   (him / enter)

5 | EDITING: A WILD VISITOR

Read an e-mail from Susan to her friend, Dina. There are nine mistakes in the use of **make,** **have, let, help,** *and* **get.** *The first mistake is already corrected. Find and correct eight more.*

Hey Dina,

I have an exciting experience to share with you. Last week I saw a deer come into my

backyard. It made my daughter ~~yelling~~ *yell* when she saw it while she was playing in the yard. I

hurried to get my child to coming in the house and then called the police. Two policemen from

Animal Control came right away. One policeman, Officer Malloy, had his partner, Officer Perez,

to chase the deer into the corner of the yard. Then they helped each other catching the deer.

Officer Malloy had Officer Perez threw a rope around the deer's neck. Of course, this made the

deer to try to run away. But they held onto it and had it walks to their van. Officer Malloy

helped Officer Perez putting the deer in a cage. I don't know what they're going to do with it.

Hopefully, they'll let it to go back to a national park.

Take care,

Susan

PART IV Achievement Test

60 Items
Score: _____

1 | LISTENING: PET'S HEALTH

🎧 *Listen to an interview with the author of a new pet book. Complete the interview by writing the words that you hear. Use words from the box. You will hear the recording two times.*

achieve	finding	preventing	to function	to look
believing	healing	to care	~~to have~~	to meet

INTERVIEWER: Hi, George. We're glad _____*to have*_____ you with us. Can you tell us about
0.

your new book?

GEORGE: Well, this book is for consumers who have been tricked into _____
1.

that they're feeding their pets healthy foods. Actually, they're giving them food

that is not healthy at all and that contains cheap grains and dangerous chemicals.

This book will tell you how to help your pets _____ a balanced diet
2.

so their bodies can operate at maximum efficiency. The food should provide all of

the nutrition that is important for a pet's body _____ properly. A
3.

body that is working properly does an amazing job of _____
4.

disease and _____ itself. However, good health requires the
5.

nutrients of a well-balanced diet. In terms of _____ the proper diet
6.

for our pets, we must learn _____ beyond our own beliefs and
7.

needs so we can begin _____ for the animals that are so important
8.

to us in a proper way.

INTERVIEWER: That's very interesting . . .

2 | DOG FOOD

Read the conversation between two neighbors. Complete the conversation with the correct verb forms. Write the letter of the best answer on each line.

LAURA: What kind of food do you feed your dogs?

BECKY: I've just started ____*a*____ (a. buying b. did buy c. bought d. buy) organic dog food. I used
      0.

      to prepare fresh food for them before, but I found that it's not very convenient

      _____ (a. do b. done c. doing d. to do) that every day.
      1.

LAURA: So you buy organic dog food?

BECKY: It's easier _____ (a. fed b. to feed c. feed d. feeds) them that way. And you can let them
                2.

      _____ (a. to eat b. to eating c. eat d. eaten) anytime by just _____ (a. to put b. putting
      3.   4.

      c. put d. to putting) it in an automatic food dispenser.

LAURA: That makes sense. It lets them _____ (a. eat b. eating c. to eat d. ate) when they're
                                          5.

      hungry.

BECKY: Yeah, they get the vitamins, minerals, and fats important for them _____ (a. to grow
                                                                            6.

      b. grew c. growing d. to growing), but you don't have to worry about _____ (a. be prepare
                                                                      7.

      b. prepared c. preparing d. to prepare) food for your pets after _____ (a. working b. works
                                                                  8.

      c. to work d. to working) hard all day.

LAURA: I'll have my husband _____ (a. buying b. buys c. to buy d. buy) some on his way home
                          9.

      tonight.

3 | A TEEN CONCERT

Read the article about going to a teen concert. Complete the article by writing the gerund or infinitive forms of the verbs. Some items may have more than one right answer.

Is being a "teenager" just a state of mind? I think so. ____*Being*____ young is all about
                                                          0. (be)

how you think. I am 41 now, but I still go to pop music concerts. This month I went to a Bobbie

Williams concert. I was surprised _____ tickets and happy _____
                                  1. (to get)   2. (see)

him perform. He has a great voice, and he writes awesome lyrics. He's also really cute!

Of course, I made a big sign for the concert. It said, "Sing Forever!" Before Bobbie sang his

hit single, he announced he needed three fans _____ him. He picked two guys from
                                                    3. (help)

the front and then said, "And . . . how about you with the sign?" I ran onto that stage, excited

_____ close to one of the greatest guys in music. And I got to help him
   4. (be)

_____ the song.
   5. (sing)

The concert lasted for a couple of hours, but _____ that long didn't slow
                                                  6. (perform)

Bobbie down at all. In fact, even at the end of the concert, Bobbie was still going strong, and he

had the audience _____ every word of the last song of the night with him.
                     7. (sing)

I know I'm not so young anymore, and I can never get anyone _____ I'm a
                                                                8. (believe)

teenager (although I think about _____ my age is 19 sometimes). But I hope
                                    9. (claim)

_____ true to myself and not let my "old age" _____ my opinions or
   10. (stay)   **11. (change)**

tastes.

4 | A COOL CAREER

Read the article about an interesting career. Complete the article by writing the gerund or
infinitive forms of the verbs. Some items may have more than one right answer.

I've just found out that one of my aunts is a pet policeperson. I met her yesterday at a family

get-together. She had a normal police job for many years, but she decided ____*to change*____
                                                                              0. (change)

jobs. She couldn't stand _____ to sad stories from people. She's also not good at
                            1. (listen)

_____ people from _____. She decided to let all the other police
   2. (stop)   **3. (fight)**

_____ that job. So, it's not surprising that she left her full-time police work. But it
   4. (do)

did surprise me that she left her job _____ an investigative pet detective. With her
                                         5. (become)

special training, she's working _____ people _____ their lost pets.
                                   6. (help)   **7. (find)**

She has trained dogs _____ the missing pets. The dogs have helped her
                        8. (track)

_____ more than 800 lost dogs, cats, snakes, and iguanas. I admire my aunt's job a
   9. (locate)

lot. She's very happy _____ a job she likes. It reminds me _____ job
                         10. (have)   **11. (consider)**

satisfaction as a priority for my future.

5 | AN ADVERTISEMENT

A. *Read the advertisement for Smart Sugarless Preserves. Complete the advertisement. Use the gerund or infinitive forms of the verbs in parentheses.*

Now It Comes with Tasty Ingredients

Once you taste our Smart Sugarless Preserves, you'll be eager _____*to try*_____ more.
0. (try)

Smart Sugarless Preserves has worked hard _____ a new product
1. (create)

that combines great-tasting goodness with brand sweeteners. Our delicious,

low-calorie preserves will make you _____ , and our jam
2. (smile)

will prevent you from _____ weight! After
3. (gain)

_____ to our loyal customers and by
4. (listen)

_____ new recipes with better ingredients,
5. (try)

we have created a new jam that everyone in your house will love!

Try Smart Sugarless Preserves Today!

_____ the best products to you and your family is our job.
6. (Bring)

If you need _____ a store or want _____
7. (locate) **8. (make)**

comments, call 1-888-553-8858 or visit us online at

www.smartsugarless.com

B. *Complete the following sentences about the advertisement. Use the gerund or infinitive forms of the verbs in parentheses. Some items may have more than one right answer.*

1. The advertisement suggests the jam helps _____ you from gaining weight.
   (keep)

2. The company wants to get customers _____ their product.
   (buy)

3. The customers' loyalty makes the company _____ good products.
   (produce)

6 | EDITING: JOB INTERVIEW ADVICE

Read the letter to the editor of a school newspaper with advice on job interviews. There are 11 mistakes in the use of gerunds and infinitives. The first mistake is already corrected. Find and correct 10 more. (Note: There can be more than one way to correct a mistake.)

Dear Editor,

My name is Carole Ford. I would like ^{to} share my experience about job interviews. I've interviewed for many jobs and most companies offered me the positions I wanted. Interviewing well is not difficult achieving. I have many useful stories and tips pass along. First, did you know that some companies are looking for people solving their problems? They will hire you if they truly believe that you have the skills helping them. In an interview, if your answer is too brief, you may leave your interviewer unsatisfied. Talk too much during an interview will make your interviewer wanting to get rid of you, even if you ARE the best candidate for the job. Give answers that you think the interviewer wants hearing may cause a stressful and unsatisfying interview. A job interview is an intimidating process, and even the most self-confident, outgoing, and friendly person can easily give the impression of to be tongue-tied and incompetent. The best solution to this common problem is come to the interview prepared, knowing exactly what to expect.

PART V Diagnostic Test

1 | LISTENING: STUDY HABITS

A. 🎧 *Listen to Brian talk about his study habits. Complete the passage by writing the words that you hear. You will hear the recording two times.*

Now that I'm in college, I'm a good student. But when I was younger I almost dropped

_____*out*_____ of school. I thought the teachers gave out too much homework, and then I'd
    0.

put _____ doing the homework until the last minute. I also found it difficult to
  1.

turn down my friends. If they wanted to make trouble, I usually went _____ with
                                          2.

them. Worst of all, I let my parents down with my poor grades. But after high school, I guess I

grew _____ a little. Now I set up a study schedule for myself every week and stick
   3.

_____ it. I show up to all my classes and keep _____ my homework.
  4.   **5.**

I sure wish I had figured out these study skills in high school!

B. *Reread the passage above. Write down five more phrasal verbs from the passage next to their meanings below. Do not use phrasal verbs you wrote down in the previous exercise.*

0. _____*gave out*_____ distribute

1. _____ establish

2. _____ solve / understand

3. _____ disappoint

4. _____ appear

5. _____ reject / say no

2 | FRIENDSHIP

Read this article about friendship. Find eight phrasal verbs and write them in the first column of the table below. Seven of the verbs have direct objects. Write the direct objects in the second column. An example is given.

If you want to throw away your friendships, criticize your friends. Criticism tears people down. Soon your friends will want to cut off all contact with you. Praise, on the other hand, never brings people down, but cheers them up. Pick out the good qualities in your friends. Then, when you run into them, watch their faces light up when you give them a sincere compliment. Try it, and you'll soon find out the importance of your friendships.

PHRASAL VERB	DIRECT OBJECT
0. *throw away*	0. *your friendships*
1. _____	1. _____
2. _____	2. _____
3. _____	3. _____
4. _____	4. _____
5. _____	5. _____
6. _____	6. _____
7. _____	7. _____
8. _____	8. _____

3 | A ROBBERY

*Read this passage from a mystery novel. All of the phrasal verbs are underlined and listed below. In each blank, write **S** if the phrasal verb is separable, and **I** if the verb is inseparable. Remember that a verb may be separable even if it is not separated in the passage.*

Donna's computer had been <u>acting up</u>. She was <u>going away</u> on a business trip the next day, and wouldn't <u>get back</u> for a week. She <u>called in</u> the company computer repair man. He <u>picked up</u> and <u>took away</u> the computer. A week later, Donna <u>came back</u> from her business trip. She <u>went up</u> the stairs to her office. She was <u>counting on</u> her computer being fixed. But instead, she found that someone had robbed her office. Could the robber have been the repair man?

0. __I__ acting up

1. _____ going away

2. _____ get back

3. _____ called in

4. _____ picked up

5. _____ took away

6. _____ came back

7. _____ went up

8. _____ counting on

4 | A DREAM COME TRUE

Read about Ralph Price, who climbed Mount Everest. Complete the information. Use the correct forms of the phrasal verbs from the boxes.

| use up | put off | grow up | go after | take on | ~~lay off~~ |

When Ralph Price was _____*laid off*_____ from his job, he had a chance to

0.

_____ his lifelong dream, to climb Mount Everest! Price _____

1. **2.**

dreaming of climbing Everest, but he had _____ it _____ for years.

3.

Now he had the opportunity to _____ the challenge.

4.

| fight off | find out | put on | set up | move around | take off |

He read and _____ all he could to prepare himself. He bought special clothes

5.

to _____ the bitter cold. Then he _____ to Nepal to fulfill his

6. **7.**

dream. His first night on the mountain, he _____ his tent, but it was too cold to

8.

sleep. He had to _____ all his clothes to stay warm.

9.

| take in | look up | give up | pay off | let down | keep on |

Ralph had to _____ his warm clothes _____ the entire trip.

10.

Before he reached the top, he was almost ready to _____ because of the cold. But

11.

when he arrived at the top, he _____ from the ground and _____

12. **13.**

the beautiful view. All of his efforts had _____.

14.

| think over | turn down | come down | go back | end up with |

Unfortunately, Ralph _____ some frozen toes. When he _____

15. **16.**

the mountain, doctors had to cut off two of his toes. When he was asked if he would ever

_____ and climb Everest again, he said, "I've _____ it

17.

_____ and the answer is no. I've already made my dream come true, and I don't

18.

want to lose any more toes!"

PART V

5 | PREPARING FOR A PARTY

Complete the phone conversation between Carol and Jim by writing the correct forms of the phrasal verbs and pronouns in the blanks.

CAROL: I'm afraid we may have to call off our party tonight! There's too much we

still have to do!

JIM: Please don't _____*call it off*_____. I've already done everything!
                              0.

CAROL: Did you pick up all the papers that were in the front yard?

JIM: I _____ this morning after you left.
              1.

CAROL: Great! Did you get a chance to cut down all the weeds, too?

JIM: Yes, I _____ earlier today.
                  2.

CAROL: What about all the dishes that we needed to put away?

JIM: I _____ already.
            3.

CAROL: Wonderful! Oh, did you turn the couch cushion over to cover up that spot?

JIM: Yes, I _____, which _____ pretty well.
                    4.   **5.**

CAROL: Good! What else? Oh, we needed to take out the garbage.

JIM: I already _____.
                      6.

CAROL: Did you also happen to throw out that old rug that we have in the kitchen?

JIM: Yes, I _____ when I took out the garbage.
                  7.

CAROL: Also, I was really hoping we could straighten up the living room.

JIM: I _____ about an hour ago.
            8.

CAROL: Wow! Well, so all we'll have to do when I get home is to put up decorations?

JIM: I just _____.
                  9.

CAROL: Amazing! How did you manage to do it all?

JIM: I haven't done anything else today! I think I'm too tired to have a party!

6 | EDITING: NEW TV

*Read this phone conversation between Diego and Luisa. There are eight mistakes in the use
of phrasal verbs. The first mistake is already corrected. Find and correct seven more.*

DIEGO: Did the TV arrive today?

LUISA: Yes, and I tried ~~out it~~ *it out*. I turned it in, but I couldn't hear anything. So I turned away the

volume as high as it would go, but I still couldn't hear anything. So I called the

company. I was on hold for an hour, so I hung off. I even tried to look out information

on the Internet, but I couldn't come up any reason with why the sound didn't work. So I

turned off it, and I'm planning to send back it today.

DIEGO: That's too bad!

Unit 11 Achievement Test

---

1 | LISTENING: JOB HUNTING

A. 🎧 *Listen to Helen and Tim's conversation about job hunting. Complete the conversation by writing the words that you hear. You will hear the recording two times.*

HELEN: Hi, Tim! Have you found _____*out*_____ about any jobs yet?
0.

TIM: No, and I'm about to give _____. Maybe I'll just have to stay at my old
1.

job.

HELEN: I wish I could cheer you _____. Let's talk it _____. Have
2.   **3.**

you looked _____ working with your brother?
4.

TIM: I thought it _____, but I don't think it would work _____.
5.   **6.**

His restaurant has really been struggling lately.

HELEN: OK. Well, have you set _____ an appointment with that job agency I told
7.

you about?

TIM: I left a message on their answering machine, but they haven't called _____
8.

yet.

HELEN: Keep trying. If you try hard to find a job, I'm sure your efforts will pay

_____.
9.

B. *Reread the conversation. Then read each statement and circle* **T** *(true) or* **F** *(false).*

Ⓣ   F   0. Tim is ready to quit looking for a new job.

T   F   1. Helen wants to help Tim be happy.

T   F   2. Helen thinks Tim doesn't need any help finding a job.

T   F   3. Tim thinks he can help at his brother's restaurant.

T   F   4. Tim hasn't made an appointment with a job agency.

T   F   5. Tim can't work because he has a bad back.

T   F   6. Helen thinks Tim will get paid.

2 | JOB HUNTING MESSAGE BOARD

Read this posting on a job hunting message board. Complete the posting by circling the correct particle.

Q: I've been looking for a job for a month now, and I can't figure <u>off / out / up</u> what's wrong.
   0.
   Nine employers have already turned me <u>down / off / in</u>. What am I doing wrong?
   1.

A: First, you should look <u>up / over / out</u> your resume again. Find a friend to help you pick
   2.

   <u>out / up / at</u> any problems with your resume. Then, take <u>off / out / up</u> any mistakes or put
   3.   **4.**

   <u>on / together / up</u> a new resume. Second, you should put <u>up / in / on</u> some nice clothes
   5.   **6.**

   before your interview. Sit up straight in your chair and keep <u>up / on / in</u> smiling. And
   7.

   remember, if you get turned <u>down / up / in</u>, keep looking! You'll get <u>over / under / ahead</u> in
   8.   **9.**

   your job search if you sit <u>up / down / through</u>, figure <u>over / out / down</u> a plan, and then let
   10.   **11.**

   opportunity in when it knocks!

3 | EDITING: A NEW JOB

Read Tim's journal entry about finding a job. There are five mistakes in the use of phrasal verbs. The first mistake is already corrected. Find and correct four more. (Note: There can be more than one way to correct a mistake.)

   Now that I've moved into my new office, I have so much to do! First, I need to

straighten ~~away~~ *up* my old office. Second, I have to clean up all my papers and throw away them.

Also, I should take over the garbage. Then, I need to take down my picture in the old office and

hang up it in the new one. Finally, I need to put around some shelves.

Unit 12 Achievement Test

| 30 Items |
| Score: _____ |

1 | LISTENING: A FAKE CONTEST

🎧 *Listen to this conversation between Donna and Franco. You will hear the recording two times. Then read each statement and circle* **T** *(true) or* **F** *(false).*

(T) **F** 0. Donna wanted help.

T F 1. Donna was trying to draw figures.

T F 2. Donna didn't want to leave the form outside.

T F 3. Franco agreed to look at the form.

T F 4. Donna wanted to buy a house.

T F 5. Franco believed the vacation contest offer.

T F 6. Franco told Donna that she should throw away the form.

T F 7. Donna agreed to enter a contest over the phone.

T F 8. Donna agreed to hold on to something.

T F 9. Franco wanted Donna to end the call.

2 | DIET AND EXERCISE

Read this article about weight gain and underline the phrasal verbs. Then write down each phrasal verb from the article next to its meaning.

Are you gaining weight? If you're like most people, you need to cut down on your food portions and get off the couch. Write down a plan to eat right and get regular exercise, and stick to it. At the very least, turn music up in your room and dance for exercise. And turn down offers of candy or dessert. Don't fill up on empty calories such as soda and sports drinks. Watch out for your old habits and don't let yourself come up with excuses to cheat. If that happens, you could end up with severe health problems!

Phrasal Verb	Meaning
0. _____ *cut down on* _____	reduce
1. _____	be careful about
2. _____	eventually have
3. _____	write on a piece of paper
4. _____	increase the volume
5. _____	leave
6. _____	continue doing
7. _____	create
8. _____	do not accept
9. _____	eat too much of

3 | IN THE BOOKSTORE

Read these conversations about shopping. Complete the conversations by writing the correct forms of the phrasal verbs and pronoun object in the blanks.

Conversation 1:

A: I just love bookstores! Did you pick out the magazines you wanted?

B: Yeah, I _____ *picked them out* _____, but they're so expensive!
0.

A: That's OK. I have a discount card. You can't pass up this offer!

B: Well, OK. I guess I can't _____. . . . Oh look, have you
1.

read this book? It was hard to put down!

A: Oh yes, I've read it. I couldn't _____ either!
2.

Conversation 2:

A: Let's sit down over there. I want to take off my shoes. They're killing me!

B: I don't think you're allowed to _____ in the store. I saw a

                          3.

    sign that read, "Shirt and shoes required."

A: Seriously, if I keep my shoes on, I'm going to die!

B: No, you won't. Come on please, _____. Let's go to the

                                 4.

    shoe store next door and buy you some new shoes, and then you can take them off.

Conversation 3:

A: What are you looking for?

B: I wrote down the title of a book I saw on TV yesterday so I could buy it today.

A: Where did you _____? Did you throw the piece of paper

                        5.

    away?

B: Oh, you're right! I did _____.

                       6.

---

4 | EDITING: CAR DEALERSHIP AD

Read this ad from a car dealership. There are seven mistakes in the use of phrasal verbs. The first mistake is already corrected. Find and correct six more.

                in on

Cash ~~on in~~ this sale of a lifetime! Come to Car World and check up our new line of cars.

Keep up to the newest technology and buy a new model. We'll give back you $1,000 in cash.

We'll even fill on your gas tank for the first month, FREE! You can always count us on for good

deals. You can't turn this opportunity up!

PART V Achievement Test

---

1 | LISTENING: TOO MUCH HOUSEWORK

A. 🎧 *Listen to Jean and Sam's conversation about housework. Complete the conversation by writing the words that you hear. You will hear the recording two times.*

JEAN: You sure look tired. What have you been doing?

SAM: Housework! First, I picked _____*up*_____ a ton of garbage from my yard and cut
0.

down some bushes. Then I folded clothes and put them _____. I had to
1.

turn over my living room rug to cover _____ a big spot on it. Then I threw
2.

away some old food in the refrigerator and took _____ the trash.
3.

Finally, I straightened up my bedroom. And I just finished putting some shelves

_____.
4.

JEAN: Wow! You *have* been busy! Can I help out with anything?

SAM: If you don't mind, you could help me turn this couch _____. Then I think
5.

I'll sit down and rest!

B. *Reread the conversation above. Find five more phrasal verbs. Write them below, next to their meanings. (Note: Only use words that are given in the passage. Do not use any words that you wrote.)*

0. _____*cut down*_____ cut

1. _____ discarded

2. _____ give assistance

3. _____ be seated

4. _____ put upside down

5. _____ made orderly

PART V

2 | BROKEN RADIO

Read this conversation between Eric and Katya. Find eight phrasal verbs and write them in the first column of the table below. Seven of the verbs have direct objects. Write the direct objects in the second column. An example is given.

ERIC: Would you mind turning the radio on? I want to listen to the weather.

KATYA: Oh, didn't I tell you? The radio's broken. You can't hear anything. I tried to turn up the volume, but I couldn't figure out any way to fix it. I even tried calling your dad to see if he could look it over, but he's gone away on a business trip.

ERIC: That's too bad. I just took it in to be repaired a month ago. Maybe we should send it back to the company. Or maybe your brother could check it out.

KATYA: The last time my brother tried to fix something of ours, we never got it back!

PHRASAL VERB	DIRECT OBJECT
0. *turning on*	0. *the radio*
1. _____	1. _____
2. _____	2. _____
3. _____	3. _____
4. _____	4. _____
5. _____	5. _____
6. _____	6. _____
7. _____	7. _____
8. _____	8. _____

3 | AN ACTOR'S STORY

Read this passage from a magazine story. All of the phrasal verbs are underlined and listed below. In each blank, write S if the phrasal verb is separable, and I if the verb is inseparable. Remember, a verb may be separable even if it is not separated in the passage. (Note: Some phrasal verbs have more than one meaning. Consider only the meaning of each verb in this passage.)

Harold loved acting, but he <u>dropped out</u> of acting school when he was 21. He was told that he should <u>look into</u> other careers because he just didn't have any talent. Then he <u>ran into</u> a friend who invited him to be in a play. At first, Harold <u>turned down</u> the offer, but he later decided to <u>take on</u> the part. A local theater critic wrote a great review about Harold's acting, and soon after his career <u>took off</u>! A Hollywood producer <u>signed up</u> Harold to appear in his first film last year. He said, "My story is proof that if you <u>hold on</u> to your dreams and <u>keep on</u> working to achieve them, you will succeed."

0. __I__ dropped out

1. _____ look into

2. _____ ran into

3. _____ turned down

4. _____ take on

5. _____ took off

6. _____ signed up

7. _____ hold on

8. _____ keep on

PART V

4 | BUGS!

Read this magazine article about bugs. Complete the article. Use the correct forms of the phrasal verbs in the boxes.

take out	go away	build up	show up	~~turn up~~	figure out

Have bugs been _____*turning up*_____ in your house? Have you been trying to
0.

_____ how to make them _____? One of the biggest reasons bugs
1.   **2.**

may _____ is because there is food. Little pieces of food can _____
3.   **4.**

in corners, under cabinets, or behind the refrigerator, so be sure to clean!

throw out	take away	use up	put down	put off

Always _____ any garbage that may attract bugs. Don't _____
5.   **6.**

cleaning food spills. Also _____ any plants brought in from outside where the bugs
7.

may live. You could also _____ some poison in places were you see the bugs.
8.

sign up for	take in	light up	look into	leave on	call in

Another suggestion is to _____ any dark places where you've seen the bugs,
9.

and _____ the light _____ at night. You may want to
                                       10.

_____ companies who offer extermination. And _____ someone
11.   **12.**

who specializes in bugs. Some companies offer free bug inspections that you could

_____.
13.

go back	look up	protect from	pay off	leave out	keep out

Finally, there is a lot of information on the Internet that you can _____ about
                                                 14.

_____ yourself _____ bugs. Any efforts that you take to educate
                              15.

yourself will _____. Hopefully, some of the suggestions given here will help you get
16.

the bugs to _____ outside where they belong and to _____!
17.   **18.**

5 | PREPARING FOR A BUSINESS TRIP

Complete this conversation between an attorney and her secretary, Noemi. Write the correct forms of the phrasal verbs and pronouns in the blanks.

ATTORNEY: Noemi, while I'm gone on my business trip, I'll need you to do a few things for me.

First, would you contact Mr. Irvine and call off our lunch meeting for tomorrow?

NOEMI: Actually, he already told me that he needed to _____*call it off*_____ himself.

0.

ATTORNEY: Fine. Next, I'll need you to check out a book from the law library for me. Here's the

title and author.

NOEMI: Sure, I'll _____ before you get back.

1.

ATTORNEY: Thank you. Will you also fill out these tax forms by Thursday?

NOEMI: OK. I can probably _____ by tomorrow afternoon.

2.

ATTORNEY: Great. Also, can you give these files back to Ann tomorrow?

NOEMI: Oh, I forgot! She asked me today when we could _____ to her.

3.

ATTORNEY: That's OK. Could you also look over the numbers on this report and make sure they

are correct?

NOEMI: Sure, I'll _____.

4.

ATTORNEY: Now, while I'm gone, we should be getting a new painting for the lobby. Would you

mind putting the painting up by the door?

NOEMI: Sure. I'll probably have Tom help me _____.

5.

ATTORNEY: That's fine. And just leave the old painting out for the janitor to put away.

NOEMI: OK. I'll just _____ with a note on it for him.

6.

ATTORNEY: Great. Also, please fill up the fish tank if it looks low.

NOEMI: All right. I'll _____ if it needs it.

7.

ATTORNEY: Great, and just keep the filter on while I'm gone, too.

NOEMI: OK, I'll _____.

8.

ATTORNEY: Oh, one last thing. Can you drop this package off at the post office tomorrow?

NOEMI: Sure, I'll _____ in the morning. Have a good trip!

9.

6 | EDITING: A MISLEADING AD

Read this description of a misleading TV ad. There are eight mistakes in the use of phrasal verbs. The first mistake is already corrected. Find and correct seven more.

    I saw a TV ad that said to call ~~on~~ *up* this company and cash on in a great opportunity to own

my own business. I thought I should check it up and find off more about it. When I called, the

guy I talked to wanted to sign me out to sell a product I had never heard of. He said he could set

up me to start earning thousands of dollars a week. All he needed was $50 to send me my kit. It

didn't take me long after that to hang off the phone. I can't believe I fall in those kinds of ads.

PART VI Diagnostic Test

1 | LISTENING: AN INTRODUCTION TO NEW ZEALAND

A. 🎧 *Listen to this passage about New Zealand. Complete the passage by writing the words that you hear. You will hear the recording two times.*

New Zealand is a small country _____*that has*_____ geographic, political, economic,

0.

and cultural features _____ unique. The two islands of New Zealand,

1.

_____ from volcanic activity in the South Pacific Ocean, have lush farmland and

2.

beautiful landscapes.

Despite its relatively small size, New Zealand has established its own position in global

affairs. For example, New Zealand doesn't allow any ships _____ nuclear weapons

3.

to visit its ports. Ships _____ nuclear energy are not welcome either.

4.

In addition, New Zealand has been a strong advocate of the United Nations,

_____ an organization that tries to resolve conflicts around the world. New

5.

Zealand also supports the World Trade Organization, _____ to break down

6.

international trade barriers. The products _____ in international markets are

7.

primarily agricultural ones such as milk, lamb, and beef.

B. *Read the rest of the passage about New Zealand. Complete the passage with the correct relative pronouns and verbs. Write the letter of the best answer on each line.*

The international interests of New Zealand have resulted in a multi-ethnic society _____c_____
                                                                                        0.
(**a. which consist   b. who consists   c. that consists   d. that consist**) of immigrants from Asia, the South Pacific,

and southern and eastern Europe. This is a change from the early years of New Zealand's history

_____ (**a. where a large number   b. when a large number   c. which a large number   d. whose large number**) of
    1.
immigrants from England, Scotland, and Ireland joined the indigenous population of the Maori

people. New Zealand's blend of different populations creates a unique island nation _____
                                                                                        2.
(**a. that is   b. whom mostly live   c. whom is   d. that mostly live**) interesting and full of life. The people,

_____ (**a. which mostly live   b. whom mostly live   c. who mostly live   d. that mostly live**) on the South
    3.
Island, mainly depend on agriculture as a way of life.

New Zealand also has many interesting geographical features _____ (**a. that make   b. who**
                                                                              4.
make   c. in which make   d. which they make) it a great place to visit. The North Island has many

mountains _____ (**a. which make   b. that it makes   c. which they make   d. where make**) it beautiful at
              5.
sunrise. On the South Island, natural hot springs _____ (**a. who provide   b. which they provide**
                                                                  6.
c. that provide   d. where provide) relaxing vacation spots are everywhere. There are many hotels

_____ (**a. who allow   b. in which allow   c. that allow   d. where allow**) access to the springs, and tourists
    7.
_____ (**a. which visit   b. with whom visit   c. whom visit   d. who visit**) can relax in their healing waters.
    8.
Other features include many rivers and lakes _____ (**a. where contain   b. that contain   c. in which**
                                                            9.
contain   d. for which contain) clean, clear water. New Zealand's forests, _____ (**a. which have**
                                                                                    10.
b. that have   c. where have   d. who have) many unique trees and plants, are one of a kind.

2 | A NEW ZEALAND VACATION DIARY

Read these diary entries about Solange's recent trip to New Zealand. Circle 18 adjective clauses. Be sure to circle the full adjective clause.

January 5

I flew into Auckland this morning. The city, which is surrounded by volcanic hills, harbors, bays, beaches, and islands, is absolutely beautiful! A New Zealand native who I met on the plane told me that Auckland used to be the capital of New Zealand. But now the capital is Wellington, which I will visit the day after tomorrow. After checking into my hotel, which is clean and not too crowded, I spent all day at the beach.

January 7

Yesterday I went to Mount Eden and One Tree Hill, where I enjoyed amazing views. I also spent some time at the Auckland Domain, which is a huge park. Then I went to the Auckland Museum, where many Polynesian artifacts are on display. I saw a 150-year-old Maori war canoe that was 30 meters long! I spent the rest of the day at the beach. Some Australians who needed another player for a game of volleyball asked me to play. I did, and I had a lot of fun!

This morning I drove to Wellington, which is on the southern coast of the North Island. I rode a cable car that took me all over the city. The cable car driver, who had lived in Wellington his whole life, told me to eat at Cuba Mall, which is a popular place for street performers. My meal, which was inexpensive, was delicious.

January 8

This morning I took the InterIslander Ferry to Picton, which is on the South Island. On the ferry I met a girl named Jill who works in Nelson, and we drove to Nelson together. My destination was Abel Tasman National Park, where they offer guided walks. Surprisingly, that was Jill's workplace! I took her guided walk. On the walk, which was two miles long, I saw a baby penguin! My trip to New Zealand, which I've been looking forward to all year, has been amazing so far!

3 | FUN FACTS ABOUT NEW ZEALAND

Read these facts about New Zealand and its history. Combine the pairs of sentences. Make the second sentence in each pair an adjective clause with an object relative pronoun or **when** *or* **where**. *Make any other necessary changes. Some items may have more than one right answer.*

0. New Zealand is located southeast of Australia. Australia is in the South Pacific Ocean.

New Zealand is located southeast of Australia, which is in the South Pacific Ocean.

1. New Zealand is a country. The country consists of two islands, the North Island and the South Island.

_____

_____

2. Eighty percent of New Zealand's population lives in cities. New Zealand's population is a mixture of many different ethnic groups.

_____

_____

3. In A.D. 800, the Polynesian Maori arrived in New Zealand. They were the first inhabitants there.

_____

_____

4. The Maori survived by hunting and fishing. They lived along the coast.

_____

_____

5. The first European traveler to see New Zealand was Abel Tasman. The Dutch had sent Tasman to explore the area.

_____

_____

6. The first Europeans in New Zealand were whalers and missionaries. The Maori traded with them extensively.

_____

_____

7. In 1840, New Zealand and Great Britain signed The Treaty of Waitangi. The Treaty of Waitangi gave power over the islands to Queen Victoria.

_____

_____

8. People established new cities in New Zealand after the Waitangi Treaty. These people were citizens of Great Britain.

_____

_____

9. The British citizens and the native Maori had conflicts. These conflicts turned into a war during the 1940s.

_____

_____

10. The capital of New Zealand is Wellington. Wellington is the southernmost capital in the world.

_____

_____

PART VI

4 | FOOD FRENZY: AN INTERVIEW ABOUT NEW ZEALAND DAIRY PRODUCTS

*Read this radio interview with Donovan Epps, the president of the New Zealand Dairy Alliance. Complete the interview. Write relative pronouns or **when** or **where** and the correct form of each verb in parentheses. Some items may have more than one right answer.*

FRANKS: Thanks for tuning in to Food Frenzy on radio 101.5 AM. I'm your host, Freddy Franks.

Today we're talking to Mr. Donovan Epps, _____who_____ _____is_____
0. (be)

the president of the New Zealand Dairy Alliance. Mr. Epps is in town for the

International Cheese Festival. The festival, _____ _____
1. (happen)

this week at the Park City Convention Center, offers people the chance to taste and

purchase cheeses from around the world. The festival also provides a place

_____ cheese manufacturers can _____ large amounts of
2. (sell)

cheese to suppliers. Welcome, Mr. Epps.

EPPS: Thank you for inviting me.

FRANKS: Can you tell our listeners a little about the dairy industry in New Zealand?

EPPS: Sure. Although New Zealand is a country _____ many sheep farmers

_____, there are also many dairy farmers. The dairy industry in New
3. (live)

Zealand, _____ _____ most of its products to other
4. (send)

countries, is quite large. Waikato is the region _____ many dairy farmers

_____.
5. (work)

FRANKS: Interesting. Now, can you explain the function of the New Zealand Dairy Alliance?

EPPS: The New Zealand Dairy Alliance, _____ _____ and sells
6. (process)

products made from milk, often helps farmers sell their products abroad.

FRANKS: What kinds of products?

EPPS: Well, we sell a lot of cheese and butter, _____ we _____
7. (make)

most of our money from.

FRANKS: Why does New Zealand send most of its dairy products to other countries?

EPPS: Most New Zealanders _____ I _____ love dairy products.
8. (know)
But they cannot consume all the products made in their home country. In fact, it may be

interesting to know that the United States is a country _____ people

_____ a lot of New Zealand cheeses.
9. (buy)

FRANKS: The New Zealand cheese _____ I _____ the most is
10. (love)
cheddar. Delicious! We'll be back after this commercial break.

---

5 | EDITING: A BUSINESS OPPORTUNITY IN NEW ZEALAND

Read this letter from a businessman in the United States to a businessman in the Bay of Islands, New Zealand. There are six errors in the use of adjective clauses. The first mistake is already corrected. Find and correct five more. (Note: There can be more than one way to correct a mistake.)

Dear Mr. Higgins:

    I am the Chief Executive Officer for Michigan Wood Designers, ~~that~~ *which* is a small company in

the northern part of the United States. We design and produce wooden souvenirs for the tourist

industry. Through market research I have discovered that the Bay of Islands region of New

Zealand, which it attracts many tourists, has few souvenir shops. In addition, there are no

souvenir shops that they sell natural wood products. We believe that our experience in wood

design, which have led to great success in the northern Michigan tourist region, could help

increase sales of souvenirs in the Bay of Islands. We hope to work directly with people which live

in the Bay of Islands. Our business plan offers both Michigan Wood Designers and the Bay of

Islands area a valuable opportunity for development.

    I am planning a trip to New Zealand at the end of the month, and I would like to schedule a

meeting at your convenience. At that time, we can discuss any issues what you are concerned

about. Thank you for your kind consideration.

Sincerely,

James F. Dalley

President and CEO of Michigan Wood Designers

Unit 13 Achievement Test

| 30 Items
Score: _____ |

1 | LISTENING: TYPES OF GOVERNMENT

🎧 *Listen to this lecture about two types of governments. Complete the lecture by writing the words that you hear. You will hear the recording two times.*

PROFESSOR WAHAL: Good morning, class. Today we have a guest speaker _____*who comes*_____
                                                                          0.

from Heights University. This lecturer is a _____ research
                                                          1.

on world governments is widely known. Our guest, _____
                                                                    2.

courses in the history of government, will explain some basic principles

of democracies and dictatorships. Please welcome Professor Marilyn

Feinberg.

PROFESSOR FEINBERG: Thank you, Professor Wahal. It's a pleasure to be here. I'll start today

by talking about governments. Governments are institutions

_____ decisions about the lives of people in a particular
        3.

area. Some governments promote values and beliefs _____
                                                                  4.

acceptable to the people. These governments try to make policies

_____ citizens and society as a whole. People
        5.

_____ the benefits of the government's policies will follow
        6.

its wishes. When people obey the government, one can say that it has

legitimacy. Yet any government must be able to enforce its decisions against

_____ do not obey its wishes. This is the power of coercion.
        7.

Political scientists differentiate among types of governments by

considering the degree of legitimacy and the degree of coercion

_____ use to make and enforce decisions. Governments
        8.

_____ democracies have a high sense of legitimacy and a low
        9.

level of coercion. In this type of government, people elect their leaders in

periodic elections, and leaders pass laws _____ normally
                                                          10.

accept and follow. If leaders fail to pass laws and make decisions

_____ accept, citizens will elect new leaders in the next
    11.

election.

2 | DICTATORSHIPS

Now read the second part of Professor Feinberg's lecture. Find three identifying and four nonidentifying adjective clauses. Write them in the table below. An example is given.

PROFESSOR FEINBERG: Now let's look at another type of government which is the second topic of this talk. Unlike democracies, dictatorships are governments that operate with a low level of legitimacy and a high level of coercion. People who live under a dictatorship do not have any influence on who becomes leader. Instead, leaders, who usually seize power through military force, rule with a small group of supporters largely through coercion. In some dictatorships one individual dominates the political process. Saddam Hussein, who ruled in Iraq, illustrates this type of dictatorship. In other dictatorships, one political party dominates the system. Communist states, which have the Communist party in power, are an example. A third type of dictatorship is an oligarchy, or a powerful group of families which dominates a political system. El Salvador, whose government consisted of members of about 13 families, was an oligarchy until the early part of the last century.

IDENTIFYING ADJECTIVE CLAUSES	NONIDENTIFYING ADJECTIVE CLAUSES
0. *which is the second topic of this talk*	4. _____
1. _____	5. _____
2. _____	6. _____
3. _____	7. _____

3 | PARLIAMENTARY AND PRESIDENTIAL DEMOCRACIES

Read one student's summary of part of Professor Feinberg's lecture. Complete the passage with the correct relative pronouns. Write the letter of the best answer on each line.

I found today's lecture very useful because it dealt with a topic ___*b*___ (a. whose b. that
0.
c. who) I'm interested in. In her lecture, _____ (a. which b. that c. whose) was about dictatorships
1.
and democracies, Professor Feinberg talked about two different types of democracies. One type is the parliamentary system, and the other is the presidential system.

Parliamentary systems are those _____ (a. who b. that c. whose) give power to the
2.
parliament, _____ (a. that is b. which is c. who is) an institution of representatives elected by the
3.
people. The political party _____ (a. which it b. who c. that) has the most members in parliament
4.
forms the government and makes decisions. The head of the government, _____ (a. whose
5.
b. who c. that) has the title of prime minister, depends on the support of the parliament. Great Britain and Canada are two important examples of parliamentary democracies.

Presidential systems also include a group of elected representatives and one person _____
6.
(a. whose b. which c. who) is the head of government. However, people call this system's head of government a president. The president works independently of the elected representatives. The United States is a principle example of a presidential democracy.

Professor Feinberg, _____ (a. who b. that c. who she) has written a book about the
7.
presidential system in the U.S., concluded her talk by handing out a list of sources for further reading on the topic. These sources, _____ (a. which b. that c. whose) include Professor
8.
Feinberg's book, explore the historical development of the U.S. presidential system.

PART V

4 | EDITING: ASKING FOR INFORMATION

Read this e-mail from Steve in the United States to his friend Ian in Canada. There are five mistakes in the use of adjective clauses. The first mistake is already corrected. Find and correct four more.

Dear Ian,

I'm hoping that you can help me with some homework for my world government class, which ~~it~~ is due on Friday. I need to answer a question about the Canadian government. I already asked one of my friends whose grandparents lives in Canada, but she didn't know the answer.

I think that your country has a parliamentary system of government, right? I don't understand the timing of the elections for a new prime minister there. As you know, the system in the United States is different. Every four years there is an election for a new president, who he will then serve for the following four years. But in Canada, who seems very similar to the United States in some ways, I can never predict when the next election will be. My friends Josh and Tim, which I'm doing the homework with, think that there is no set day that everyone recognizes as election day in Canada. Are they right?

Thanks for any help you can give me on this.

Steve

Unit 14 Achievement Test

30 Items
Score: _____

1 | LISTENING: AN INFLUENTIAL CANADIAN AUTHOR

A. 🎧 *Listen to Samantha's class presentation about her favorite Canadian author. Complete the presentation by writing the words that you hear. You will hear the recording two times.*

Have you ever read a novel that took place in Canada? If you have, then there's a good chance that it wasn't written until the mid 1900s. This is because until that time, many people thought that Canada was only a place _____*where people went*_____ to get away from

0.

Europe. Some people even considered it the absence of civilization. This was a time

_____ books or stories about Canada.

1.

But one writer did a lot to change that. Hugh MacLennan, _____

2.

among the greatest Canadian writers, was one of the first authors to write about the country. Before him, most Canadian authors wrote novels about the United States, Europe, or traveling the world. They thought that people wanted to read about these important and interesting places—not about the forests, snow, and wind of Canada. This was the opinion

_____ until Hugh MacLennan published his first novel in 1941.

3.

Barometer Rising, _____ in his hometown of Halifax, Nova Scotia, was

4.

one of the first Canadian novels. In this and his other works, MacLennan wrote about situations

and themes _____ were uniquely Canadian.

5.

*B. Read the rest of Samantha's presentation. Circle nine adjective clauses with object relative pronouns or **when** or **where**. Be sure to circle the complete clause.*

One Canadian theme (that MacLennan wrote about in his book, *Two Solitudes,*) is the tension between English-speaking and French-speaking Canadians. This book was also set in an environment with which MacLennan had a lot of experience. MacLennan grew up in Halifax, Nova Scotia, the son of English-speaking Scottish immigrants. However, he lived most of his life in the province of Quebec, where French is the official language. *Two Solitudes* describes how the French and English languages meet in daily life in Quebec.

Another of MacLennan's Canadian themes is the magnificence of the country's geographical features. MacLennan developed this theme, which he made clear throughout his novels, by focusing on features of Canada's landscape. For example, *Rivers of Canada* is a book in which MacLennan discussed important rivers in Canada's history. Immigrants from Europe traveled down the St. Lawrence River on which Quebec City and Montreal are located. From there they continued westward on the Ottawa River to the place where the capital of Canada sits today. He wrote stories about the people who made those voyages and asked readers to think about the times when these people lived and the hardships that they endured. MacLennan attempted to show the relationship between the geography of Canada and the character of Canadians.

2 | MACLENNAN'S LIFE

*Read these statements about MacLennan's life. Combine the pairs of sentences. Make the second sentence in each pair an adjective clause with an object relative pronoun or **when** or **where**. Make any other necessary changes.*

0. MacLennan attended Dalhousie University. He studied Greek and Latin there.

   MacLennan attended Dalhousie University where he studied Greek and Latin.

1. MacLennan won a men's doubles tennis championship in 1928. Many people supported him.

   _____

   _____

2. In 1928, MacLennan went on a trip to England with his only sister. Their parents had named her Frances.

_____

_____

3. In 1931, MacLennan wrote a book of poetry. Three London publishers rejected the book.

_____

_____

4. Dorothy Duncan became his wife in 1936. He met her in 1932.

_____

_____

5. The Lower Canada College is in Montreal, Canada. MacLennan taught at The Lower Canada College from 1935 to 1945.

_____

_____

6. *Two Solitudes* reflected MacLennan's own experiences living in Quebec. Canadians and Americans made this book a bestseller.

_____

_____

7. The MacLennans bought a house. They called this house Stone Hedge.

_____

_____

8. In 1954, MacLennan published a collection of essays. Dorothy Duncan edited this collection for him.

_____

_____

9. In 1951, MacLennan started working at McGill University. He taught in the Department of English there.

_____

_____

10. MacLennan published a second version of *Two Solitudes* in 1963. He translated it into French then.

_____

_____

11. In 1968, MacLennan became a full professor at McGill University. He had taught there since 1951.

_____

_____

12. In 1980, MacLennan published his seventh novel. He called it *Voices in Time*.

_____

_____

3 | EDITING: AN E-MAIL TO A FRIEND

*Read this e-mail from Sally to her friend Peichi. There are five mistakes in the use of adjective clauses with object relative pronouns or **when** or **where**. The first mistake has already been corrected. Find and correct four more. (Note: There can be than one way to correct a mistake.)*

Peichi,

    What do you think about a trip to Canada this summer? There are a lot of places ~~which~~ *where* we

could have a great vacation. In fact, I've been reading a wonderful book that I found it at the

library last week. It's called *Rivers of Canada,* and it describes places like Niagara Falls and tells

interesting historical stories. It's by the author his stories I already told you about. I like all the

stories that this particular author write because they are based on facts about Canada's history.

Another Canadian author which I saw on TV the other day will be at The Corner Bookstore

tomorrow for a book signing. Do you want to go? We could find out a lot more about Canada

while we're there. Let me know!

Sally

PART VI Achievement Test

60 Items
Score: _____

1 | LISTENING: SOME DIFFERENCES BETWEEN CANADA AND THE UNITED STATES

A. 🎧 *Listen to this passage about some differences between Canada and the United States. Complete the passage by writing the words that you hear. You will hear the recording two times.*

Many people think that Canada and the United States are very similar, perhaps partly because of how close they are. In fact, Canada, _____ *which is* _____ the second largest country
0.

after Russia in terms of area, is similar to the United States in many ways. However, important

differences _____ Canada apart from the United States exist as well.
1.

Canada, _____ a democratic country like the United States, has a style of
2.

democracy called a parliamentary system. This is a system _____ from
3.

the American one in several ways. For example, in a parliamentary system, members of

parliament in the political party _____ the largest select a prime
4.

minister to lead the nation. The United States has a presidential system of government

_____ each citizen to vote for a president. The candidate
5.

_____ the most votes from a sufficient number of states becomes
6.

president. A team of leaders _____ work with him or her at the highest
7.

levels of government.

PART VI

B. *Read more information about some differences between Canada and the United States. Complete the passage with the correct relative pronouns and verb forms. Write the letter of the best answer on each line.*

A second difference between Canada and the United States ____*a*____ (a. that is b. who is c. that

0.

are d. which are) important is their economies. Canada is a country _____ (a. that is b. where is

1.

c. who is d. which it is) heavily dependent upon international trade. Canada especially depends on

trade with the United States, _____ (a. when it sends b. which it sends c. where it sends d. who it sends)

2.

more than 80 percent of its exports. This differs from the United States, _____ (a. who sends

3.

b. which sends c. where sends d. that sends) only 20 percent of its exports to Canada. Canada has more

exports _____ (a. which they are b. who are c. that they are d. that are) national resources (such as oil

4.

and gas) and agricultural products than the United States.

Another difference between Canada and the Unites States is health care. In Canada, the

health care system is a universal program _____ (a. which they provide b. that provides c. who

5.

provides d. in which provides) medical care to all residents. All people _____ (a. who lives b. which

6.

live c. who live d. which lives) in Canada receive health care _____ (a. that is b. where is c. which it is

7.

d. that it is) the same regardless of their ability to pay. This is a system _____ (a. that the

8.

government pays for b. for who the government pays c. for that the government pays d. who the government pays

for). In contrast, the United States government only provides health care to those citizens

_____ (a. which cannot pay b. whom cannot pay c. whose cannot pay d. who cannot pay) for it

9.

themselves. Instead, most people have jobs _____ (a. who provide b. that provide c. which they

10.

provide d. in which provide) payment plans for health care.

2 | CULTURAL DIFFERENCES BETWEEN CANADA AND THE UNITED STATES

Read this information about some cultural differences between Canada and the United States. Circle 18 adjective clauses. Be sure to circle the full adjective clause.

Canada and the United States are countries (that people often think have very similar cultures). However, social scientists point out significant cultural differences between them. These differences, which partly result from their histories, make the countries very interesting. For example, today's Canadians include people whose ancestors wanted to remain a British colony during the American Revolution. (The American Revolution, which took place in the late 1700s, was a war to separate the United States from British rule.) Other Canadians come from families whose ancestors were French immigrants. Many of these immigrants settled in eastern Canada, where they established the province of Quebec. Canada, where French and English are both official languages, is a bilingual nation. The country is an example of a mosaic society in which citizens preserve the ethnic and cultural traditions of its immigrant populations.

By contrast, social scientists describe the United States as a melting pot society. Citizens who came from many different cultures have joined their ethnic and cultural traditions and created a larger American culture. Many of the first immigrants, who came from England, Ireland, Italy, Germany, Poland, Scotland, and other European countries, began to create one culture that combined elements from all of their cultures. These early immigrants, who often spoke their native languages in their homes, communicated with each other in English. Today, the United States is a country that has only one official language: English.

American media and entertainment that reflect the cultural values of the United States are popular and widely available in Canada. As people who are concerned with preserving their culture, some Canadians worry that the things which they see will influence their culture. During the 1930s, Canada created a national public broadcast system that citizens can watch and listen to as an alternative to American media.

Above all, it's important to remember that Canada and the United States are countries with distinct cultures that represent their people. These cultures, which many people value, are influenced by the histories of the countries.

3	FUN FACTS ABOUT CANADA

Read these statements about Canada and its history. Combine the pairs of sentences. Make the second sentence in each pair an adjective clause with an object relative pronoun or **when** *or* **where**. *Make any other necessary changes.*

0. The first people probably arrived in Canada thousands of years ago. Thousands of years ago there was a land bridge between Siberia and Alaska.

   The first people probably arrived in Canada thousands of years ago when there was a land bridge

   between Siberia and Alaska.

1. The first Europeans in Canada were probably Vikings from Iceland. These Europeans arrived there about 1,000 years ago.

   _____

   _____

2. The French gave it to Great Britain in 1763. The French first claimed the land of Canada.

   _____

   _____

3. The government of Great Britain divided it into four colonies. The government of Great Britain controlled the area.

   _____

   _____

4. On July 1, 1867, the four colonies became one country. People called the country Canada.

   _____

   _____

5. The first prime minister was John A. Macdonald. Many people know Macdonald as the founding father of Canada.

_____

_____

6. Canada covers about 10 million square kilometers. This is an area slightly larger than the United States.

_____

_____

7. The Canadian flag pictures a maple leaf. The government named the maple leaf the national symbol.

_____

_____

8. Canada's two official languages have caused problems in the past. The languages are French and English.

_____

_____

9. Each year 12 million tourists visit Niagara Falls. The tourists want to see the second-largest waterfall in the world.

_____

_____

10. Canada has a population of almost 30 million people. These people are mostly of British, French, other European, American Indian, and mixed backgrounds.

_____

_____

PART VI

| 4 | AN INTERVIEW ABOUT CANADA'S NATIVE PEOPLE |

*Read this radio interview about Canada's native people. Complete the interview. Write relative pronouns or **when** or **where** and the correct form of each verb in parentheses. Some items may have more than one right answer.*

JANET HOLM: Hello. You're listening to *Around the World* on radio 91.5. I'm your host, Janet

Holm. I am pleased to have with me today Mr. John Foster, _____who_____

_____is_____ the Director of Governmental Affairs for the First Nations
        0. (be)

people in Canada. Welcome, Mr. Foster.

FOSTER: Thank you for inviting me.

HOLM: So tell us: Who are the First Nations people?

FOSTER: These Canadians are descendants of the original inhabitants of North America

_____ _____ in Canada long before the English,
              1. (live)

French, and other settlers came. Many First Nations people live in the Yukon

Territory, the Northwest Territory, and Nunavut.

HOLM: As the Director of Governmental Affairs for the First Nations people, what is your

job?

FOSTER: My job, _____ _____ to represent the interests of
                2. (be)

First Nations people, is quite rewarding. Really, I am just a person

_____ the government _____ to protect the rights of
                3. (trust)

First Nations people.

HOLM: In a recent news story _____ I _____ on television,
                4. (see)

reporters explored some of the issues _____ First Nations people

_____ .
5. (encounter)

FOSTER: Yes, that television program, _____ I _____ too,
                6. (view)

explained the issues well. For example, it focused on economic development,

_____ I _____ . I encourage First Nations people to
                7. (promote)

make and sell traditional cultural tools and pieces of art _____

many people _____ about. This is a way to maintain their cultural
        8. (not know)

heritage and help people _____ _____ unfamiliar with
                                                  9. (be)

Canada's history learn about its original inhabitants.

HOLM: Another interesting thing _____ the television program

_____ was the oral histories of the First Nations people. We'll talk
     10. (mention)

about these right after our commercial break. Stay tuned!

---

5 | EDITING: A BUSINESS OPPORTUNITY IN CANADA

Read this letter to a director of international trade development in Canada. There are six errors in the use of adjective clauses. The first mistake is already corrected. Find and correct five more.

Dear Mr. Bothham:

    I am the president and chief executive officer of Wisconsin Sign Makers, ~~that~~ *which* is a small American company that make all kinds of signs for businesses. I am seeking to expand our business into the province of Ontario. We believe that Toronto and Ottawa are areas that is particularly good markets for our products. In those areas, there aren't any companies that they offer services as extensive as ours. We believe that Wisconsin Sign Makers, that offers more services than any other sign-making business, can serve the area well.

    In order to proceed, I am writing to request any information that you can give us. Is there a particular person with which I should work to carry out these plans? Thank you for your consideration. I look forward to hearing from you.

Sincerely,

Joseph A. McDuffie

President and CEO of Wisconsin Sign Makers

PART VII Diagnostic Test

1 | LISTENING: PLANNING A VACATION

A. 🎧 *Jane and Eric are planning their vacation. Listen to their conversation. Complete the conversation by writing the words that you hear. You will hear the recording two times.*

JANE: Hey, Eric. Where do you think we _____ *should go* _____ on vacation

                        0.

    this year?

ERIC: I've been thinking about it, but I haven't been able to come up with a good idea

    yet. Last year we went to the beach, and that was a disaster! The beach

    _____ our ideal vacation spot!
                       1.

JANE: This year we should go somewhere really exotic! Last year we

    _____ for a big vacation, but this year we can!
                      2.

ERIC: How about Egypt? There must be a lot of really interesting sites to see there, like the

    Pyramids.

JANE: OK, let's consider Egypt. We should also consider England. I've always wanted

    to see Stonehenge. Do you know what I've always wondered? Why

    _____ Stonehenge? I have questions about a lot of
                      3.

    ancient places. I'm sure the tourists who visit them are able to learn about their histories

    while they're there.

ERIC: I'm sure they are. But remember that we _____
                                     4.

    between Egypt and England right now. In fact, we had better research both places before

    deciding.

JANE: You're right. We should find out about the history of each place before we decide because

    we might discover that we're really more interested in one place than the other.

    _____ that last year?
                      5.

ERIC: I think so. Last year we made our decision too fast.

JANE: Oh well, that was last year. Now we can learn from our past mistakes. We

_____ our time and do some research first. We might

          6.

make a better decision this year if we do that.

ERIC: Travel guides might have helpful information. They're full of both history and useful

travel tips. Do you want to meet at the bookstore tomorrow to research Egypt and

England? I _____ free at noon, but I've got to check

                    7.

my schedule first.

JANE: OK. The bookstore might be busy then, so let's plan on being there for two hours.

***B.** Reread the conversation between Jane and Eric. Find 13 modal verb phrases. Write them in the table below. (Note: Only use modal verb phrases that are given in the passage. Do not use any modal verbs that you wrote.) An example is given.*

ABILITY	ADVICE	NECESSITY	ASSUMPTION	FUTURE POSSIBILITY
0. *haven't been able*				
1. _____	4. _____	7. _____	9. _____	11. _____
2. _____	5. _____	8. _____	10. _____	12. _____
3. _____	6. _____			13. _____

2 | THE MYSTERY OF STONEHENGE

Complete this conversation between Jane and Eric about Stonehenge. Circle the correct word(s).

JANE: This travel guide claims that every visitor to England (should)/ may visit Stonehenge
0.
because of its great historical importance. It's so magnificent! Those stones look heavy. It

had to <u>have / had</u> been a lot of hard work to build this.
1.

ERIC: This book says no one knows exactly why Stonehenge was built. It says it <u>had to / could</u>
2.
have been a type of prehistoric calendar.

JANE: Well, regardless of why Stonehenge was built, it <u>ought to / must</u> have been really
3.
important for the people to put so much time and effort into building it.

ERIC: England stopped allowing visitors to touch the stones in 1978. This book says they

<u>can't / might not</u> touch the stones because it damages them.
4.

JANE: I guess they should <u>stop / have stopped</u> letting people touch the stones sooner. Is there
5.
anything else they <u>ought to / were able to</u> have done to protect it?
6.

ERIC: I'm sure they could <u>have / had</u> done something, but I don't know what.
7.

JANE: How <u>could / should</u> people have moved all these giant stones 5,000 years ago?
8.

ERIC: This book says the people must have <u>move / moved</u> the stones by floating them down a
9.
nearby river on boats. Hey, do we know for sure who built Stonehenge?

JANE: I don't think so. The Druids <u>may / must</u> have. They were Celtic priests who probably
10.
lived in the area during that time. . . . Wow, we've been here an hour! We should

<u>of / have</u> started looking at information about Egypt by now.
11.

ERIC: Let me ask this store clerk for help. . . . Excuse me. We <u>aren't able to / might not</u> find
12.
the travel books for Egypt.

CLERK: There <u>must / can</u> be a few here somewhere. . . . Here they are, on the left.
13.

ERIC: People <u>must / should</u> like reading about Egypt! This whole row is on Egypt!
14.

JANE: Well, we <u>shouldn't / can't</u> read them all, so pick one and let's get started.
15.

3 | EGYPTIAN PYRAMIDS

A. Read these questions Jane and Eric had about Egypt's pyramids. Use the modals in parentheses to write short answers.

0. **Q:** Did the Egyptians believe in life after death?

   A: _They must have_____. Some say the pyramids acted as a stairway for
             (must)
   the pharaohs to climb to enter the heavens.

1. **Q:** Were the Egyptian pharaohs important to their society?

   A: _____. The pyramids were built as tombs for them.
            (had to)

2. **Q:** Could the pyramids have been a symbol of more than a passage to the heavens?

   A: _____. Some people say the size and design of a
            (might)
   pyramid showed the pharaoh's wealth and power.

3. **Q:** Did the secret passages in the pyramids keep out thieves and robbers?

   A: _____. Many of the pharaoh's treasures were missing by
            (must not)
   the time modern archaeologists explored the pyramids.

4. **Q:** Was King Khufu the richest and most powerful pharaoh?

   A: _____. His pyramid is the largest of the three at Giza.
            (may)

B. Read these statements about Egypt's pyramids. Use the meanings of the underlined phrases and the word in parentheses to write sentences with modal phrases.

0. It's been suggested that the Egyptian pharaohs started planning their pyramids right after they

   ascended to the throne. (might)

   The Egyptian pharaohs might have started planning their pyramids right after they ascended to

   the throne.

1. It's possible the Egyptians brought the huge stones from 500 miles away. (may)

   _____

2. It's likely that the Egyptians also built the Sphinx, a giant statue. (must)

   _____

3. The Sphinx <u>perhaps</u> guarded the pyramids and the treasure they held. (might)

_____

4. <u>Most likely</u> the Egyptians had many tools for cutting stones. (had to)

_____

5. <u>Probably</u>, the Egyptians didn't build the pyramids quickly. (couldn't)

_____

C. *Read these regrets other tourists had that are printed in the travel guide Jane and Eric looked at. Use the modals in parentheses to write sentences expressing what the tourists should have done.*

0. We didn't take any water with us when we visited the pyramids. We were thirsty most of the

day! (should)

We should have taken water with us when we visited the pyramids.

1. We didn't visit the pyramids at Giza. They're the most famous ones! (should)

_____

2. We only visited the pyramids at Giza. There are many other interesting pyramids too.

(should not)

_____

3. We didn't check out the Sphinx while we were at Giza. It's so close, so it was a waste not to.

(could)

_____

4. We didn't hire a personal tour guide when we explored the pyramids. They can teach you so

much history about the pyramids! (ought to)

_____

5. We forgot our cameras in the hotel. Now we're sad we don't have any pictures of the

pyramids! (should not)

_____

4 | EDITING: MAKING A DECISION

Jane and Eric are still trying to make a decision on where they should go on their vacation. Read Jane's e-mail to her friend Seema. There are 12 mistakes in the use of modals. The first mistake is already corrected. Find and correct 11 more. (Note: There can be more than one way to correct a mistake.)

Dear Seema,

Well, it's time for Eric and I to decide for sure where we should ~~to~~ go on our vacation this year. It's getting kind of late. Remember when you asked me if we should've already gotten tickets? Well, we should of. We should to decide where we're going tonight because the travel agent who's helping us arrange the trip says we should buy plane tickets by next week. I guess that should be when ticket prices start to really go up for the summer.

What should we had spent less time on? I guess we ought a have spent less time researching the different places, but it was so interesting! I enjoyed learning why ancient people might built magnificent structures like Stonehenge and the pyramids. I still can't believe these people could not have built them without today's machines. These ancient structures has to have taken a long time to build, and a lot of people must work on them before they were finished!

The problem is that both places sound so interesting! England musts have better weather in the summer because that's when most tourists go there. Perhaps we are able to go to England this summer and then to Egypt next winter. What do you think?

Jane

PART VII

Unit 15 Achievement Test

30 Items
Score: _____

---

1 | LISTENING: READING NEWS AND MAGAZINE STORIES

🎧 *Ben and Ann are talking about reading news and magazine stories. Listen to their conversation. Complete the conversation by writing the words that you hear. You will hear the recording two times.*

BEN: Ann, I read a story yesterday that you __*have got to read*__ . It said the city
                                     0.
    _____ a new park right next to your house next year.
                 1.

ANN: Really? What else did it say?

BEN: Well, I _____ much more. I think it said the city _____
                  2.   **3.**
    citizens pay extra money to help build the park.

ANN: Really? I haven't heard anything yet. My neighbors _____ something about
                                                 4.
    it, though. I'll ask around.

BEN: That's a good idea. Somebody _____ some information about it.
                                        5.

ANN: You know, the city _____ citizens pay more money without a city-wide vote.
                             6.
    That story can't be right. Good reporters always consider all the facts, but irresponsible

    reporters often leave out important information. That's why it's important to read articles

    carefully, and remember, don't assume everything you read is true!

2 | A JOURNALIST'S DILEMMA

Complete this speech by journalist Francis Pennymore. Circle the correct modal verbs.

Thank you for inviting me to talk to you about my job as a journalist for *News World*

magazine. You (might)/ have got to think that working as a journalist is exciting and glamorous.
        0.

There may / ought to be some truth to that, but as a good journalist, I can / have to tell both
        1.   **2.**

sides of the story regardless of where that story takes me.

The most difficult part of my job ought to / might be choosing stories. Many important
                                    3.

things happen every day. Which ones should / can we report on? We might / have to choose
                                        4.   **5.**

only a few to write about in depth. I tend to ask myself, what must / should people read about? I
                                                                6.

want to write stories that could / must change the world. But people might not / shouldn't want
                                7.   **8.**

to read such stories! So a journalist always has to think about both the stories and the readers.

Another difficulty is the travel. Once there was a big oil spill in Alaska. Our boss told us we

had to / might write a story about it. It happened suddenly, so he told us we could / had better
9.   **10.**

move quickly. We had difficulty getting to the spill site because of bad weather. Finally, we

ought to / were able to find someone to take us there. But after all that, we couldn't / shouldn't
        11.   **12.**

write anything because no one had to / was able to talk to us! There's always a possibility that
                                    13.

problems may / couldn't come up that will prevent us from getting a story.
        14.

Deadlines are also a real challenge. Every Thursday at 10:00 A.M. I should / must submit my
                                                                    15.

story. Almost every week I feel I could write a better story if I were given a little more time. . . .

Well, I probably ought to / can stop at this point and ask if you have any questions. We'll run
                    16.

out of time if I don't.

3 | RESPONSIBLE REPORTERS

Read each sentence about reporters. Write **AB** *if the sentence expresses ability,* **AD** *if the sentence expresses advice, and* **AS** *if the sentence expresses assumption.*

0. _AD_ Reporters shouldn't lie.

1. _____ Reporters must do a lot of research about the issues they write about.

2. _____ Reporters can call sources to check facts before turning in their stories.

3. _____ Reporters should interview people on both sides of the issue.

4. _____ Reporters are able to get good jobs in respectable newspapers and magazines.

4 | EDITING: A LETTER TO THE EDITOR

Read this letter to the editor of NewsAtlanta *newspaper. There are five mistakes in the use of modals. The first mistake is already corrected. Find and correct four more. (Note: There can be more than one way to correct a mistake.)*

Dear Editor in Chief,

    I was very disturbed last week when a friend showed me an article published in your

newspaper. The article reported that the city ~~mights~~ *might* force citizens to pay extra money next year

in order to build a new park in the downtown area. Might the city really build this park without

asking the citizens what they want? Of course it won't! The reporter who wrote that article

musts not know very much about city affairs, because the city can't to make these types of

decisions without making a formal proposal and holding a public vote on the issue. The city

knows this, and any good reporter should too! As the editor of this newspaper, you should take

responsibility for the quality of reporting that you print. You don't have to allow irresponsible

reporters to leave out these details that make citizens worry. If you monitor your reporters more

carefully in the future, your readers will be much happier.

Sincerely,

Ann Matthews

Unit 16 Achievement Test

1 | LISTENING: MOVING TO COSTA RICA

A. 🎧 *Listen to this conversation between Mark and Dan two weeks before Mark married Marisa. Complete the conversation by writing the words that you hear. You will hear the recording two times.*

DAN: We're really going to miss you, Mark, when you move to Costa Rica.

MARK: I'll miss you too, Dan, but I'm excited to move to Marisa's country—excited but really

unprepared!

DAN: What do you mean? What _____*could you have done*_____ to prepare better?
                                      0.

MARK: Well, for one thing, I _____ Spanish for more than the
                                              1.

past five months.

DAN: Oh, yeah. That _____.
                                    2.

MARK: I _____ taking Spanish in elementary school. I should
                        3.

have taken it in high school and college, too.

DAN: But at least you have your Master's degree in Business Administration from New York

University!

MARK: That's another thing. I should have studied international business. I

_____ about international currencies and trade at
                        4.

NYU. I _____ on U.S. business so much. We
                        5.

studied a little about international markets, but really focusing on them

_____ me a lot in Costa Rica.
                        6.

B. Read each numbered statement about what Mark did or didn't do to prepare for moving to Costa Rica. Then circle the letter of the sentence that best describes Mark's situation.

0. Mark should have taken more Spanish classes.
   a. Mark took enough Spanish classes.
   b. Mark didn't take enough Spanish classes.

1. Mark should have visited Costa Rica more often.
   a. Mark didn't visit Costa Rica enough.
   b. Mark visited Costa Rica enough.

2. Should Mark have taken a history class about Costa Rica?
   a. Mark didn't take a history class about Costa Rica.
   b. Mark took a history class about Costa Rica.

3. Mark shouldn't have focused his education on U.S. business practices.
   a. Mark didn't focus his education on U.S. business practices.
   b. Mark focused his education on U.S. business practices.

4. Mark might have practiced speaking Spanish with his friends.
   a. Mark practiced speaking Spanish with his friends.
   b. Mark didn't practice speaking Spanish with his friends.

5. Mark shouldn't have ignored his Spanish homework to focus on work.
   a. Mark focused on work and ignored his Spanish homework.
   b. Mark didn't ignore his Spanish homework.

6. Mark ought not to have waited so long to learn Spanish.
   a. Mark learned Spanish early in life.
   b. Mark waited a long time to learn Spanish.

7. Mark could've spoken only Spanish with his fiancée.
   a. Mark spoke only Spanish with his fiancée.
   b. Mark didn't speak only Spanish with his fiancée.

8. Mark should've listened to Spanish tapes while driving to work.
   a. Mark didn't listen to Spanish tapes.
   b. Mark listened to Spanish tapes.

9. Mark ought to have learned about Costa Rican business practices.
   a. Mark learned about Costa Rican business practices.
   b. Mark didn't learn about Costa Rican business practices.

10. Mark shouldn't have turned down a part-time job in international business.
    a. Mark had a part-time job in international business.
    b. Mark didn't have a part-time job in international business.

2 | MARK'S UNFORTUNATE EXPERIENCE TRAVELING

Read Mark's regrets about his trip to Costa Rica. Use the modals in parentheses to write sentences expressing what Mark should have done.

0. I didn't sleep the night before leaving on the trip. I felt very tired the whole trip. (should)

I should've slept the night before leaving on the trip.

1. I didn't get to the airport early enough. Everyone else gets to the airport early enough, so why can't I? (could)

_____

2. I brought only credit cards on the trip. Now I need some cash. (should not)

_____

3. I didn't pack any extra clothes in my carry-on bag. Now my luggage is lost and I have no clean clothes to wear. (could)

_____

4. My sister knew that luggage often gets lost. She didn't tell me that. (might)

_____

3 | A DISCUSSION BETWEEN MARISA AND MARK

Read this conversation about a problem that Marisa and Mark encountered soon after they married. Complete the conversation. Use the correct form of the verbs in parentheses or short answers.

Scenario: Mark and Marisa just got married, and Mark needs to find a job. But his boss, Mr. Torte from the United States, refused to write a letter of recommendation for Mark when he applied for a new job in Costa Rica. Mark and Marisa don't know why Mr. Torte refused to write the letter.

MARK: Marisa, _____*should*_____ we _____*have invited*_____ Mr. Torte to the wedding?
0. (should / invite)

MARISA: I guess we _____*should have*_____. I didn't think he would want to come all the way here
0.

for the wedding. It's expensive to travel that far. Regardless, _____ he

_____ to write you a recommendation letter?
1. (should / refuse)

MARK: No, he _____. I worked for him for two years and was a good employee.
2.

But I really don't think he would have refused just because we didn't invite him. Maybe

he refused because I didn't tell him I was leaving until a week before the wedding.

When _____ I _____ him?
3. (should / tell)

MARISA: I don't know. Could you have told him any sooner?

MARK: I _____. Oh, well . . . it's too late now. But what _____ I
4. (could)

_____ to fix the situation? It would have been nice to have a positive
5. (should / do)

letter of recommendation in my file.

4 | EDITING: A LETTER TO A FRIEND

Mark is now settled in his new home and job in Costa Rica. Read this e-mail from Mark to his friend Dan in the United States. There are six mistakes in the use of modals. The first mistake is already corrected. Find and correct five more. (Note: There can be more than one way to correct a mistake.)

Dear Dan,

Well, Marisa and I are all settled in our new home. We could ~~of~~ *'ve/have* bought a house right on the beach, but we decided on a house in San Juan instead.

I finally found a new job working for a Costa Rican company that sells coffee beans all over the world. Like I told you before, I might not have studied only U.S. business while I was in college. It was hard to find a job. It shouldn't have been so hard. In fact, I really ought a have found a job before Marisa and I got married and we moved down here. Didn't you have trouble finding a job when you moved to another state? You might had reminded me how difficult it would be! Just kidding! I know that I have started looking much earlier. I should have known it would be more time-consuming in a foreign country.

Oh, I wanted to ask you a question. Should we of sent you that coffee? I sent it, and then remembered that you don't like coffee all that much. Hopefully you can enjoy it.

Talk to you soon.

Mark

Unit 17 Achievement Test

| 1 | LISTENING: THE LOST CITY OF ATLANTIS |

A. 🎧 *Listen to this speech about Atlantis, an ancient lost city. Complete the speech by writing the words that you hear. You will hear the recording two times.*

Plato, an ancient philosopher, wrote about the city of Atlantis. Atlantis

_____*may have been*_____ an ancient city located on an island in the Atlantic Ocean. The
　　　　　　0.

legend says that Atlantis _____ a paradise where a great empire existed.
　　　　　　　　　　　　　1.

Because of the stories, many people believe that the people of Atlantis must have been brilliant

engineers who built palaces, temples, and waterways.

Then, around 9,500 B.C.E., the whole island disappeared. Some think that a series of

earthquakes _____ Atlantis to sink to the bottom of the ocean.
　　　　　　　　2.

Despite the fact that many explorers have tried to find the ancient city under water, they

_____ much because we don't have any physical evidence that the city of
　　　3.

Atlantis actually existed.

_____ Atlantis _____? Many people think
　　　　　　　　　　　　　　　　　4.

that Atlantis couldn't have existed because humans at that time _____
　　　　　　　　　　　　　　　　　　　　　　　　　　　　5.

the technology the legends describe. Some believe that Atlantis did exist, and that it

_____ in the Americas, the Canary Islands, or even Antarctica.
　　　6.

Due to some recent archaeological findings, others are convinced that Atlantis

_____ a city on the Greek island called Thera. If Thera and Atlantis were
　　　7.

the same place, Plato may have been wrong about where, how, and when the island was

destroyed. Or, Plato might have based his stories about Atlantis on ancient Egyptian stories

about the island of Thera.

Perhaps we will never know if the lost city of Atlantis ever really existed. But one thing is for

sure—the myth of Atlantis _____ this long without Plato's stories.
　　　　　　　　　　　　　　　8.

B. Reread the speech above. Find one modal that expresses impossibility and two modals that express speculations. Write the verb phrases below. (Note: Only use modals that are given in the passage. Do not use any verbs that you wrote.) An example is given.

MODAL OF IMPOSSIBILITY	MODAL OF SPECULATION
1. _____	0. _must have been_
	2. _____
	3. _____

2 | PLATO AND THE LOST CITY OF ATLANTIS

Match these facts with the conclusions. There are more conclusions than you need.

Facts	Conclusions

__c__ **0.** Plato wrote about the lost city of Atlantis.

a. Atlantis had to have been a real place.

b. They might have gone there because they believed Thera and Atlantis were the same place.

_____ **1.** The Athenians conquered the people of Atlantis.

_____ **2.** Many people have searched for Atlantis.

~~c.~~ He must have had some information about the city.

_____ **3.** Thera is an actual Greek island.

d. If Thera and Atlantis are the same place, Atlantis had to have been real.

_____ **4.** The remains of the city discovered on Thera revealed a wealthy Bronze Age city that resembled the descriptions of Atlantis.

e. People must like watching stories about ancient mysteries.

f. Plato must have lived in Atlantis.

_____ **5.** Many tourists have visited Thera.

g. The Athenians must have been more powerful than the people of Atlantis.

_____ **6.** A volcanic eruption buried Thera in 15 feet of ash.

h. This city could have been the lost city of Atlantis.

_____ **7.** Many movies have been made about the lost city of Atlantis.

i. They must have believed that Atlantis existed.

j. Many people had to have died at Thera.

3 | WHAT HAPPENED AT POMPEII?

A. *Read this story about another ancient lost city, Pompeii. Use the meanings of the underlined phrases and the word in parentheses to write sentences with modal phrases.*

Pompeii, an ancient city in Italy, was destroyed in A.D. 79 when the volcano called Mt. Vesuvius erupted and buried the city under volcanic ash. This eruption killed all the inhabitants of the city. Why didn't the people flee?

0. <u>It's probable</u> that the inhabitants of Pompeii did not know the volcano would erupt.

(must not)

The inhabitants of Pompeii must not have known the volcano would erupt. _____

1. <u>It's likely</u> that it was too late to flee once they realized what was happening. (might)

_____

2. Since the volcano erupted very early in the morning, <u>it's probable</u> that everyone was sleeping.

(must)

_____

3. <u>It's very unlikely</u> that the people of Pompeii recognized the signs that the volcano would erupt.

(couldn't)

_____

4. <u>It's possible</u> that the people of Pompeii didn't have a safe place to go to. (may)

_____

B. *Read these questions a student had about Pompeii. Complete the teacher's answers. Use the modals in parentheses to write short answers.*

0. Q: Did the volcanic eruption happen very quickly?

   A: __*It must have*_____. It doesn't seem like people had time to flee.
         (must)

1. Q: Did the ash that fell on the city preserve the artifacts we have today from Pompeii?

   A: _____. They are too old to have survived on their own.
         (must)

2. Q: Did the archaeologists who rediscovered Pompeii expect to find all the artifacts in such

   good shape?

   A: _____. No one knew at that time that the ash from the

(could not)

   volcano would preserve them.

3. Q: Was the city forgotten after the eruption?

   A: _____. No one talked about the city until it was

(might)

   rediscovered hundreds of years later.

---

4 | EDITING: SHARING KNOWLEDGE

Read this e-mail from Manuel to his penpal Tom. There are six mistakes in the use of modal verbs. The first mistake is already corrected. Find and correct five more.

Dear Tom,

In my history class we've been discussing whether or not Atlantis may ~~had~~ been a real city.
We've read a translation of Plato's story about Atlantis, and it must of been a magnificent city
because Plato describes grand temples and palaces and complicated waterways. What kind of
people might have built this advanced technology such a long time ago? I imagine they had to
had been very intelligent to be capable of this. It had to have been hard to build without modern
machines.

The legend says Atlantis must have disappeared under the ocean. How could this really
happened? I think it might not have really disappeared completely, because if the city were really
at the bottom of the ocean, we would have found it by now. Don't you think so? Please write me
back and tell me what you think!

Manuel

PART VII Achievement Test

1 | LISTENING: TRAVELING BY TRAIN

A. 🎧 *Harry and Jason are traveling to Barcelona, Spain on a train. Listen to their conversation. Complete the conversation by writing the words that you hear. You will hear the recording two times.*

HARRY: Jason, here are our seats. Look, there _____*might be*_____ room for our bags either
0.

underneath the seat or in these compartments above the seats. Where should we put

them?

JASON: I think we ought to put them underneath our seats. My bag is pretty heavy, and I

_____ it high enough to get it into the overhead bins.
1.

HARRY: OK. Wow, it's really a tight fit. My bag _____ too big!
2.

JASON: You have to put yours in the overhead compartment. Look, the train conductor is

coming around to collect our tickets.

HARRY: Where _____ mine? Oh, I remember. I thought the bottom of my bag
3.

might be the safest place for it. _____ my passport out too?
4.

JASON: Yes. You had better get it out.

HARRY: I didn't know I needed my passport on the train.

JASON: The conductor _____ sure you have a ticket and a passport.
5.

HARRY: This must be a long train ride. I see a lot of people who brought meals along.

JASON: Well, everyone might not be going to the same place. People will come and go with each

stop.

HARRY: Each stop? Do you mean this train isn't going straight from here to Barcelona?

JASON: That's right. The train _____ at as many as 10 or 15 other cities along the
6.

way. And Barcelona may not be the last stop either. That means we have to pay

attention to where we are and remember to get off.

HARRY: But all the announcements are made in Spanish! We can't speak Spanish. We might not

know when to get off.

JASON: I can understand some Spanish even though I _____ it.

                                                 7.

HARRY: That's a relief! That means you shouldn't sleep during the trip.

JASON: I can't ever sleep on the train anyway. It's too noisy.

HARRY: Well, it's not too noisy for me! Wake me up when we get there!

B. *Reread the conversation between Harry and Jason. Find 13 modal verb phrases. Write them in the table below. (Note: Only use modal verb phrases that are given in the passage. Do not use any modal verbs that you wrote.) An example is given.*

ABILITY	ADVICE	NECESSITY	ASSUMPTION	FUTURE POSSIBILITY
1. _____ 2. _____ 3. _____	0. *should we put* 4. _____ 5. _____ 6. _____	7. _____ 8. _____	9. _____ 10. _____	11. _____ 12. _____ 13. _____

---

2 | A WALK THROUGH BARCELONA

Harry and Jason are walking through Barcelona. Complete their conversation. Circle the correct word(s).

JASON: We (shouldn't)/ couldn't waste a minute of our time here in Barcelona. How do you like
                     0.

the walk so far?

HARRY: It's OK. I think we should take / have taken our bags to the hotel first.
                                       1.

JASON: Today let's just take a short walk and tomorrow we'll really explore the city.

HARRY: Right. We don't have to / must not see everything now. We're here all week!
                              2.

JASON: I studied Barcelona at school last year. I can / must tell you a little bit about the city's
                                         3.

history if you like.

HARRY: OK. Should I had read / have read something about Barcelona too?
                             4.

JASON: I don't think it was really necessary, but it might be interesting to hear now. The city was

actually founded around 230 B.C.E. It's not entirely clear who might <u>have / has</u> lived
                                                                        5.

here at that time. Many people say it could have <u>been / be</u> people called the
                                                    6.

Carthaginians, the Visogoths, or the Muslims. But Barcelona <u>should / might</u> never have
                                                              7.

become a great city if people from Southern France hadn't taken it over around A.D. 800.

These people came to be known as Catalans, and they <u>could / were able to</u> finally put
                                                      8.

Barcelona on the world map.

HARRY: Being located on the Mediterranean Sea <u>had to / should</u> have been a plus.
                                               9.

JASON: Yes, it was. In fact, the oldest part of the city is located right by the harbor and is called

Barri Gotic. It must <u>have been / be</u> a very busy place in those days!
                      10.

JASON: Oh look! That's the Sagrada Familia. It's a huge cathedral, and it <u>can / might</u> be the
                                                                           11.

most famous building in Barcelona. A man named Gaudi designed it.

HARRY: How <u>could / might</u> one man have designed such a complicated building? I have so many
            12.

questions. I <u>might / should</u> have learned something about Barcelona before we left after
              13.

all. I could <u>have / had</u> made the trip much more meaningful!
              14.

JASON: We <u>were able to / could have</u> cover a lot of material about Gaudi in my class, so I can
          15.

tell you more about him tomorrow. Now let's head back to the hotel and get some rest.

3 | ANTONIO GAUDI: THE FAMOUS ARCHITECT

A. Read these questions that Harry had about architect Antonio Gaudi. Use the modals in parentheses to write short answers.

0. Q: Did people know the quality of Gaudi's work while he was alive?

A: <u>They must have</u>. You can see more than a dozen buildings and parks
        (must)
   designed by Gaudi in Barcelona.

1. Q: Was Gaudi a religious man?

A: _____. Many of his works depict religious scenes.
        (might)

2. Q: Did Gaudi like to publish articles on architecture?

A: _____. He only published one article during his whole life.
        (must not)

3. Q: Could Gaudi have devoted himself to his works at the expense of everything else in
   his life?

A: _____. He even lived in the Sagrada Familia while he was
        (must)
   building it.

4. Q: Did Gaudi know the Guell family well?

A: _____. They hired him to build five different buildings and parks.
        (may)

B. Read these statements about Gaudi. Use the meanings of the underlined phrases and the word in parentheses to write sentences with modal phrases.

0. <u>It's likely</u> that the Guell family was very wealthy. (must)

   The Guell family must have been very wealthy.

1. <u>It's been suggested that</u> Gaudi was Spain's most famous architect. (might)

   _____

2. <u>Most likely</u> Gaudi had both natural talent and excellent training. (had to)

   _____

3. <u>It's likely</u> Gaudi spent all his time designing and building his masterpieces. (must)

   _____

4. <u>Gaudi probably</u> didn't use computers to help him design his buildings. (couldn't)

_____

5. <u>It's possible</u> people wanted Gaudi to design buildings in other parts of the world as well. (may)

_____

C. *Read these regrets Jason had from his last trip to Barcelona. Use the modals in parentheses to write sentences expressing what the tourist should have done.*

0. I didn't visit Gaudi's home in Barcelona. It was turned into a really interesting museum about his life. (should)

   I should have visited Gaudi's home in Barcelona. _____

1. I didn't climb the 340 steps to the top of one of the Sagrada Familia's towers. The view must be amazing from there! (could)

_____

2. I didn't buy a poster of Park Guell. I wanted one to hang in my bedroom. (should)

_____

3. I didn't take pictures of the Sagrada Familia at night. It's beautiful then because of all the lights! (should)

_____

4. I didn't go to Park Guell. It's supposed to be a good place to relax and eat lunch! (ought to)

_____

5. I threw away our entrance tickets to the Sagrada Familia. They have historical information printed on the backs. (should not)

_____

4 | EDITING: A POSTCARD FROM BARCELONA

Read this postcard Harry sent to his parents from Barcelona. There are 12 mistakes in the use of modals. The first mistake is already corrected. Find and correct 11 more. (Note: There can be more than one way to correct a mistake.)

Dear Mom and Dad,

Yesterday we visited Park Guell, which is a city park designed by Antonio Gaudi. To

get there, we had to climb up a large hill. It was so high that we could ~~of~~ *have* seen the whole city if it

hadn't been cloudy. The park is very beautiful, with lots of curving structures. Gaudi must liked

using mosaics, because everything is decorated with a mosaic. Artists make mosaics by setting

small colored tiles into a surface to make an image. There are so many tiny little pieces that it

couldn't have taken a really long time to build the park, and the builders must be very skillful.

We only got to stay at the park for two hours because it closed. We must have checked to see

when the park closed.

Barcelona was great! It's such a beautiful and busy city. It musts be a popular vacation spot. I

feel like we missed so many interesting sights. You've been to Barcelona. Where else should we

had gone?

Jason and I are on the train going to Paris from Barcelona now. Remember when you asked

me if we should have made train reservations so early? Well, we shouldn't of! We might stay for

two weeks instead of one, but we had to keep our train reservations.

We'll be visiting Paris for the next week. We must not forget to visit the Eiffel Tower and the

Louvre, which is the world's largest museum. I'm sure Paris must to be a great city to visit too.

I'm worried that we should not have time to see everything there either. I guess I'll just have to

come back again next year! Hey, you guys ought a come with me!

Love,

Harry

PART VIII Diagnostic Test

60 Items
Score: _____

🎧 *Listen to this lecture about hybrid cars. Complete the lecture by writing the words that you hear. You will hear the recording two times.*

Hybrid cars _____*are powered*_____ by two sources: gasoline and a rechargeable
0.

electric battery. These cars were first made available to consumers in the late 1990s. They quickly

became very popular, and now companies are introducing new models, including trucks and

SUVs. In the future, even hybrid sports cars _____.
1.

The primary reason for hybrid cars' popularity is their energy efficiency. Hybrid cars produce

less pollution than regular gas cars. This _____ in a few ways. When a
2.

hybrid car speeds up, energy _____ from the battery, not gas, so less gas
3.

_____. Also, when a hybrid car stops, even at a traffic light, the gas
4.

motors shut off, and the car is powered by electricity. A hybrid car's battery recharges each time

the driver steps on the brakes. When a car is moving, it has energy. When the brakes

_____, this energy is removed. Some of this energy
5.

_____ by hybrid cars and stored in the battery to use later.
6.

Energy-efficient cars are a trend of the future. This _____ in
7.

changing laws. In some countries, strict laws _____ to limit the amount
8.

of pollution that cars can produce. The requirements of these laws _____
9.

by hybrid cars. With hybrid cars, drivers save money on gas, and our earth's environment

_____, too. Yes, it looks like the days of buying regular gas-powered cars
10.

_____.
11.

PART VIII

2 | BICYCLE: THE TRIP

Read these diary entries from Joe's bicycle trip with his friends in California. Circle 17 passive verbs and passive causative verb phrases. Be sure to circle the complete verb or phrase.

June 1

We biked 20 miles today in warm weather. I (was challenged) by the trip, and now I'm exhausted. My body hasn't been trained to perform in such warm weather. But I will be rested after a good night's sleep. I hope I can go faster tomorrow, or I might not be taken seriously by Ari and Tomas.

June 2

Today we biked into the redwood forests around Big Sur. The trees were awesome! I hope that these trees are never cut down so that their beauty may be respected forever. They should be enjoyed by many future generations. We decided to camp overlooking the ocean. Less than 30 minutes after we had stopped, the tent was set up and the fire was built. I prepared the meal, and it was eaten very quickly! I don't know who the meal will be prepared by tomorrow night, but I doubt it will be as good as mine!

June 3

It was so hot today! The back of my neck was burned by the sun. Although I had considered shaving my head to be cooler, I won't cut my hair now that I've seen Ari's sunburned head! He had his hair shaved before we went on the trip, but I think he regrets it now.

June 4

What a morning! My bike broke after only 10 miles. I realized that all bikers ought to be taught how to fix their bikes! Ari, Tomas, and five other bikers examined it, and they all said that it had to be fixed by a bike mechanic. We had to walk three miles to a bike shop where I had my bike taken apart by a mechanic. I got a tire replaced, too, and I got my brakes checked.

3 | PLANES: *THE AVIATOR*

Read this text about the movie The Aviator. *Complete the sentences. Use the passive form of each verb in parentheses. Some items may have more than one right answer.*

The Aviator ___was written___ by John Logan, and it _____ by Martin
          0. (write)   **1. (direct)**

Scorsese. It _____ in 2004. The movie is about Howard Hughes, a famous
          2. (release)

American movie director and pilot, or aviator. He _____ by Leonardo DiCaprio.
                                           3. (portray)

This movie, which _____ a masterpiece by many viewers, depicts Hughes' life from
                  4. (consider)

the late 1920s to the mid-1940s. It tells the story of how Howard Hughes' small fortune

_____ into a large one. Hughes, who _____ in Texas, became a
      5. (transform)   **6. (raise)**

successful movie producer when he was still young. Later he _____ to aviation
                                          7. (attract)

(flying planes), which became his passion. Throughout the film, Hughes _____ as a
                                                   8. (portray)

man obsessed with perfection.

The story of Hughes' relationship with actress Katharine Hepburn _____ in the
                                                 9. (include)

movie. Because Hughes _____ with his work, his relationship with the actress
             10. (obsess)

suffered.

The Aviator _____ five Academy Awards at the 2005 awards ceremony. Cate
           11. (award)

Blanchett, who depicted actress Katharine Hepburn, _____ an award for best
                                         12. (give)

actress in a supporting role. In addition, the movie _____ for its excellence in art
                                      13. (recognize)

direction, cinematography, costume design, and film editing.

4 | BOATS: A CRUISE

Read this conversation about a cruise. Complete the conversation. Write the correct passive, passive with a modal or similar expression, or passive causative form of each verb in parentheses.

MELANIE: Hey, Kelly. How was your Caribbean cruise?

KELLY: It was amazing! The boat was beautiful. And we _____*were shown*_____ a great time!
                                                    0. (show)

MELANIE: I've never been on a cruise. What did you do?

KELLY: Well, I relaxed, and I got all kinds of beauty treatments.

MELANIE: Your nails look great! Did you _____ on the boat?
                                            1. (have / them / do)

KELLY: Yes. I also had back massages.

MELANIE: How often did you _____?
                            2. (get / your back / massage)

KELLY: Every day. And I _____ once. I also
                         3. (have / my feet / rub)

_____ one evening for a formal dinner.
4. (get / my hair / do)

MELANIE: That sounds great! What else did you do?

KELLY: Well, during the day, I sat on the deck most of the time, and I

_____ to me.
5. (have / drinks and snacks / deliver)

MELANIE: What _____?
              6. (you / serve)

KELLY: All kinds of foods and fruity drinks. Everything was delicious.

MELANIE: So _____ by the service?
            7. (you / impress)

KELLY: Definitely.

MELANIE: Well, it sounds like you relaxed a lot. _____ to any
                                                  8. (you / take)

historic sites?

KELLY: Yeah. My favorite tour was in Costa Maya, Mexico. It

_____ one of the best tours because you can see
9. (must / consider)

Mayan ruins, beautiful beaches, and jungles.

MELANIE: _____ in the price of the cruise?
          10. (the tour / include)

KELLY: No, we had to pay extra for it.

MELANIE: Well, it sounds like you had a wonderful time.

KELLY: It was fantastic. Everyone _____ like that on a

          11. (ought to / take care of)

  vacation. You know, you and your husband should think about taking a cruise. You

  _____ like a queen!

     12. (will / treat)

| 5 | EDITING: TRAIN COMPLAINT |

Read this letter of complaint to a train company. There are eight mistakes in the use of the passive and passive causative. The first mistake is already corrected. Find and correct seven more.

Dear Deluxe Train representative,

  I am writing to complain about the service I received on a recent trip with Deluxe Train. I
decided
~~was decided~~ to travel with Deluxe Train after friends told me of its excellent service and

reliability. On my trip, however, I was extremely disappointed. When I got on the train, I had one

of the attendants to carry my bag. But he wasn't careful with it, and he threw it on a shelf. A

bottle of perfume in my bag was breaking by him. Then, I was asked a train attendant for a

second blanket, and he told me that only one blanket was allowed per person. But I saw extra

blankets in a closet! Later I had some coffee bringing to me. But it took over half an hour to

arrive, and by then it was cold.

  I thought you should be informing of my terrible experience. Passengers ought to be respect

by Deluxe Train employees. Your company's service had better been improved if you want more

business from the Smith family.

Sincerely,

Cynthia Smith

Unit 18 Achievement Test

30 Items
Score: _____

🎧 *Listen to this lecture about the 1936 Summer Olympics in Berlin, Germany. Complete the lecture by writing the words that you hear. You will hear the recording two times.*

The 1936 Berlin Olympic Games ___*are remembered*___ for several historical reasons.

        0.

Forty-nine nations _____ at these Olympics, and 3,963 athletes (331 women and

        1.

3,632 men) participated in 129 events. More than 4 million tickets _____ to

        2.

people from all over the world to attend the different events.

These Games _____ best _____ for disproving Adolf Hitler's

        3.

theory of the superiority of the Aryan race. In fact, the most famous athlete of these Games was

Jesse Owens, an African-American who broke 11 Olympic records and won four gold medals.

The torch relay _____ in these Olympic Games. A torch is a long stick that

        4.

_____ on fire. This relay is now an important Olympic tradition. In the relay, a

        5.

torch _____ from Olympia, Greece, the site of the first Olympics, to the location

        6.

of the current Games by athletes or other famous people.

The 1936 Summer Games were the first ones on television. Twenty-five large TVs

_____ around Berlin. At this time most people didn't have televisions in their

        7.

homes, so the Games _____ by local people on these televisions.

        8.

Basketball, canoeing, and team handball competitions _____ for the first time

        9.

in these Games, and the sport of polo _____ for the last time.

        10.

2 | THE ANCIENT OLYMPIC GAMES

Read each sentence. Write **P** *if the sentence is passive and* **A** *if it is active.*

0. __P__ The first Olympic Games were held about 776 B.C.E., and they were dedicated to the Olympian gods.

1. _____ From their beginning in the year 776 B.C. until 684 B.C.E., the Olympic Games were a one-day event.

2. _____ Only Greek men were allowed to participate in the ancient Olympic Games.

3. _____ Married women were not permitted to watch or take part in the Olympic Games, but unmarried women were permitted to attend.

4. _____ The original Olympic stadium in Olympia, Greece was the site of most events.

5. _____ Running, long jump, shot put, javelin, boxing, equestrian, and pankration (a type of martial arts) events were included in the ancient Games.

6. _____ The ancient Olympic Games were played for almost 12 centuries, but they were prohibited in the year A.D. 393 by Emperor Theodosius.

3 | INTERVIEW: *SPORTS SPECIAL*

Read this television interview with Pam Plum, a player on a local curling team. Complete the interview by writing the passive or short answer form of each verb.

SAM: Good evening. I'm Sam Sills, and this is *Sports Special*. Today we're going to learn a bit about a sport that is not widely known—curling. With me is Pam Plum, a curler on a local curling team. Thank you for joining us today, Pam.

PAM: I'm happy to be here.

SAM: Well, I know just a little about curling. I know that stones ____are slid____ on top of
0. (slide)
ice, right?

PAM: Yes. A 19-kg stone _____ across ice towards a large circle. Players try to get
1. (push)
the stone as close to the center of the circle as possible.

SAM: That's probably harder than it sounds! _____ curling _____ by
                                                      2. (play)

       teams?

PAM: Yes, it _____. It's a competition between two teams, and each team has four
                3. (be)

       players. Basically, whichever team gets the stone closest to the center of the circle wins.

SAM: Interesting! Now tell us a bit about the history of curling. Where _____ it

       _____?
       4. (develop)

PAM: It originated in Scotland during the 16th century. The earliest curling games

       _____ around 1540.
       5. (report)

SAM: And at that time _____ the games _____ only during the
                                              6. (play)

       winter?

PAM: Yes, they _____. For many years the games _____ on frozen
                  7. (be)   **8. (hold)**

       ponds or lakes.

SAM: Curling is now an Olympic sport. When _____ it _____ an
                                           9. (make)

       Olympic sport?

PAM: It _____ to the Olympics at the 1998 Winter Games in Nagano, Japan.
          10. (add)

SAM: Fascinating! We'll be right back with Pam Plum, curler, after these messages.

---

4 | EDITING: OLYMPIC CHAMPION

*Read this short biography of Olympic gymnastics champion Nadia Comaneci. There are
five mistakes in the use of the passive. The first mistake is already corrected. Find and
correct four more. (Note: There can be more than one way to correct a mistake.)*

                                 was

Nadia Comaneci ~~is~~ born on November 12, 1961, in Onesti, Romania. She was introduce to

gymnastics at the age of six. She began competing in 1972, and she accomplished a lot during her

career. She was the first gymnast in Olympic history to be awarded a perfect score of 10.0. She

were given this score for her routine on the uneven parallel bars at the 1976 Summer Games in

Montreal, Canada. Six more 10.0s were presenting to her during those Games. In the 1976 and

1980 Games she was decorated with nine medals in total. She retired from competition in the

early 1980s and left Romania in 1989. Now she lives in the United States. Nadia's incredible

performances admire by athletes and fans as triumphant moments in Olympic history.

Unit 19 Achievement Test

30 Items
Score: _____

1 | LISTENING: JOB INTERVIEW PREPARATION

🎧 *Listen to this information about preparing for a job interview. Complete the information by writing the words that you hear. You will hear the recording two times.*

Many things ___*must be considered*___ as you prepare for a job interview. In order to
                          0.

demonstrate to the interviewer that you can meet the company's needs, your knowledge about

the company _____ apparent. How can you do that? Well, first of all,
                          1.

your knowledge of the company _____ by reading annual reports, doing
                                          2.

research on the Internet, and speaking with employees of the company. Then make sure to

mention this information during the interview.

Also, you should plan for some of the questions you might hear. You can easily find

frequently asked interview questions on the Internet. Answers to these questions

_____ and _____ ahead of time. But be careful!
                                          3.

Memorized answers from interview books or websites _____.
                                                          4.

Interviewers are familiar with these standard answers and will not be impressed by them.

In order to become comfortable in an interview situation, mock interviews

_____, even if they are with friends or family members. The more you
          5.

practice, the more comfortable you'll become with interviewing.

2 | JOB INTERVIEW

Read this passage about what to do in a job interview. Circle 10 examples of the passive with modals and similar expressions.

Interviewers will pay a lot of attention to how you act during an interview. Certain behavior (will be expected) of you. In fact, whether you are a good fit with the company will be decided within your first five minutes there! So here are few more things to consider before you arrive.

First, you will be expected to arrive on time. Make sure you know how to get to the interview location. Any problems with directions must be discovered ahead of time.

Second, your appearance can't be forgotten. Your clothing should be cleaned and pressed so you look professional.

Several copies of your resume had better be made ahead of time. If someone asks you for it, you'll want to have it ready.

Next, greet the interviewer appropriately. This includes a firm handshake, a smile, and introducing yourself. The interviewer should be greeted in the way that you would want someone to greet you.

When you answer questions, look the interviewer in the eye. Eye contact should be maintained while you talk.

And this is important! Your positive qualities must be highlighted for the interviewer; how will the interviewer know about your skills if you don't tell him or her? Although it's sometimes difficult, you must stay calm during the interview so that you can sell yourself. Act professionally, or you may not be taken seriously.

3 | INTERVIEW QUESTIONS AND ADVICE

Read this letter to an advice columnist and the columnist's response. Complete the letters.
Write the passive form with a modal or a similar expression for each verb in parentheses.

Dear Dr. Job,

I recently graduated from college. My first job interview ____*is going to be scheduled*____ for
                                                                    0. (be going to / schedule)
sometime next week. I've been coached by my professors on what to say, but I haven't

thought much about my appearance. My girlfriend keeps telling me that my hair

_____ and that I should remove my eyebrow ring. Does my beard
    1. (have to / cut)

_____? _____ my tattoos
    2. (have to / shave)   **3. (can / see)**

_____? Do I need to wear cologne? My girlfriend also tells me that my

brightly colored suit will not make a good impression on my interviewers. I believe that I

_____ because of my abilities. I think that my appearance doesn't
    4. (will / hire)

_____ for the interviewers to see my skills. Who is right, or
    5. (have to / change)

_____ both of us _____ correct?
    6. (can / consider)

Sincerely,

Jobless in Seattle

Dear Jobless in Seattle,

Although you have a good point, your girlfriend's suggestions _____.
                                                                    7. (can't / ignore)
Appearance _____ into consideration for any job interview. Although
              8. (had better / take)

your personality and individuality are important, it is also important to look professional. Body

piercings and tattoos _____ if you want to be taken seriously. Since long
                          9. (can't / show)

hair or facial hair on a man _____ inappropriate for an interview, you
                                  10. (may / consider)

may want to get a haircut and shave. Cologne is a good idea, but be careful; excessive cologne

can be a real turnoff.

Remember, if you make a favorable impression, the job _____ to

<u>11. (could / offer)</u>

you. And after you have demonstrated your abilities on the job, you may be able to grow your

hair and beard, show your tattoos, and wear bright clothing.

Good luck!

Dr. Job

---

4 | EDITING: SUMMER JOB INQUIRY

Read this e-mail about a summer job. There are five mistakes in the use of the passive with modals and similar expressions. The first mistake is already corrected. Find and correct four more.

Dear Mr. Myers,

I am writing to request additional information about the summer job you advertised in *The Town Chronicle* this week for a flower delivery person. You stated that the job requires 25 hours per week, Monday through Friday. Will the delivery person ~~allow~~ *be allowed* to work more hours on certain days and fewer hours on others? Or will the person require to work five hours each day? Also, I am planning to go on vacation for a week in June. If I get the job, can I been excused for that week and make up the time another week? Also, money was not mentioned in the advertisement. Is the new employee going to be pay minimum wage? Since the employee has to provide his or her own car, will he or she to be given additional gas money?

Thank you for your time.

Jenny Pantella

Unit 20 Achievement Test

1 | LISTENING: WEDDING PREPARATIONS

🎧 *Listen to this conversation between Suzy and Jess. Complete the conversation by writing the words that you hear. You will hear the recording two times.*

SUZY: Hi, Jess! What are you doing at the mall?

JESS: I'm ____*getting my nails painted*____ for a party tonight.
      0.

SUZY: Oh yeah? Where are you going to _____?
                                              1.

JESS: At Nell's Nails.

SUZY: Really? I need to find a nail place for my wedding. Have you

       _____ by anyone there before?
                2.

JESS: Yeah, they're really good. So, how are the wedding plans going?

SUZY: Very well! I decided that I'm going to _____ by Carla's Cake
                                                       3.

       Shop, and I'm going to _____ by my neighbor. She owns a flower
                                      4.

       shop.

JESS: And what about your hair? Are you going to _____ by a
                                                          5.

       professional stylist?

SUZY: Yeah, at the Beauty Spot. And I think I'll _____ by the stylist
                                                          6.

       about a week before the wedding so it will be really healthy.

JESS: That's a great idea. Have you _____ yet?
                                             7.

SUZY: No, not yet. I'll do that next week. Oh, I have to meet my sister in a half hour. I had

       better get going. See you soon!

JESS: See you!

2 | WEDDING ADVICE

Read this text about how to save money when planning a wedding. Circle 11 passive causative verb phrases. Be sure to circle the complete phrase.

In many places, it's becoming more common for brides and grooms to pay for their own weddings. And they're learning that weddings can be expensive! Here is some advice on how to save money on a wedding.

Some people (get their flowers delivered) from an expensive flower store. But there are other options. You can have your flowers arranged by a friend. Or you can have the wedding located in a beautiful outdoor area and have the flowers provided as part of the scenery! If you choose a location that has more than one wedding per day, schedule your wedding after someone else's. Maybe you can use the flowers from the previous ceremony for free!

Some people have their wedding photographed by a professional photographer. To save money, have only formal pictures taken by a professional. Put disposable cameras on the tables at the wedding reception, and have the reception captured on film by friends and relatives. You can also try to get your pictures taken by a photography student. This will cost less than a professional photographer.

Many people have a large meal catered by a restaurant or catering service. Instead of this, you can have the wedding scheduled for a time between meals. Then you can have appetizers served instead of a meal, which will save you money. If you really want to save money, you can have food brought to the reception by the guests. This is very informal, but it can be a lot of fun!

3 | THINGS TO BE DONE

Write sentences about the things that Suzy is going to have done for her before her wedding. Use the passive causative and the words in parentheses.

0. (get / invitations / print)

   Suzy is going to get invitations printed.

1. (have / the bridesmaids' lunch / prepare)

   _____

2. (have / the bridal party's presents / wrap)

   _____

3. (have / her wedding dress / adjust)

   _____

4. (get / her wedding dress / press)

   _____

5. (get / her hair / color)

   _____

6. (have / extra flowers / order)

   _____

4 | EDITING: HONEYMOON

Read this e-mail from Suzy to her friend Jess. There are seven mistakes in the use of the passive causative. The first mistake is already corrected. Find and correct six more.

Dear Jess,

Hi! How are you? Our honeymoon is wonderful! Sam is a great husband, and we're

                           my hair braided

having a great time. Today I got ~~braided my hair~~ on the beach. Sam laughed when he saw me!

But he got a bad fake tattoo draw on his shoulder, so he can't laugh too much. Yesterday we got

our pictures developing from the first few days here. We got some really good pictures. We're

enjoying all the hotel services. Every day I have a tropical fruit drink made it for me. Yesterday I

got my whole body massage. We had our breakfast bringed to us this morning. And last night we

champagne and strawberries delivered to us on the beach! Anyway, I'll call you when I get back!

Take care!

Suzy

PART VIII Achievement Test

60 Items
Score: _____

🎧 *Listen to this information about the Beatles. Complete the information by writing the words that you hear. You will hear the recording two times.*

The Beatles, a musical group originally formed in 1959, ____was made up____ of four
                                                          0.

young men from Liverpool, England. Although their music is over 30 years old, they still

_____ as the best rock group ever. The four musicians, John Lennon, Paul
        1.

McCartney, George Harrison, and Ringo Starr hold several records in the music industry that

some say _____. They are the only group in history to have 20 number one songs.
              2.

They have sold more albums than any other group, with global sales totaling more than 1.1

billion records.

Many of the Beatles' songs _____ by John Lennon and Paul McCartney. Early
                                    3.

on, it was decided that the Lennon-McCartney team _____ credit for all songs
                                                          4.

written by either of them. In reality, many of their songs were mainly written by just one of them

with a little help from the other. Despite this fact, Lennon-McCartney _____ the
                                                                              5.

most successful popular songwriting duo in the world.

In addition to making music, the Beatles made five movies. The band _____
                                                                            6.

starring in *A Hard Day's Night, Help!,* and *Magical Mystery Tour.* They _____ in
                                                                                  7.

animation in the movie *Yellow Submarine.* Their last movie, *Let It Be,* was a documentary which

_____ as the band recorded the album of the same title.
        8.

The Beatles played together in a recording studio for the last time in 1969. In 1970, it

_____ that Paul McCartney had left the Beatles. The group officially broke up on
        9.

December 31st, 1970. But the Beatles _____. In fact, when a CD of all their
                                              10.

number one songs was released in 2000, 31 years after the release of their previous album, it

became the fastest-selling CD of all time. Their music _____ and appreciated by
                                                                11.

fans of all ages for years to come.

2 | A MUSICAL TOUR

Read these diary entries about Tomoko's experiences traveling in Austria. Circle 17 passive verbs and passive causative verb phrases. Be sure to circle the complete verb or phrase.

July 4

My destination of Austria (was chosen) because of its importance in classical music. I started in

Salzburg because it was the home of the famous classical composer Wolfgang Amadeus Mozart.

Today I visited the place where Mozart was born in 1756. It has been converted into a museum.

His childhood violin and other musical instruments can be seen there, and letters he and his

family wrote to each other can be read. I learned that Mozart had his first music published

before he was 10 years old! That's amazing!

July 5

Today I went on the *Sound of Music* tour and saw the original home of the Von Trapp family. I

didn't know much about them. So I got their story explained to me by a tour guide, and I learned

a lot. After his wife died, Georg Von Trapp had his nine children looked after by a woman

named Maria Kutschera. Maria taught the children to sing and love music. Eventually Maria and

Georg fell in love, and they were married. When Austria was taken over by the Nazis in 1938,

the family escaped to mountains, leaving their possessions behind. They sang to make money.

Eventually they arrived in the United States, where they could be heard singing in performances

around the country. Their story was made into a Broadway musical and a very well-known

movie. The tour was a lot of fun. Well, it's late, and I should figure out my schedule for

tomorrow. Each day's activities must be planned so I get the most out of my trip!

July 6

Today I traveled to Vienna. I saw the Vienna State Opera where audiences have been treated to

some of the best opera music in the world since the 1860s. Tomorrow some of the waltzes of

Johann Strauss will be played there, including some pieces that may be considered his best. I got

a ticket, and I can't wait. I also visited the House of Music. It's a museum where you interact with music. I conducted a virtual Vienna Philharmonic Orchestra, and I sang and played

instruments and had my music recorded. It was awesome! I have learned a lot about music on

this trip that I didn't study in my music classes. I think all music students should be encouraged

to visit Vienna!

| 3 | BLUES: *RAY* |

Read this text about the movie Ray. *Complete the sentences. Use the passive form of the*
verbs in parentheses. Some items may have more than one right answer.

The film *Ray* _____ was written _____ by Taylor Hackford and James L. White, and it
                    0. (write)

_____ by Taylor Hackford. The movie _____ in 2004, and it
   1. (direct)   **2. (release)**

tells the story of Ray Charles. Ray was a famous American pianist and singer who

_____ by many people to be one of the best blues musicians and performers of
   3. (consider)

all time.

Ray Charles was born in 1930, and he _____ by his mother in Florida. He
                                              4. (raise)

_____ to blues at an early age. When it _____ that Ray was going
   5. (introduce)   **6. (discover)**

blind at the age of seven, he _____ as a normal boy by his strong-minded mother.
                                       7. (treat)

She taught Ray to stand up for himself. Her strength and determination helped Ray become a

successful musician. He _____ when people didn't agree with his artistic ideas. It
                         8. (not / discourage)

just made him work harder. His work paid off, and eventually his music _____ by
                                                                            9. (hear)

people around the country and the world.

For many years, Ray's life _____ by his addiction to drugs. After a long
                              10. (complicate)

struggle, Ray finally triumphed, and his life no longer _____ by his addiction.
                                                            11. (control)

In the movie, Ray Charles _____ by Jamie Foxx, who won an Oscar for actor
                              12. (portray)

in a leading role. *Ray* _____ one other Oscar for sound mixing.
                          13. (award)

4 | A NEW CD

Read this conversation about a new CD. Complete the conversation. Use the correct passive, passive with a modal or similar expression, or passive causative form of each verb in parentheses.

DAN: Hey, Ed, have you heard the new CD that José's band made?

ED: No. Is it good?

DAN: Yeah, it's really good. It's going _____*to be produced*_____ by a big record
0. (produced)

company.

ED: I heard the band _____ a deal by Star Records a few
1. (offer)

months ago. Is that true?

DAN: Yes, it is! Remember when they sent their first record to Star Records five years ago? The

producer said the record _____ at that time, but
2. (could not / make)

he told them their style was interesting. He said they should

_____, and he told them to send them in. So they did,
3. (have / their other songs / record)

and now they have a record deal!

ED: That's awesome! When will _____?
4. (the CD / release)

DAN: It comes out in stores next week. But José gave me copy already. Here, take a look at it.

ED: Where did they _____? It's so cool!
5. (get / the cover / do)

DAN: They _____ by a professional photographer. Then they
6. (have / their pictures / take)

_____ by a friend who is an artist.
7. (get / the other art / create)

ED: So how's the music? Did they _____ by other people?
8. (have / the songs / write)

DAN: No. They wrote them all.

ED: How much money _____ when they got their contract?
9. (they / pay)

Do you know?

DAN: Well, I know _____ a big check when they first signed
10. (the band / give)

the contract with Star Records. As for the future, the money depends on how many CDs

they sell. I think they're going to be really popular and make a lot of money.

ED: _____ for any magazines or anything?
11. (they / interview)

PART VIII

DAN: I don't know about magazines, but I heard that they _____

12. (may / feature)

on that TV program *Entertainment News* next week.

ED: That's so cool. I'll definitely buy the CD.

---

5 | EDITING: RECORD LABELING

Read this letter of complaint from a parent to a music store. There are eight mistakes in the use of the passive and passive causative. The first mistake is already corrected. Find and correct seven more.

Dear Music Mania representative,

I am writing to complain about your store's practice of not labeling CDs that contain mature content. I ~~was~~ recently bought a CD from your store for my son. I was listened to it, and I was shocked by the obscene language. These types of CDs had better been labeled so parents can be alerted to the material they contain.

There is another thing that concerns me. My 13-year-old son was purchased CDs with mature content in your store without parental consent. A 13-year-old child should not be allowed to buy something like this if his or her parents aren't present. CDs with adult content had better not to be sold to children without their parents' approval.

Your store should have its CDs label if they contain mature content, and children should have their purchases to approve by a parent or a responsible adult. If you don't make these changes, your customers may being tempted to shop at other music stores.

Sincerely,

Vonetta Hood

PART IX Diagnostic Test

1 | LISTENING: EASY TRAVEL

🎧 *Listen to this radio advertisement for Easy Travel, a travel agency. Complete the advertisement by writing the words that you hear. You will hear the recording two times.*

How long does it take you to plan a vacation? Buying plane tickets, finding a rental car, looking for activities for the kids. . . . It's a lot of work! ____*What would*____ you say
                                                                                                        0.
_____ to do all that work for you? Because that's what Easy Travel does. It's so
          1.
easy! _____ to our agency, we will ask you a few simple questions about the kind
          2.
of vacation you want. Then we do all the work. We'll research all the options, and we'll offer
you several packages to choose from. If you want a low-cost vacation, _____ you
                                                                                          3.
three low-cost options! If you're looking for a romantic getaway, _____ at least
                                                                                  4.
three possibilities. All you do is pick the one that's best for you. So, _____ to
                                                                                        5.
spend another minute planning your next vacation, then we are the travel agency for you!

2 | MAKING DECISIONS

A. *Read this passage about making decisions. Find eight present and future real conditional sentences. In each real conditional sentence, circle the result clause. Underline the clause that expresses the condition.*

Every day we are faced with decisions. Some decisions are very important while others are not. <u>If a decision has long-term effects,</u> (that decision is usually important). A decision is also important if it affects many people. If a decision is important, you should consider all the possible consequences before making a choice. Decisions made without careful consideration can often result in bad choices and regrets.

If you consider all the possible consequences, will you make the right choice? Even if you try to consider all the possibilities, you can't always think of everything. But there are some ways to improve your decision-making skills. Consider these tips when you make decisions.

1. Make a list of the positive and negative consequences of each choice.

2. Consider the people who the decision will affect. What is best for them?

3. Try to think of similar situations. What decisions did you make in the past, and what happened as a result?

4. Avoid rushing into a decision. Take time to think it over.

5. Recognize any biases you may have about the choices you are considering.

I follow these guidelines when I'm faced with an important decision, and I have learned to make good choices. If you use these tips, you might improve your decision-making skills. And if you improve your decision-making skills, you'll lead a happier life with fewer regrets!

B. *Read the numbered statements about making decisions. Then read each statement and circle* **T** *(true) or* **F** *(false).*

0. If one of my decisions hurt someone, I would apologize to him or her.

    T (F) **a.** One of my decisions hurt someone.

    T (F) **b.** I must apologize to that person.

1. If my mom were here, I could ask her what to do.

    T F **a.** My mom is here.

    T F **b.** I can't ask my mom what to do.

2. If they knew how much the trip would cost, they would make a decision right now.

    T F **a.** They're making a decision right now.

    T F **b.** They don't know how much the trip will cost.

3. Melanie would have taken a long time to make the decision if she had known its importance.

    T F **a.** Melanie knew the decision was important.

    T F **b.** Melanie took a long time to make the decision.

4. If James had decided to go to college, he could have become a lawyer.

    T F **a.** James went to college.

    T F **b.** James didn't become a lawyer.

5. I wish I had the opportunity to change my mind.

    T F **a.** I want to change my mind.

    T F **b.** I don't have the opportunity to change my mind.

6. If Cameron had decided to go to the beach, she would have gotten sunburned.

    T F **a.** Cameron decided to go to the beach.

    T F **b.** Cameron got sunburned.

7. I wish I were good at making decisions.

    T F **a.** I want to be good at making decisions.

    T F **b.** I am good at making decisions.

8. If Derek hadn't decided right then, he would have lost the opportunity.

    T F **a.** Derek decided right then.

    T F **b.** Derek didn't lose the opportunity.

3 | PLANNING A VACATION

A. *Lola and Laszlo are talking about their vacation plans. Read their conversation.*
Combine the pairs of sentences in parentheses to make present real conditional sentences.
Keep the same order and decide which clause begins with **if**. *Make necessary changes in*
capitalization and punctuation.

LOLA: We should start planning for our vacation this summer. *If we want to plan our*

trip right, we need to call a travel agent.
           0. (We want to plan our trip right. We need to call a travel agent.)

LASZLO: Let's do it ourselves this year. We can make all the reservations online.

LOLA: Why do you want to do it yourself? _____
                1. (It's much faster and easier. You use a travel agent.)

_____

Do you have the time and patience to really consider all our options?

LASZLO: Of course I do! _____
            2. (I have a lot of patience. I'm interested in the topic.)

_____

LOLA: Let's get started then. _____
          3. (You don't know any good websites. Try www.planyourvacation.com.)

_____

It gives you lots of information about activities and costs at different places.

LASZLO: Let's start there. _____
         4. (We should reserve plane tickets early. We want to pay low fares.)

_____

LOLA: I'm not sure that matters. We're going on vacation around a holiday.

_____
         5. (You travel near a holiday. Plane tickets always cost more.)

_____

LASZLO: Hmmm. That's a good point. Well, I'll go online and start checking prices.

B. *Read these statements about some of Laszlo and Lola's vacation decisions. Complete the present and future real conditional statements. Use the correct present or future form of each verb in parentheses.*

0. If the plane tickets _____*cost*_____ more than $300 a person, they _____*will choose*_____ a
(cost)   (choose)
different vacation spot.

1. If their favorite hotel _____ more than $100 per night for a room, they
(charge)
_____ at a different hotel.
(stay)

2. Now one of their children may go to summer camp during the time they had planned for a

vacation. Unless the whole family _____ available, they _____ on
(be)   (not go)
vacation.

3. Some friends of Laszlo and Lola may vacation at the Grand Canyon. Laszlo and Lola

_____ hotel rooms with their friends if they _____ the Grand
(can share)   (visit)
Canyon at the same time.

4. If they _____ a way to make the vacation less expensive, Laszlo and Lola
(not find)
_____ their money for a better vacation next year.
(save)

| 4 | **PACKING FOR A VACATION** |

A. *Read these tips for packing for a vacation. Complete the tips with **if** or **unless**.*

0. _____*If*_____ you're traveling with companions, share some items to lessen the number

of things you'll need to pack.

1. _____ you pack lightly, you will need a suitcase with wheels. You won't want to

carry a heavy suitcase around.

2. You should pack warm clothes _____ you know your destination will have cool

weather.

3. _____ you aren't sure about the weather conditions, you'll need to pack a

variety of clothes.

4. You shouldn't pack an item _____ you're sure you'll use it.

B. *Tanya is packing for a trip to Mexico City. Read her reasons for packing each item.*
Rewrite Tanya's reasons. Use present and future unreal conditionals. Some items may have
more than one right answer.

0. I don't know what the weather is like in Mexico City. That's why I'm packing both pants and

shorts.

If I knew what the weather is like in Mexico City, I wouldn't pack both pants and shorts.

1. I get motion sickness on airplanes. That's why I'm taking this medicine.

_____

_____

2. I don't know how to get to the hotel from the airport. That's why this map is so important.

_____

_____

3. I'm not familiar with the tourist attractions in Mexico City. That's why I have to take this

travel guide.

_____

_____

4. I love taking good pictures. That's why I'm taking this expensive camera.

_____

_____

5. I don't know how much money to take. That's why I'm putting this credit card in my purse.

_____

_____

6. I hate traveling without something to read. That's why I'm taking this book.

_____

_____

7. The hotel has a swimming pool. That's why I can't leave my swimsuit at home.

_____

_____

8. I can't buy this medication there. That's why I need to take it with me.

_____

_____

9. My parents want me to call them. That's why I'm packing this phone card.

_____

_____

10. Airplanes are always cold. That's why I need this sweater.

_____

_____

C. *Read some of Tanya's thoughts after her vacation in Mexico. Complete the past unreal conditional sentences. Use the correct forms of the words in parentheses.*

0. If I _____*had realized*_____ the hotel provided shampoo and soap, I
              (realize)

   _____*wouldn't have taken*_____ them along with me.
         (not take)

1. If I _____ my camera on the trip, I _____ so
        (not take)   (not get)

   many great pictures.

2. If I _____ my suitcase from the airport to the hotel, it
       (not carry)

   _____ so heavy.
      (not seem)

3. I _____ bring my postcards home if I _____
      (not have to)   (mail)

   them before I left.

4. My suitcase _____ so heavy if I _____ gifts
         (not be)   (not buy)

   for my whole family.

5. I _____ back so many souvenirs if they _____
      (not bring)   (be)

   so inexpensive.

6. I wish I _____ two more days at the beach.
      (spend)

7. My sister wishes she _____ to Mexico with me.
           (go)

8. If I _____ she wanted to go, I _____ her.
      (know)   (invite)

PART IX

5 | EDITING: A POSTCARD FROM MEXICO

Read this postcard Tanya sent her friend Molly. There are nine mistakes in the use of conditionals. The first mistake is already corrected. Find and correct eight more. (Note: There can be more than one way to correct a mistake.)

Dear Molly,

    Mexico City is warm and sunny! If I ~~knew~~ *had known* that, I wouldn't have packed two sweaters and a jacket! Tomorrow I'm going shopping. If I will find something nice, I'll get it for you. I'm so glad you suggested Mexico for my vacation. I wouldn't think of it if you hadn't mentioned it.

    Yesterday I visited the pyramids at Teotihuacan. Unless you're scared of heights, you might not want to climb to the top. Some of the pyramids are over 60 meters tall! I was there all day, but I wish I can have spent a week there! You know me. If a place is full of history, I would love it!

    When I would travel, I always make a list of places to visit again, and Mexico is definitely on it! If I would move next month, I would buy a house in Mexico. That's how much I love it here. Will you come with me if I had come again next year? If I get the chance, I'll definitely be back! See you soon,

Tanya

Unit 21 Achievement Test

30 Items
Score: _____

A. 🎧 Listen to this radio advertisement for a website. Complete the advertisement by writing the words that you hear. You will hear the recording two times.

These days many people are becoming very conscious of what they eat. Are you joining the

trend? _____*If you want*_____ to eat more healthfully, then I have the website for you! I can show
       0.

you many ways to cook healthy, delicious dishes! If you eat healthy foods, _____
                                            1.

more than your physical fitness. When you pay attention to what you eat, your energy level

_____.
    2.

So what's your reason for wanting to change your eating habits? Many people go on diets

_____ to lose weight or when they have a health problem. Different problems
    3.

require different diets, so my website offers collections of recipes for a variety of health issues.

But you don't have to start eating better because of a problem. You can actually prevent health

and weight problems _____ eating well before they happen! If you want to learn
                              4.

how to cook healthy food in your own kitchen, _____ my website,
                                                5.

www.eatrightforyourhealth.com. You'll find great meal ideas!

B. *Read this information on the website's home page. Find 11 present real conditional sentences. In each real conditional sentence, circle the result clause. Underline the clause that expresses the condition.*

<u>If you eat a lot of dairy products like milk, cheese, and yogurt,</u> (you should buy low-fat versions of them). These low-fat products usually cost the same as the higher-fat versions, and they generally taste pretty similar. If you're trying to avoid fat, then eat leaner meats. Fish, seafood, and chicken have much less fat than red meat. When you purchase any meat, try to choose pieces that are well-trimmed. Another way you can eat healthier meals at home is to buy lots of fresh fruits and vegetables. When you eat these, you get lots of important vitamins and nutrients.

You should always read the nutrition facts on food containers when you're at the grocery store. If you pay attention to what you buy, then you also pay attention to what you eat! When I go to the grocery store, I usually start in the health foods section. Even if your store doesn't have a section just for health foods, you can still find healthy foods. Look for fresh fruits and vegetables, lean meats, low-fat dairy products, and whole grains.

And finally, if you eat out often, try to cut down on that habit. If you cook at home, then you have more control over what you eat. And you can save a lot of money if you eat at home, too. These are all ways you can change your eating habits to better your health and energy levels. So if you like these tips, explore the rest of the website for more!

2 | HEALTHY EATING TIPS

Read these questions and answers posted on the website. Then use the information in each question and answer to help you write a summary. Write present real conditional sentences.

0. Q: I love to buy fresh fruit. Is there any way to find less expensive fruit?

   A: You ought to buy it when it's in season. The prices are lower then.

If you love to buy fresh fruit, you ought to buy it when it's in season.

1. Q: I want to fix a healthy meal for a friend. Any suggestions?

   A: You should check my website for great meal ideas! You'll find all kinds of healthy recipes.

_____

_____

2. Q: My friend likes low-fat desserts. Do you have any ideas?

   A: She ought to make something with fresh fruit. Fruit is sweet and healthy.

_____

_____

3. Q: I like to cook with the freshest food. Where can I buy it?

   A: Shop at a market that gets food delivered each day. They have the freshest food.

_____

_____

4. Q: My children need healthier snacks. Any ideas?

   A: Give them plenty of fresh fruit and vegetables. They are tasty and good for growing bodies.

_____

_____

5. Q: I want to start eating better. What do I need to know?

   A: Remember to eat a variety of foods. This way you will get all the nutrition you need.

_____

_____

3 | A SEAFOOD MARKET

*Read this conversation between Marla, a customer, and Young Sun, a worker at a seafood market. Combine the two sentences in parentheses to make a present real conditional sentence. Keep the same order and decide which clause begins with **if**. Make necessary changes in capitalization and punctuation.*

YOUNG SUN: Hi. Can I help you?

MARLA: Well, I'd like to get some fish for dinner, but I don't know much about seafood.

Can you recommend something?

YOUNG SUN: Sure. The salmon is really good. It's very fresh today.

MARLA: Is freshness important?

YOUNG SUN: Yes. _____*If seafood isn't fresh, it can start to taste funny*_____.
                               0. (Seafood isn't fresh. It can start to taste funny.)

MARLA: How can you tell if the fish is fresh?

YOUNG SUN: Well, there are several ways. _____

_____.
           1. (You can tell it's fresh. The fish doesn't have a strong smell.)

_____.
           2. (And you know it's good. The fish is firm, not too soft.)

MARLA: That's good to know. I guess you need to know a lot about seafood to work here.

YOUNG SUN: It does help. _____.
           3. (You know about the products. You can serve customers better.)

MARLA: So how do I cook the salmon?

YOUNG SUN: Put a little salt and pepper on it. Cook it on medium heat for about 20 minutes.

MARLA: That's it? It's so easy!

YOUNG SUN: Yep. _____.
           4. (You do that. It comes out great every time.)

MARLA: I can't believe it's so easy.

YOUNG SUN: Yeah. _____.
           5. (Most people eat a lot of seafood. They know how to prepare it.)

It's quick and easy, and it's good for you.

4 | EDITING: MAKING DINNER PLANS

Read this e-mail from Marla to her husband Darren at work. There are five mistakes in the use of present real conditionals. The first mistake is already corrected. Find and correct four more. (Note: Some errors may include punctuation.)

Darren,

    I went to the seafood market on Lincoln Avenue today. When I walk by it, I always ~~wanted~~ *want* to stop in. So today I did, and I bought some salmon for dinner. The woman who works there is a seafood expert. If she tells me something, I will believe it. She told me to cook the salmon with just a little salt and pepper. She said that when fish will be fresh, it doesn't need a lot of seasoning. I think it'll be so good. If we like this fish I can get more next week.

    I'm also planning to fix a salad and some fresh fruit. If you want anything else, just letting me know.

Love,

Marla

Unit 22 Achievement Test

---

1 | LISTENING: PUTTING TOGETHER A NEW DESK

🎧 *Listen to this conversation between Carla and Betty as they put together Carla's new desk. Complete the conversation by writing the words that you hear. You will hear the recording two times.*

CARLA: Betty, I'm glad you're here! I need help putting this new desk together. If you don't help

me, I ____*might never get it done*____!
     0.

BETTY: Well, _____ instructions, I'll be able to help you.
           1.

CARLA: There are instructions. But they're really difficult to understand! I've been looking at

them for an hour! Here, take them.

BETTY: If you get frustrated, _____ it.
                    2.

CARLA: I know that. But I can't help it!

BETTY: Don't worry. _____ it done if we work together.
              3.

CARLA: OK, what should I do?

BETTY: Here. If you hold this piece, _____ that one to it.
                       4.

CARLA: Yeah, that looks right.

BETTY: Actually, this looks pretty easy. _____ a problem, it won't take
                        5.

long at all.

CARLA: Thank goodness. If you can really do this, _____ you out to
                         6.

dinner.

BETTY: Well, then let's finish it up!

2 | CONDITIONS AND RESULTS

Match the conditions with the results. There are more results than you need.

Conditions	Results
_f_ 0. If I study a lot,	**a.** I might look for it somewhere else.
____ 1. If I find a cheap airline ticket,	**b.** I'll go see it with my friends.
____ 2. If the weather is bad,	**c.** I may spend it on a new shirt.
____ 3. If I have some extra money,	**d.** I might buy it.
____ 4. If there's a good movie at the theater,	**e.** I could ignore the letter.
____ 5. If I can't find the book I want at that store,	**f.** ~~I might do well~~ on the test.
____ 6. If I forget to turn off the lights,	**g.** I won't play outside with my dog.
	h. I'll go outside.
	i. I'll waste electricity.

3 | MAKING A SCHEDULE

Read this conversation between Byron and his new co-worker, Thomas, as they make plans
for a busy day at work. Complete the conversation with **if** or **unless**.

BYRON: _____Unless_____ we make a schedule for our work today, we'll never get
        0.

everything done.

THOMAS: Yeah, _____ we make a schedule, it'll help us organize our time.
                  1.

BYRON: How about this: _____ we finish up the Peterson presentation this
                       2.

morning, we can start on the Carlton project this afternoon.

THOMAS: What about the quarterly reports? We have to do those too. Also, we're supposed to

organize the Phillips files.

BYRON: This is a lot to do. _____ we work quickly, we won't have time to do
                            3.

everything!

THOMAS: Yeah, and we can't leave on time _____ we finish it all.
                                           4.

BYRON: Well, let's divide up some of this work. _____ I prepare the slides for the
　　　　　　　　　　　　　　　　　　　　　　　　　5.

presentation, will you be able to start the Carlton project?

THOMAS: Sounds good. _____ we share the work, we'll never leave this office!
　　　　　　　　　　　　　　　6.

4 | A CO-WORKER'S ADVICE

Read these statements of advice Byron gave to his co-worker, Thomas. Complete the statements by writing correct present or future form of each verb.

If you ____*forget*____ to do any of your tasks, the boss _____ upset with
　　　　　　0. (forget)　　　　　　　　　　　　　　　　　　　　　1. (get)

you.

You _____ successful in your job if you _____ all the rules.
　　　　2. (be)　　　　　　　　　　　　　　　　　　　3. (follow)

People _____ you as a responsible person if you _____ your
　　　　　4. (see)　　　　　　　　　　　　　　　　　　　　5. (finish)

work on time.

If you _____ your work done early, the boss _____ you.
　　　　　6. (get)　　　　　　　　　　　　　　　　　　　7. (reward)

Unless you _____ all your work correctly, the boss _____
　　　　　　8. (do)　　　　　　　　　　　　　　　　　　　　9. (be)

disappointed in your performance.

5 | EDITING: A MOTIVATIONAL E-MAIL

Read this e-mail from Byron to Thomas. There are four mistakes in the use of future real conditionals. The first mistake is already corrected. Find and correct three more. (Note: Some errors may include punctuation.)

Hey Thomas,

　　　　　　　　　　　　　　　　　　　　　　　　　　　　　　　　　　　　　practice
　　I know you're giving a big presentation tomorrow. Are you nervous? If you ~~practiced~~ a lot,

I'm sure you'll do well. I always used to get nervous before presentations. But I learned how to

deal with it. If you will relax for 15 minutes before the presentation starts, you'll do much better.

You won't be able to concentrate, unless you're calm. Remember, you do well if you prepare

yourself and relax. Good luck tomorrow! I know you'll do just fine!

Byron

Unit 23 Achievement Test

30 Items
Score: _____

1 | LISTENING: WISHFUL THINKING

🎧 *Listen to this conversation between Sasha and her husband, Joseph. Complete the conversation by writing the words that you hear. You will hear the recording two times.*

SASHA: I wish we _____*didn't have*_____ to work so much.
0.

JOSEPH: I know. If I didn't have to work, _____ up some hobbies, like playing the
1.

piano. How about you?

SASHA: If I didn't work, _____ the world. I've always wanted to see Turkey,
2.

Egypt, and Spain.

JOSEPH: _____ the chance to travel wherever I wanted, I would go to South
3.

America. I've always wanted to visit Peru to see Machu Picchu. Oh, and

_____ to see the Nazca lines if I could.
4.

SASHA: That would be so interesting! But if _____, I wouldn't suggest any more
5.

places to visit. I might get too many ideas in my head! I wish _____ my
6.

job right now!

JOSEPH: Believe me, I know. I wish _____ you to all those places. Maybe we can
7.

start to travel in a few years when we've saved some more money.

PART IX

2 | MORE WISHES

*Read each numbered statement. Then read each statement and circle **T** (true) or **F** (false).*

0. I wish I could buy my sister a new car for her birthday.

    T (**F**) **a.** I can buy my sister a new car for her birthday.

    (**T**) **F** **b.** I want to buy my sister a new car.

1. I wish I were an artist.

    T **F** **a.** I want to be an artist.

    T **F** **b.** I'm an artist.

2. I wish that my husband would take me out to dinner.

    T **F** **a.** My husband took me out to dinner.

    T **F** **b.** I want to go out to dinner with my husband.

3. I wish my wife and I could take a trip to Japan.

    T **F** **a.** I want to take a trip to Japan.

    T **F** **b.** My wife and I have the ability to go to Japan.

4. I wish we had a pet kitten.

    T **F** **a.** We have a pet kitten.

    T **F** **b.** We want a pet kitten.

5. If I had a new stereo, I would listen to it all the time.

    T **F** **a.** I have a new stereo.

    T **F** **b.** I listen to my new stereo all the time.

6. I would have a huge garden if I knew about plants.

    T **F** **a.** I have a huge garden.

    T **F** **b.** I know about plants.

7. If I bought a new car, I would buy a convertible.

    T **F** **a.** I'm not able to buy a convertible right now.

    T **F** **b.** I recently bought a new car.

| 3 | WHAT IF . . . |

Sasha asks Joseph some questions. Use the correct forms of the words given to write present unreal conditional questions.

0. What / you / buy / if / you / have a million dollars?

   What would you buy if you had a million dollars? _____

1. What / you / do / if / you / never have to worry about money?

   _____

2. If / you / can work anywhere / where / you / want to work?

   _____

3. If / you / can buy any car / what / it / be?

   _____

4. Who / you / like to have dinner with / if / you / can eat with anyone in the world?

   _____

4 | EXCUSES, EXCUSES

Children often make excuses to avoid doing what they're supposed to do. Rewrite the excuses below. Use present and future unreal conditionals. Some items may have more than one right answer.

0. I don't have my schoolbooks. That's why I can't do my homework.

If I had my schoolbooks, I could do my homework.

1. I don't have a book to read. That's why I don't stop watching TV.

_____

2. I'm not good at sports. That's why I won't play basketball with my friends.

_____

3. I'm not hungry. That's why I won't eat supper.

_____

4. I like my room dirty. That's why I won't clean my room.

_____

5. I'm afraid of water. That's why I can't take a bath.

_____

6. The knob on the radio is broken. That's why I can't turn down the music.

_____

7. My favorite TV show is on. That's why I won't wash the dishes.

_____

8. My sister doesn't want help. That's why I can't help her with her homework.

_____

9. I'm not tired. That's why I won't go to bed.

_____

5 | EDITING: E-MAIL CHAIN LETTERS

A chain letter is a letter sent to several people asking them to send a copy of the letter to several more people. Read this information about e-mail chain letters. There are four mistakes in the use of present and future unreal conditionals. The first mistake is already corrected. Find and correct three more.

If you have e-mail, you may have received a message like this: "What would you do if

you had
~~you'll have~~ three wishes? Now you do! Make your wishes and send this message to 10 more

people. If I was you, I'd hurry and send the message on before you forget!"

People all around the world receive e-mails like this frequently. The messages usually come

with instructions to make a wish and then send the message on to other people. The messages

often warn that if you don't send the e-mail to more people, your wish won't come true.

If you would receive a message like this, what would you do? Would you delete it, or would

you send it to other people? If you decided to send it on, what would you wish for? Many people

will wish for health, happiness, and wealth if they had the opportunity.

Unit 24 Achievement Test

30 Items
Score: _____

---

1 | LISTENING: AN UNSUCCESSFUL BAND

A. 🎧 Listen to this conversation between Amy and Ben about their band. Complete the conversation by writing the words that you hear. You will hear the recording two times.

BEN: Why do you think our band didn't get any jobs? Would we have succeeded

_____*if we had done something differently*_____ ?
                              0.

AMY: Well, if we had advertised the band, people might have known who we were. Or

_____ a manager, he or she could have helped us find jobs.
              1.

BEN: You know what else would have helped? If we had recorded a sample of our music for

potential clients, people _____ what kind of music we played.
                                           2.

AMY: That would have been a great idea _____ of it earlier. If our band
                                                          3.

had gotten a good reputation, people might have wanted to hire us.

BEN: If we had done some of these things before, our band _____ a
                                                                                    4.

success!

AMY: You know, maybe it's a *good* thing that the band didn't succeed. I mean,

_____ successful, I wouldn't have gone back to school.
              5.

BEN: That's true. I wouldn't have started dating Jennifer _____ to work
                                                                              6.

a lot of nights. I guess sometimes things just work out for the best, even if they don't turn

out the way you expected.

AMY: That's so true. I'm glad we started the band even though it didn't work out. Although I

wouldn't have bought a new guitar if I had known I wouldn't need it!

BEN: I guess sometimes lessons like that can be expensive.

B. Reread the conversation between Amy and Ben. Then read each statement and circle
T *(true)* or **F** *(false).*

T Ⓕ 0. Amy and Ben's band succeeded.

T **F** 1. Amy and Ben advertised their band.

T **F** 2. People didn't know who Amy and Ben were.

T **F** 3. A manager helped Amy and Ben find jobs.

T **F** 4. The band recorded a sample of their music.

T **F** 5. The band didn't get a good reputation.

T **F** 6. People wanted to hire Amy and Ben's band.

T **F** 7. Ben started to date Jennifer.

T **F** 8. Amy bought a new guitar.

T **F** 9. Amy knew she would not need a new guitar.

2 | SOME THOUGHTS ABOUT WORK

*Read some people's thoughts about their past experiences with work. Complete the past
unreal conditional sentences by writing the correct forms of the words in parentheses.*

0. I always worked too much each week. If I _____*hadn't worked*_____ so much, I
   (not work)

   _____*could have spent*_____ more time with my children.
   (could / spend)

1. My boss taught me how to manage my time. I _____ how to manage
   (would / not know)

   my time if he _____ me.
   (not taught)

2. I drove 45 miles to work each day. If I _____ so far to work, I
   (not drive)

   _____ extra free time.
   (would / have)

3. When I was young, I always wanted to be a lawyer, but I became a dentist instead. I

   never really liked being a dentist. If I _____ a lawyer, I
   (be)

   _____ happier.
   (might / be)

4. I didn't go to college. If I _____ to college, I
   (go)

   _____ medicine.
   (would / study)

5. I broke the copy machine at work and had to pay to fix it. I _____
   (could / go)

   on a vacation this year if I _____ the copy machine.
   (not break)

6. I didn't know some teaching jobs allow you to take the summer off. If I

_____ that some teaching jobs allowed this, I
      (know)

_____ a teacher.
     (would / become)

7. Some salespeople travel around the world for work. I _____ a lot if I
                                           (might / travel)

_____ as a salesperson.
     (work)

8. My job required a lot of extra hours, and I never liked that. I wish I

_____ a different job.
     (choose)

9. I am not a licensed mechanic. I wish I _____ courses to become
                                        (take)

licensed.

10. My boss didn't say the job required heavy lifting. I wish he _____ me
                                        (tell)

all the job requirements.

---

3 | EDITING: LOSING A JOB

Read this e-mail from Sunny to Isabel. There are six mistakes in the use of past unreal conditionals. The first mistake is already corrected. Find and correct five more.

Dear Isabel,

    I have some bad news. The supermarket where I work is going out of business, and now I

don't have a job. I don't know what I'll do! It has been a great job for me. I never would ~~meet~~ *have met*

my boyfriend Mark if I wouldn't have worked there. And if I haven't worked there at night, I

can't have attended college courses during the day.

    I guess the situation isn't all that bad. I can always find another job. But if I knew the store

was closing sooner, I may have found a new job already! I really wish I had heard about this

sooner. Anyway, I'll keep you updated on my job hunt.

Sunny

PART IX Achievement Test

60 Items
Score: _____

⌒ *Chess is a kind of board game. Listen to this radio advertisement for a chess tournament. Complete the advertisement by writing the words that you hear. You will hear the advertisement two times.*

Do you want to challenge your mind? Would you like to win $5,000? You can do both

_____*if you come*_____ to the May Madness chess tournament next Saturday! Hundreds of chess
　　　　0.

players from all over come each year to play this tournament. _____ together,
　　　　　　　　　　　　　　　　　　　　　　　　　　　　　　　　　　　　1.

excitement fills the air! If you stop by to watch, _____ the matches played in
　　　　　　　　　　　　　　　　　　　　　　　　　2.

record time! If you come to compete, _____ against some of the most talented
　　　　　　　　　　　　　　　　　3.

players in the area. And _____, you'll receive a prize of $5,000! What would you
　　　　　　　　　4.

do with the money _____?
　　　　　　　　　5.

2 | COMPETITIONS

A. *Read this passage about competitions. Find eight present and future real conditional sentences. In each real conditional sentence, circle the result clause. Underline the clause that expresses the condition.*

<u>If you enjoy testing your skills against other people,</u> (you should participate in a competition). A competition is a contest in which individuals or teams test their abilities against others'. If the result of the competition is very important, we call it a high-stakes competition. Professional sports are one example of high-stakes competition. In some professional sports, athletes earn a living by winning competitions. If they never win, they will not make very much money. Other competitions do not have such important results. We call these low-stakes competitions. A chess game between friends is one example of a low-stakes competition. If you want to take part in an activity for fun, you should participate in a low-stakes competition.

When you participate in a competition, you become part of a community. Even if it's an individual competition, you are still a part of the community of people who compete in that type of contest. If you love challenging yourself and want to be part of a community, then you'll really enjoy competitions!

Competitors are often superstitious. Regardless of the superstition, all competitors who believe in superstitions believe one thing. If they perform a certain ritual before the competition, they have a better chance at winning. What do you think? If competitors follow a ritual, will they increase their chances of success?

*B. Read the numbered statements about competitions. Then read each statement and circle **T** (true) or **F** (false).*

0. If I liked playing chess, I would enter the competition next month.

   T Ⓕ **a.** I like playing chess.

   T Ⓕ **b.** I'm going to enter the chess competition.

1. If Tony reviewed the rules, he would know how to play the game.

   T   F   a. Tony already reviewed the rules.

   T   F   b. Tony already knows how to play the game.

2. If Randy played tennis a lot, she could win a tournament.

   T   F   a. Randy plays tennis a lot.

   T   F   b. Randy doesn't have the ability to win a tournament.

3. If the players had cheated, the officials would have caught them.

   T   F   a. The players didn't cheat.

   T   F   b. The officials caught the players.

4. If I had chosen a different partner, I might've won the competition.

   T   F   a. I chose a different partner.

   T   F   b. I won the competition.

5. I wish I were a good basketball player.

   T   F   a. I want to play basketball well.

   T   F   b. I am not a good basketball player.

6. If Olivia had been the last contestant, she would have won.

   T   F   a. Olivia won.

   T   F   b. Olivia wasn't the last contestant.

7. The other team wouldn't have beaten us if we had practiced.

   T   F   a. The other team beat us.

   T   F   b. We practiced.

8. I wish I could quit my job to train for the Olympics.

   T   F   a. I can quit my job.

   T   F   b. I want to quit my job.

| 3 | **MAKING A TEAM FOR THE QUIZ BOWL** |

A. *Read this conversation between Pablo and Kai. Combine the pairs of sentences in parentheses to make present real conditional sentences. Keep the same order and decide which clause begins with* **if***. Make necessary changes in capitalization and punctuation.*

PABLO: Hey, Kai. _____*If you're available, you should be on my Quiz Bowl team.*_____
                          0. (You're available. You should be on my Quiz Bowl team.)

KAI: What's a Quiz Bowl? Is it some sort of competition?

PABLO: Yeah. It's an academic contest. Teams compete against each other. A judge asks

   questions about different subjects, like history, math, physics, and music.

   _____.
                          1. (I have enough people to make a team. I compete each year.)

KAI: Tell me a little more about how it works.

PABLO: Well, two teams compete in each round. A judge asks questions. Each team

   member has a buzzer to signal that he or she wants to answer a question.

   _____.
                          2. (You push your buzzer. You know the answer to the question.)

KAI: What's the scoring like?

PABLO: _____.
                          3. (You're right. The judge gives your team points.)

   A wrong answer means your team loses points.

   _____.
                          4. (The other team has a chance to answer correctly. You say the wrong answer.)

KAI: What happens when you beat the other team?

PABLO: _____.
                          5. (Your team wins. You advance to the next round of the tournament.)

KAI: That sounds like fun. Count me in!

B. *Read these statements about some of the team's strategies for the Quiz Bowl. Complete the present and future real conditional sentences by writing the correct present or future form of each verb.*

0. Kai is the member with the strongest math skills. If the question ____*deals*____ with
                                                                        (deal)

   math, Kai ____*will answer*____ the question.
             (answer)

1. Pablo also knows a lot of math. Pablo _____ the math questions when Kai
                                                      (answer)

   _____ the answer.
      (not know)

2. Carol, another team member, hates history. Carol _____ her buzzer to answer if
    (not push)

    the judge _____ a history question.
    (ask)

3. Each team member has an area of expertise. If each team member _____ on his
    (concentrate)

    or her own area, the team _____ the competition.
    (can win)

4. The team loses points for wrong answers. The team _____ to questions unless
    (not respond)

    they _____ sure their answer is correct.
    (be)

C. *Read some of the team's thoughts after they lost the Quiz Bowl. Complete the past
unreal conditional sentences. Use the correct forms of the words in parentheses.*

0. If we ____*had had*____ five members, we ____*might have won*____ the Quiz Bowl.
    (had)   **(might / win)**

1. If one member _____ a lot about history, we _____ the
    (know)   **(win)**

    competition.

2. Our team _____ chemistry if we _____ some questions would be
    (study)   **(realize)**

    about that subject.

3. We _____ more questions if the other team _____ their buzzers
    (could / answer)   **(not press)**

    first.

4. If we _____ up late last night, we _____ so tired for the
    (not stay)   **(not be)**

    competition.

5. I wish we _____ more often.
    (practice)

6. Kai _____ more if he _____ experience with Quiz Bowls.
    (might / contribute)   **(had)**

7. Carol wishes she _____ the answer to the last question.
    (know)

8. If our team _____ the Quiz Bowl, we _____.
    (won)   **(celebrate)**

4 | A CANOE RACE

A. *A canoe is a long, light boat. You use a short pole that is wide and flat at the end to move it through water. Read this conversation between Tamara and Connie before they begin training for a canoe race. Complete the conversation with* **if** *or* **unless**.

CONNIE: That canoe race we're competing in is next month. We'll need to come up with a

strategy _____*if*_____ we want to beat Nancy and Shawna.
          0.

TAMARA: I know! They're really good, and they practice a lot. _____ we practice a
                                                                  1.

lot too, we won't win.

CONNIE: We also need to do some endurance training. _____ we aren't in good
                                                      2.

physical shape, we won't be able to finish the race.

TAMARA: And it's really important to work together. We'll lose the race _____ we
                                                                          3.

work together.

CONNIE: I think we can do it. We should be able to win _____ we really train
                                                         4.

hard.

TAMARA: So let's do it! Want to meet tomorrow at 2:00?

CONNIE: Sounds good! See you then.

B. Read Robert's excuses for not being involved in this year's canoe contest. Rewrite his excuses. Use present and future unreal conditionals. Some items may have more than one right answer.

0. I know Tamara and Connie. That's why I can't be a judge for the race.

If I didn't know Tamara and Connie, I could be a judge for the race.

1. I don't have a lot of free time. That's why I won't help organize the competition.

_____

2. I'm helping with a tennis tournament this year. That's why I don't have free time.

_____

3. I'm too old. That's why I can't get up early to watch the race.

_____

4. I have to work that day. That's why I can't go to the race.

_____

5. I have a meeting that day. That's why I won't take a vacation day from work.

_____

6. My wife is afraid of water. That's why she won't be my racing partner.

_____

7. My canoe has a leak. That's why I can't race.

_____

8. I don't know how to cook. That's why I can't prepare food for the picnic after the race.

_____

9. My children can't swim. That's why they won't compete in the kids' competition.

_____

10. I am not rich. That's why I can't give money for a prize.

_____

5 | EDITING: CELEBRATING A VICTORY

Read Connie's e-mail to her parents after she and Tamara won the canoe race. There are nine mistakes in the use of conditionals. The first mistake is already corrected. Find and correct eight more. (Note: There can be more than one way to correct a mistake.)

Dear Mom and Dad,

  The canoe race was yesterday, and Tamara and I won! If we ~~didn't practice~~ *hadn't practiced* so much, we wouldn't have beaten Nancy and Shawna. I guess all the hard work paid off! Tamara and I always bought each other ice cream when we win a race, so afterwards we went to the Ice Cream Shoppe. We saw Nancy and Shawna there. I wish we could buy them ice cream too, but we didn't have enough money. If we will win next year, we'll buy them ice cream then. We have them to thank for our success. If we hadn't met them, we wouldn't train for yesterday's race so much.

  We might go to a new competition next month in Rochester, but I doubt we could win. But if we would won the race, we would get $500! Then we could afford a new canoe. What would you buy if you win $500?

  Well, I've go to run. I'm meeting Tamara at the river in an hour. If we practice, we won't stay in shape for next week's race in New Town. And you know us! If it was nice outside, you can find us on the river! Are you coming to visit next week? If you come, you can get a canoe and race us for practice!

Love,

Connie

PART X Diagnostic Test

---

1 | LISTENING: TRIP TO EUROPE

🎧 *Listen to this phone conversation between Yelena and her mom. Complete the conversation by writing the words that you hear. You will hear the recording two times.*

YELENA: Hello?

MOM: Hi. It's Mom. What have you been up to?

YELENA: Well, I've been thinking that I should take a trip to Europe.

MOM: Really?

YELENA: Yeah. My friend Paul travels there all the time, so I asked him

_____ *to help me* _____ plan a trip. I told him that
     0.

_____ something amazing.
     1.

MOM: Did he have any suggestions?

YELENA: Yeah. I asked him _____. He told me that Italy
     2.

and Greece _____ awesome. He asked me
     3.

_____ going to one of those countries. I
     4.

know he really loved Greece. In fact, he said, "Greece is the best place

_____."
     5.

MOM: Those sound like two pretty good options!

YELENA: Yeah, but he also told me _____ about France. That
     6.

would be pretty amazing, too.

MOM: I'm sure it would. Who do you think you'd go with?

YELENA: Well, I asked Paul _____ with last time. It
     7.

turns out that he went alone on his last trip, and he really liked it. He

_____ lots of people traveling by himself. So I think I
     8.

want to go by myself, too.

MOM: How long are you going to be gone?

YELENA: Paul said _____ for at least three weeks. He usually
                                    9.

stays at least that long. He said _____ home before
                                                            10.

that because I would regret not staying longer.

MOM: Oh, three weeks is a long time. Did you ask him when

_____?
                11.

YELENA: Yeah, I did. And he gave me some advice. He said, "You

_____ to go in July because it can get really hot." He
                12.

told me _____ best to go in May. The weather is
                            13.

milder, and there aren't so many tourists then.

---

2 | MOTHER'S QUESTIONS

*Yelena's mother has some more questions about her trip. Read her direct questions and
change them into embedded questions.*

0. Do you have hotel reservations yet?

   I don't know _____*if you have hotel reservations yet*_____.

1. How much will the plane ticket cost?

   Do you know _____?

2. When will you book your ticket?

   Can you tell me _____?

3. Are you still planning to go alone?

   I can't remember _____.

4. Is your luggage sturdy enough?

   I wonder _____.

5. Should you change some money before you leave?

   You need to find out _____.

3 | RESORT VACATION

Read this story about Rick's trip to a beach resort. Circle 17 reporting verbs. Underline the examples of direct speech once. Underline the examples of indirect speech twice. An example is given.

In July, Rick decided to take a vacation to the beach. He (asked) his well-traveled friend Tim where he should go. Tim said he had gone to a place called Sea Breeze Resort a few years earlier, and he said it was a lot of fun. He advised Rick to go there, too. Rick asked him if he had any information about the place, but Tim told him to call the resort for the most accurate information.

Rick called Sea Breeze Resort and asked the receptionist how much a room cost. She told him that a package trip for seven days/six nights was only $750. He asked her what he could do at the resort, and she said, "We have so many activities you won't be able to do them all!" Rick was excited, and he told the receptionist to book him the package.

Rick left for Sea Breeze Resort the next week. When he arrived at the resort and tried to check in, the receptionist told him his name was not in the registry. He told her to check again. She checked and told him, "I'm sorry, sir, but your name is not registered." He told her he could get the registration information from his backpack. Suddenly he realized that he had left his backpack in the taxi that brought him to the resort. So he asked the receptionist if he could use the phone. He called the taxi service, and two hours later the taxi arrived with his backpack. He found the registration information and was finally able to check in. "Now may I please have the keys to my room?" he requested. She replied, "I'm sorry, sir, but we don't have any clean rooms right now." Rick had to wait two more hours for his room to be ready!

4 | RESORT VACATION DIARY

Read this e-mail Rick wrote to his friend Tim. Complete the e-mail with the correct answers.
Write the letter of the best answer on each line.

Tim,

What a disaster this vacation is turning out to be! After my terrible first day I thought things

would get better. They haven't. I'm not sure ____*b*____ (**a. when will things start to improve b. when**
0.

things will start to improve c. when thing starting to improve). After I finally got into my room, I called

and asked room service _____ (**a. if they could bring b. if they can bring c. can they bring**) me a
1.

hamburger and fries. They told me _____ (**a. they can't fill my order b. we can't fill your order**
2.

c. they couldn't fill my order) because they didn't have any hamburgers left, and they _____
3.

(**a. asked please choose b. asked to choose c. asked me to choose**) another item from the menu. I _____
4.

(**a. asked please make me b. asked to make me c. asked them to make me**) a steak well done. An hour later

they brought me my meal. I didn't know _____ (**a. how much tipping b. how much to tip c. how**
5.

much should I tip), so I gave the man two dollars. It was two dollars too much. I cut into the steak,

and it was barely cooked. But I was so hungry that I ate the whole thing. Later that night, I got

sick to my stomach. I've been sick all day today. I asked the receptionist _____ (**a. can you**
6.

recommend b. to recommend c. where to recommend) a pharmacy so I could get some medicine. She told

me that _____ (**a. the closest one had been b. the closest one it is c. the closest one was**) 20 miles away!
7.

I have five days left of my vacation, and I'm not sure _____ (**a. whether I'll be able to enjoy b. can I**
8.

enjoy c. if I could enjoy) any of it. I can't imagine what else _____ (**a. is going wrong b. could go**
9.

wrong c. had gone wrong). I wonder _____ (**a. if you had more fun here b. if you're having more fun there**
10.

c. did you have more fun there) than I'm having here.

Rick

5 | PACKING ADVICE

Read this conversation between Ying and Joe. Complete the direct and indirect speech sentences with the correct forms of the words in parentheses.

YING: So, did your brother tell you what to take when you visit him in Europe?

JOE: Yes. He _____*told me to be very careful*_____ when I pack.
        0. (tell / me / be very careful)

He _____, " _____."
                         1. (say / not / pack / too much)

YING: That's good advice! What about money?

JOE: He _____. He
        2. (say / that / a combination of cash, traveler's checks, and credit cards / be / best)

also _____ with me.
      3. (tell / me / that / should I take / euros)

YING: What did he tell you about clothes?

JOE: He _____, " _____." He said it over and
                         4. (say / not / bring / too many clothes)

over again.

YING: When I went to India, one of my friends _____,

" _____ because you can throw them
  5. (tell / me / you / should / travel / with old clothes)

away and pack souvenirs."

JOE: That's a good idea.

YING: She also _____, " _____ as many pictures
                                6. (tell / me / you / ought / take)

as you can. You never know when you'll be back."

6 | EDITING: TRAVEL DIARY

Read this diary entry about Paula's trip to Italy. There are 10 mistakes in the use of direct and indirect speech and embedded questions. The first mistake is already corrected. Find and correct 9 more. (Note: There may be errors in punctuation. There can be more than one way to correct a mistake.)

May 31

Today was my first full day in Florence, and it was great! I got up and ate breakfast at a little café down the street from my hotel. I asked my waiter what ~~did~~ he recommended doing during the day. He told me that I will enjoy everything in Florence. He said me he had lived there his whole life, and he said that "I don't want to live anywhere else." I asked him what things were there to see. He said that the Uffizi Gallery had been wonderful. It's one of the most famous art galleries in the world. He also told me to visit the Duomo, one of Italy's most beautiful cathedrals. I wondered what did he think of the Piazza Della Signoria, or central square of the city, and he told me don't miss it. He told me take a boat ride down the River Arno, too. Then he invited me to eat supper at the restaurant with his family. I don't know if have I ever met such a nice waiter before. And I can't remember when I've had such a lovely vacation!

Unit 25 Achievement Test

1 | LISTENING: HE SAID, SHE SAID

🎧 *Listen to this conversation about Greg and Alice's date. Complete the conversation by writing the words that you hear. You will hear the recording two times.*

LAURA: Hey, Sue! Guess who I talked to yesterday?

SUE: Who?

LAURA: Greg. He told me about his date with Alice last Friday. He said he _____*thought*_____
   0.
the date went well. It sounds like they had a great time.

SUE: Really? I talked to Alice and she said, "It _____ the worst date I've ever
   1.
had."

LAURA: Oh, no! I wonder what happened. Greg told me dinner _____ nice.
   2.
They went to a new Korean restaurant downtown, and he said that the food

_____ delicious.
   3.

SUE: Alice didn't think so. She said that it _____ her heartburn because it was
   4.
too spicy. In fact, when I talked to her, she said that she still _____ well.
   5.

LAURA: Well, Greg told me that they _____ a great conversation during dinner and
   6.
that they had really gotten to know each other.

SUE: Alice said that Greg _____ through the entire dinner and that she had
   7.
suggested a movie so she wouldn't have to listen to him talk anymore. But she said he

_____ talking during the movie, either.
   8.

LAURA: Oh . . . Wow. Poor Greg! He told me that he _____ to ask her out again.
   9.

SUE: Oh, no. What a mess.

LAURA: I know. I think I should talk to Greg before he calls her.

2 | DATING ADVICE

Read this letter to Dr. Date, a dating expert, and his response. Circle 16 reporting verbs.
Underline the examples of direct speech once. Underline the examples of indirect speech
twice. The first answer is already given.

Dr. Date,

Last weekend I went on a date with a woman named Alice. I had a great time, and I thought she did, too. She said she liked Asian food, so I took her to a Korean restaurant. She also told me she wanted to see a movie, so we went to see a show that she picked. I enjoyed being with her, and at the end of the night, she told me that she had had a good time, too. She even said, "We should do this again." But when I talked to my best friend Laura, she told me that her friend Sue had talked with Alice about the date too. But she got a different story. Laura said Alice hadn't enjoyed the date as much as I had. I wanted to know what Alice had said. But Laura just told me, "Alice is very picky when it comes to men." She said that Alice liked me only as a friend. Then she told me "You're too good for Alice. You can do better." She said Alice was lucky to go out with me once.

Laura always tells me I'm handsome, kind, and considerate. I'm confused. If I'm so great, then why doesn't Alice want to date me? What did I do wrong, and what should I do next?

Sincerely,

Clueless in Memphis

Dear Clueless in Memphis,

Women often use nonverbal communication instead of verbal communication. You said that Alice had had a good time. Think back to your date. Did she look like she was having a good time? You said she liked Asian food, but did she seem to enjoy the Korean food? You said she had wanted to see a movie, but did she appear to like it or did she look bored? She told you she had enjoyed herself, but what did her body language suggest?

I'm actually very interested in your relationship with Laura. You say she's your best friend. She says you are handsome, kind, and considerate. Is it possible that this relationship could develop into something more than a friendship? As far as what to do next, I suggest this: Forget about Alice and consider dating Laura. She's the winner.

Good luck!

Dr. Date

---

3 | EDITING: A BLIND DATE

A blind date is an arranged meeting between a man and woman who have not met each other before. Read this story about a blind date. There are six mistakes in the use of direct and indirect speech. The first mistake is already corrected. Find and correct five more. (Note: There can be more than one way to correct a mistake.)

Chris had not been on a date for a long time. His friend Tom said that he ~~knows~~ *knew* the perfect girl for Chris. Her name was Megan. In fact, Tom also said that he had already talked to Megan about Chris. Megan said she had wanted to meet him. During that conversation, Megan even says that she was excited about the date. The night of the date, Chris arrived at the restaurant a little early. He looked around for Megan. Tom had said Chris that Megan had long black hair and blue eyes. Finally, Chris saw a beautiful woman sitting at a table by the window. He went over and introduced himself. She said she had been Megan. They had a wonderful dinner together. When Chris suggested having dinner again later that week, Megan says, "I think that's a great idea."

Unit 26 Achievement Test

---

1 | LISTENING: APARTMENT PROBLEMS

🎧 *Listen to this conversation about Sean's new apartment. Complete the conversation by writing the words that you hear. You will hear the recording two times.*

JULIE: Hi, Sean! I saw your mother yesterday, and she said you ____*had moved*____ into a new
0.

apartment.

SEAN: Yes, I did. One of my friends lives in an apartment in the same building, and she told me

the apartments _____ really nice. But I'm having some problems.
1.

JULIE: Really? Like what?

SEAN: Well, there are insects in my apartment. I called the apartment manager last week, and he

said, "I _____ care of it." But he hasn't been there. Then I discovered the
2.

air conditioner didn't work, so I called the manager again. He told me, "We

_____ it tomorrow." But that was four days ago, and no one has come.
3.

When I complained to my friend, she told me I _____ too picky.
4.

JULIE: That's ridiculous!

SEAN: I know! And I didn't sleep well last night because the neighbors were having a loud party.

I asked them to be quiet, and they told me I _____ them. Can you believe
5.

it? I told them, "I _____, not have a party." When I asked them to be quiet
6.

the second time, they told me their party _____ until the next morning. I
7.

was so mad! I said, "If you don't quiet down, I _____ the police."
8.

JULIE: Why don't you move again?

SEAN: I can't. Before I moved in, the apartment manager told me that I _____ a
9.

one-year lease. Well, really he convinced me to do it. He told me I _____
10.

the apartment soon because there weren't many left. So I decided to sign the lease and get

the apartment before they were all rented.

JULIE: Maybe you should write a complaint letter to the management company.

SEAN: I think I will.

---

2 | CHOOSING AN APARTMENT

Fatima and her husband got a lot of advice when they were choosing an apartment. Read the sentences of advice as Fatima reports them in indirect speech. Then circle the letter of the direct speech that is being reported.

0. The real estate agent said we might want to look in the newspaper for apartment ads.
   a. "You looked in the newspaper for apartment ads."
   b. "You would look in the newspaper for apartment ads."
   c. "You may want to look in the newspaper for apartment ads."

1. She said that we should drive around that week to look for apartments for rent.
   a. "You should drive around this week to look for apartments for rent."
   b. "You should have driven around that week to look for apartments for rent."
   c. "You would drive around this week to look for apartments for rent."

2. She told us that we could view apartments by appointment the following week.
   a. "You could view apartments by appointment next week."
   b. "You could have viewed apartments by appointment the following week."
   c. "You can view apartments by appointment next week."

3. She said that if we had a limited budget, we ought to consider living in the suburbs.
   a. "If you have a limited budget, you ought to have considered living in the suburbs."
   b. "If you have a limited budget, you ought to consider living in the suburbs."
   c. "If you had a limited budget, you ought to consider living in the suburbs."

4. She told us that before we moved to the suburbs, we should think about the time spent traveling to work.
   a. "Before you move to the suburbs, you should think about the time spent traveling to work."
   b. "Before you move to the suburbs, you would think about the time spent traveling to work."
   c. "Before you move to the suburbs, you should have thought about the time spent traveling to work."

5. She said that we had to consider what each apartment would look like with our furniture.
   a. "You had to consider what each apartment would look like with your furniture."
   b. "You must consider what each apartment will look like with your furniture."
   c. "You have to consider what each apartment will have looked like with your furniture."

6. She told us that we should check the walls, the closets, and the plumbing before signing a lease.
   a. "You should check the walls, the closets, and the plumbing before signing a lease."
   b. "You would check the walls, the closets, and the plumbing before signing a lease."
   c. "You should have checked the walls, the closets, and the plumbing before signing a lease."

7. She said that we had to ask about the heating and water costs, city taxes, and parking.
    a. "You might ask about the heating and water costs, city taxes, and parking."
    b. "You have asked about the heating and water costs, city taxes, and parking."
    c. "You must ask about the heating and water costs, city taxes, and parking."

8. She told us that we shouldn't purchase more furniture until we decided on an apartment.
    a. "You shouldn't purchase more furniture until you decide on an apartment."
    b. "You shouldn't have purchased more furniture until you decided on an apartment."
    c. "You shouldn't purchase more furniture until you decided on an apartment."

3 | HOW TO DECORATE AN APARTMENT

Read the following statements Sean heard from a design expert about decorating her new apartment. Then rewrite each statement as Sean reports it in indirect speech.

0. "You can make the apartment attractive without a lot of money."

    He said I could make the apartment attractive without a lot of money.

1. "You should evaluate your apartment's good points and bad points."

    _____

2. "You must decide on a theme for your apartment."

    _____

3. "This old living room furniture can be mixed with new items."

    _____

4. "A color scheme will make a visual impact in the main room."

    _____

5. "Warm colors can create an intimate, welcoming feeling, while cool colors can make a room feel elegant."

    _____

6. "If you decide to keep white walls, you can use curtains, pillows, and rugs to add color."

    _____

7. "You may want to shop at secondhand stores to save money."

    _____

8. "If you want to spend less on furniture, you should buy self-assembled furniture."

    _____

4 | EDITING: COMPLAINT LETTER

Read Sean's complaint letter to the apartment management company. There are five mistakes in the use of direct and indirect speech. The first mistake is already corrected. Find and correct four more.

To Whom It May Concern:

    I am writing to complain about the poor service I have received over the past month from the manager at Grand Street Apartments. When I signed my lease, the apartment manager told me that if I had any problems, ~~you~~ should call him. Well, I've had to call about a few things. I recently had a problem with the air conditioning. He said, "I will take care of it." When I called again two weeks later, he said that he is very busy right then. He said he would fix the problem this week. The next day I saw him relaxing by the swimming pool for two hours. When I said that he could take a look at my apartment then, he said that he can't help me then. He was busy. When I told him that it was very important, he said, "I may do it the next day." This behavior is unacceptable. If someone doesn't fix my air conditioning by next Saturday, I will move out and expect a full refund of this month's rent.

Sincerely,

Sean McIntyre

Unit 27 Achievement Test

| 1 | LISTENING: SICK IN BED |

🎧 *Listen to this phone conversation between Ana and her mother. Complete the sentences by writing the words that you hear. You will hear the recording two times.*

ANA: Hello?

MOM: Hi Ana, it's Mom. Are you still sick in bed?

ANA: Yes. I'm feeling a little better, but the doctor _____*advised me to stay*_____ in bed for a

0.

few days.

MOM: Will you be able to miss work?

ANA: I called my boss, and he _____ today and tomorrow off, so

1.

that's good. Hopefully, I can sleep a lot. But he _____ in

2.

on Thursday for the staff meeting. I have so much work to do, but the doctor

_____ too much. He really recommends resting as much as

3.

possible. He also _____ away from others because I might be

4.

contagious.

MOM: Do you think you should go to work then?

ANA: Well, my boss _____ in. I guess I'll just wait and see how I feel.

5.

MOM: Are you taking any medicine?

ANA: The doctor _____ aspirin, so I went to the pharmacy and got

6.

some, and I think it's helping a little. He also _____ a lot

7.

of fluids, so I'm drinking a couple kinds of hot tea and plenty of water. He

_____ lots of chicken soup, too.

8.

MOM: I can bring you some soup for dinner.

ANA: That would be great! Oh, no! I just remembered that I'm supposed to eat dinner with

Jennifer tonight. She _____ out for pizza. I'd better call her right

9.

now and tell her I can't go. I'll see you later, Mom.

MOM: OK, I'll be there around 7:00.

2 | SICK AT HEART

*Read this letter to Dr. Manners, an advice columnist. Circle the reporting verbs and
underline the indirect instructions, commands, requests, and invitations.*

Dear Dr. Manners,

One of my good friends (invited) me <u>to go to her house for dinner</u> last week because I had
gotten a promotion at work. She said to arrive about 7:00, and she told me not to bring
anything. When I arrived, she told me to come in and she said to sit down and relax. I sat down
in the living room, but after 10 minutes, I went into the kitchen. She was busy preparing the
food. I told her to let me help, but she told me not to touch anything. She said to wait in the
living room. About half an hour later, she asked me to sit at the table. We ate the meal, and to be
honest, it was terrible. She didn't say anything about the food, and she even invited me to eat a
second helping. After dinner, she said not to clear the table. I have invited her to eat dinner at my
place, and when she comes over we always enjoy cooking together. Why didn't she let me help,
and why didn't she say anything when the food was so bad? I don't know what's going on or
what to do.

Sincerely,

Sick at Heart

3 | DR. MANNERS' ADVICE

*Read Dr. Manners' response to Sick at Heart. Seven indirect instructions, commands,
requests, and invitations are underlined. Circle the letter of the direct speech that is being
reported.*

Dear Sick at Heart,

There are a few things to consider. Your friend <u>invited you to eat dinner with her</u> ___*c*___
                                                                                        0.
(a. "Eat dinner with her." b. "You eat dinner?" ©"Eat dinner with me.") as a present for your promotion. If

she <u>told you not to bring anything,</u> _____ (a. "Don't bring anything." b. "I told you not to bring
                                          1.

anything." c. "You not to bring anything.") then she probably wanted to do the work. It's possible that

<u>she told you not to help</u> _____ (a. "You not to help." b. "I told you not to help." c. "Don't help.") because
                              2.

she wanted you to relax. Or if she's not a very good cook, it could be that she was embarrassed

PART X

by her lack of skills. Maybe she <u>told you not to touch anything</u> _____ (a. "You not to touch
3.

anything." b. "I told you not to touch anything." c. "Don't touch anything.") because she was trying a new

recipe. I don't know why <u>she asked you to eat more.</u> _____ (a. "Eat more." b. "I ask you to eat
4.

more." c. "You should eat more.") Maybe she <u>invited you to take another helping</u> _____ (a. "I invited
5.

you to take another helping." b. "Take another helping." c. "I invite you to take another helping.") because she

wanted to seem gracious. The point is that you'll never know what happened if you don't ask

her. Maybe you could <u>invite her to join you at your house for a meal</u> _____ (a. "Invite me to join
6.

you at your house for a meal." b. "Join me at my house for a meal." c. "Join you at your house for a meal.")

sometime soon. Take that opportunity to ask her about it.

4 | EDITING: A TOUGH BOSS

*Read Jan's diary entry about her frustration with her boss. There are five mistakes in the use
of indirect instructions, commands, requests, and invitations. The first mistake is already
corrected. Find and correct four more.*

November 9

    I'm sick and tired of my boss! I arrive to work early every day, but today I got caught in

traffic so I was a few minutes late. When my boss saw me walking in, he advised me to

   make
~~making~~ sure I'm on time every day. I was so mad! Then he said finish the quarterly report by

tomorrow when yesterday he told me to have it done by next week. Now I have to stay up all

night to finish it. But it gets worse! This afternoon he advised me to don't take such long coffee

breaks. But I hadn't even taken a break—I had been working in another room! The absolute

worst part of the day was when he said rewriting an entire report because he had changed his

mind about a few things. My friend told me that to quit my job, but my parents told me to keep

trying. I don't know what to do.

Unit 28 Achievement Test

| 30 Items |
| Score: _____ |

🎧 *Listen to this conversation about Ed's meeting with one of his professors, Dr. Gupta. Complete the conversation by writing the words that you hear. You will hear the recording two times.*

SAM: How did your meeting with Dr. Gupta go?

ED: Well, he asked me some questions I didn't know the answers to.

SAM: Like what?

ED: He asked ___*what I was planning to do*___ after graduation. When I didn't respond right
0.

away, he asked _____ for a higher degree.
1.

SAM: I know you've been thinking about that. What did you say?

ED: I said I hadn't decided. Then he asked me _____ biology. I told
2.

him I had always wanted to be a doctor, but I wasn't sure I could. When he asked me

_____ that, I told him I wasn't sure my grades were high enough.
3.

But he said they were fine.

SAM: That's great!

ED: Yeah! He asked _____ to specialize in. When I told him I wanted
4.

to become a heart specialist, he seemed surprised.

SAM: Didn't he specialize in heart medicine?

ED: Yes, he did. He asked me _____ me in the heart, and I told him
5.

that I had become interested in it after taking his course last semester. I think he was happy

about that. I asked _____ a letter of recommendation for me, and
6.

he said yes.

SAM: That's good news!

ED: Yeah. So I think I'll start applying to some medical schools.

2 | LOOKING FOR A ROOMMATE

Ed owns an apartment, and he's looking for a new roommate to help with living expenses. Read his journal entries about two people he met. Circle four direct questions and underline four indirect questions.

March 5

Today I met with a guy named Patrick to see if he would be a good roommate. I asked <u>whether he would spend</u> a lot of time at the apartment, and he said no because he works a lot. I asked him where he worked. He told me he had a full-time job with Fisher Corporation. I asked what had happened with his last living situation, and he said his two roommates had moved away. He wants to rent for a full year. He seems very reliable.

March 7

Today I met with another guy, Jonathan. Before I could ask my questions, he asked "What happened to your last roommate?" After I answered, he asked, "Do you mind if I smoke in the apartment?" I told him no smoking was allowed, and then he asked, "Do parties in the apartment bother you?" I told him that I needed eight hours of sleep each night but that I didn't mind a small gathering of friends. Then he asked, "Do you make a lot of money?" I told him that it was no concern of his and that I had a few questions to ask. I asked him how much he worked each week, and he said his dad would pay the rent. I was not impressed.

3 | ANOTHER MEETING

Read another of Ed's journal entries about another meeting with a prospective roommate. Then read the list of questions. Put a ✓ next to the direct questions that Ed asked. Put an X next to the questions he didn't ask.

March 9

Today I met with a guy named Boris. When I asked him what he did for a living, he told me that he didn't have a job at the moment. I asked him why he had left his last job, and he asked me if it was any of my business. I told him I needed to be sure he could pay the rent, and I asked him if he had enough money to pay rent this month. Instead of answering, he asked me why my roommate had decided to move out. I asked who had told him about the apartment. It turns out that Boris already lives in this building. He said he had heard me talking about it at the swimming pool. When I asked him why he had decided to change apartments, he said his roommate was always bothering him about paying the rent and the bills. I don't think he'll be my next roommate. I think I'll choose Patrick.

0. __✓__ What do you do for a living?

1. _____ Is it any of your business?

2. _____ Do you have enough money to pay rent this month?

3. _____ Why did your roommate decide to move out?

4. _____ Who told you about the apartment?

5. _____ Did you hear me talking about it at the swimming pool?

6. _____ Why did you decide to change apartments?

7. _____ Does your roommate always bother you about paying the rent and bills?

4 | TALKING TO THE PARENTS

Read these questions that were part of a phone conversation between Ed and his parents.
Rewrite each question as indirect speech.

0. Ed's mom asked, "Did you have a good week?"

Ed's mom asked if he had had a good week.

1. Ed asked his parents, "How have you been?"

_____

2. Ed's mom asked, "Did you meet with the professor yet?"

_____

3. Ed's dad asked, "When will you start applying to medical schools?"

_____

4. Ed asked his parents, "Did I ever introduce you to Dr. Gupta?"

_____

5. Ed's mom asked, "Did you decide on a roommate yet?"

_____

6. Ed's dad asked, "When are you coming to visit us?"

_____

5 | EDITING: E-MAIL TO GRANDMA

Read this e-mail Ed wrote to his grandmother. There are five mistakes in the use of direct questions and indirect questions. The first mistake is already corrected. Find and correct four more. (Note: There may be errors in punctuation.)

Dear Grandma,

    This has been a busy week. I met with one of my professors, and we talked about my future.

                             I wanted

He asked me what ~~wanted I~~ to do with my life, and I told him I wanted to become a heart

specialist. When I asked him if whether he would help me with my medical school applications,

he said yes. This week I also interviewed some guys who are interested in being my roommate.

One guy asked, "whether I minded if the rent was late." Another guy asked if could I wait for his

rent money until he got a job. I did have one good applicant, though, and he'll move in next

week. Mom and Dad called yesterday. They asked me if I could come home sometime soon for a

visit? I think I'll go next weekend. Hope to see you then.

Love,

Ed

Unit 29 Achievement Test

| 1 | LISTENING: PUTTING A NAME WITH A FACE |

🎧 *Kate and Lee are at a party. Listen to their conversation. Complete the conversation by writing the words that you hear. You will hear the recording two times.*

KATE: Lee, can you tell me _____*how I know*_____ that man? I'm talking about
0.

the guy with the dark hair and beard. He looks so familiar, but I don't know

_____.
1.

LEE: He looks familiar to me, too. We must know him. But I can't remember

_____ him.
2.

KATE: Have we met him before, or have we just seen him somewhere? I'm not sure. Oh, I

wonder _____ the owner of the new Italian restaurant
3.

downtown. It sort of looks like him.

LEE: It could be. But I'm not sure _____ a beard. I haven't
4.

been to that place in a while, though, so maybe he has one now.

KATE: Let's ask Paul _____.
5.

LEE: OK. Hey, Paul!

PAUL: What's up?

LEE: Well, I wonder _____ about the people at this party.
6.

PAUL: Why? Who do you want to know about?

LEE: Do you know _____?
7.

PAUL: Yeah, that's Gino de Selva. He owns the Italian restaurant Gino's downtown.

KATE: I was right! Does he speak English? I'd like to talk with him, but my Italian isn't very

good.

PAUL: No problem. He speaks English really well.

KATE: Good. I'm going to go introduce myself.

2 | MAKING AN ACQUAINTANCE

Read Kate's conversation with Gino de Selva. Circle nine embedded questions.

KATE: Hi, I'm Kate Wilder. I wanted to introduce myself and compliment you on your restaurant. I had dinner there last week, and I can't remember (when I ate such delicious food).

GINO: Thank you. Do you remember what you ordered?

KATE: I don't know how I could forget! I had the Italian stuffed mushrooms, the linguini with clams, and the tiramisu.

GINO: I'd like to know what you thought of the stuffed mushrooms. I recently created a new recipe, and I'm not sure how it compares to the old one.

KATE: Well, I never had the other mushrooms, but I can't imagine how they could taste any better! Can you tell me where you got the recipes for your dishes?

GINO: Yes, my father was a chef in Italy, and he taught me everything I know.

KATE: Can you remember what your first dish was?

GINO: Yes! When I was seven years old I made a dish of penne pasta with diced tomatoes, fresh mozzarella cheese, and fresh parsley. It's still one of my favorite dishes.

KATE: It sounds delicious! I don't even know how to cook macaroni and cheese!

GINO: Maybe I can give you a cooking lesson.

KATE: That would be great! I wonder if you can help me improve my cooking skills. They're pretty bad.

GINO: Don't worry, anyone can learn with the right teacher!

3 | TALKING ABOUT A PROBLEM

Complete this conversation between two friends. Change the direct questions in parentheses to embedded questions. Use correct punctuation.

FIONA: I have a problem. I don't know ___what I should do about my sister Annie___ .
                                         0. (What should I do about my sister Annie?)

SUZY: Why? What's going on?

FIONA: She wants to enter a talent show, and I don't know

_____. I wonder
          1. (Should I support her or not?)

_____.
          2. (Can I encourage her not to perform?)

SUZY: Why wouldn't you support her?

FIONA: Well, I want to, but I'm worried about her. I don't know

_____. And I don't know
          3. (Is she talented enough?)

_____.
          4. (Can she handle losing?)

SUZY: What's her talent?

FIONA: Well, she calls it modern dance. But it's really strange. I'm not sure

_____.
          5. (How can I tell her that?)

SUZY: I can't imagine _____. I'm sure talent shows get a lot
                         6. (What would the problem be?)

of strange entries.

FIONA: That's true. But the last time she competed in something like this, she got last place.

SUZY: Oh, no! I can't imagine _____.
                                7. (How did she feel?)

FIONA: It was awful. I don't know _____. I don't want her to
                       8. (Have I ever seen her so disappointed?)

get so disappointed again. That's why I can't decide what to do.

4 | EDITING: FORGETTING A NAME

Read this letter to Dr. Manners, an advice columnist. There are seven mistakes in the use of embedded questions. The first mistake is already corrected. Find and correct six more.

Dear Dr. Manners,

    I've gotten myself into an uncomfortable situation, and I don't know what ~~doing~~ *to do*. I wonder you can help me out. Yesterday I was shopping downtown when a familiar-looking woman greeted me by name. I wasn't sure who was she, but instead of asking her name, I just said hello and talked to her for a few minutes. Then she invited me to lunch next week. I couldn't think of an excuse quickly enough, so now I'm supposed to meet her next week! Can you tell me what should I say? Should I simply ask her what is her name? I'd like to find out who she is, but I don't want to embarrass her or myself. I can't imagine what will she think. I'm not sure to approach the situation politely.

Sincerely,

Please help!

PART X Achievement Test

1 | LISTENING: MISUNDERSTANDING AT WORK

🎧 *Listen to this conversation about a misunderstanding at work. Complete the conversation by writing the words that you hear. You will hear the recording two times.*

JAMAL: What a day!

SCOTT: What happened?

JAMAL: Well, my boss _____*told me that we had*_____ a meeting at 12:00 with important clients.
0.

He wanted me there early. I clearly remember him saying, "_____
1.

in the conference room at 11:45." So I arrived at the conference room at 11:40, but the

meeting was already in progress. Afterwards, my boss _____ my
2.

behavior was unacceptable.

SCOTT: He really said that? Why? He told _____ there at 11:45! I guess
3.

he forgot what he'd said.

JAMAL: Apparently, because he insisted that he _____ at 10:45!
4.

He really thought that he was right. I didn't want to argue with him, but I

_____ me 11:45. I didn't want him to think I was irresponsible,
5.

so I asked if maybe _____ a mistake. He got really mad at that
6.

comment. He asked me _____ to keep my job!
7.

SCOTT: What? That's really ridiculous.

JAMAL: I know. At that point I asked myself _____ for someone like
8.

that.

SCOTT: I believe it! So then what happened?

JAMAL: Well, he calmed down a little. He _____ one of the most
9.

responsible workers in the office. That made me feel better. Then he asked me

_____ going to fix this problem.
10.

SCOTT: Wow!

JAMAL: Yeah. I was really surprised. I told him _____ a good idea to
11.

document all meeting times in e-mails to avoid these types of misunderstandings. He

agreed and said, "We _____ an electronic schedule of all
12.

meetings." Then he talked to his assistant and asked _____ the
13.

schedule.

SCOTT: Thank goodness!

JAMAL: I know! I was really stressed out for a while.

2 | STRESS AT WORK

*Scott went to see a doctor because he wasn't feeling well. Read the doctor's direct questions
and change them into embedded questions.*

0. Do you feel tired during the day?

   I'd like to know _____*if you feel tired during the day*_____.

1. What is the cause of your anxiety?

   I'd like to find out _____.

2. Do you take any medicines on regular basis?

   It does not say in your file _____.

3. Have you had nightmares lately?

   I wonder _____.

4. How would you rate your ability to concentrate?

   Can you tell me _____?

5. When did you last feel completely at ease?

   Can you remember _____?

3 | MISUNDERSTANDING BETWEEN FRIENDS

Read this story about a misunderstanding Josie had with her friends. Circle 17 reporting verbs. Underline five examples of direct speech once. Underline 12 examples of indirect speech twice. An example is given.

Josie had plans to meet her friends Carrie and Paula at an Italian restaurant downtown. Carrie told her to be at the restaurant at 8:00. She said to get there on time because it got very busy. Josie asked Carrie to give her directions, but Carrie just said, "You'll see it. It's right on Main Street." Paula said the restaurant had just opened, and she also told them that most people dressed formally. She asked them to wear nice clothes.

That evening Josie got a taxi and she said to the driver, "Please take me to the new Italian restaurant downtown. It's on Main Street." She asked if it would take long to get there, and he said it would take about 20 minutes. When they stopped in front of the restaurant, Josie got out and paid the driver.

She entered the restaurant and looked around for her friends, but she didn't see them. She told the host, "We have a reservation for Carrie Smith." He checked, but he couldn't find the reservation. Josie was confused, but she decided to wait. After 10 minutes, she called Carrie's cell phone. When Carrie answered, she asked Josie, "Where are you?" Josie said she was at Rico's. Carrie laughed and said, "That restaurant has been open for years." Carrie said that she and Paula were at Gino's, the new Italian restaurant across the street. She told Josie to go there.

Josie walked across the street to Gino's and saw her friends. Both of them were wearing T-shirts and jeans. Josie asked them why they hadn't dressed up. Paula asked her if she had checked her e-mail that day. Josie hadn't. It turned out that Paula had learned that the restaurant wasn't fancy and that they didn't need to dress up after all. She had written an e-mail to let Carrie and Josie know, but Josie didn't get the message. Josie decided that she didn't care if she was overdressed, and they all sat down to eat.

4 | E-MAIL

Read this e-mail Paula had written to Josie before they met for dinner. Complete the e-mail with the correct phrases. Write the letter of the best answer on each line.

Josie,

Hi! I just ran into a friend of mine who ate at Gino's last week, and ___a___ (a. she said the
0.

food was b. she said the food has been c. she says the food had been) great. I said I _____ (a. wondered
1.

which dress should I b. had wondered which dress to c. wonder which dress to) wear, but I was surprised

when she _____ (a. told me to wear casual clothes b. told, "Wear casual clothes!" c. suggested wear casual
2.

clothes). So I wanted to ask _____ (a. you knew b. do you know c. if you knew) what to wear to
3.

dinner tonight. I know I said _____ (a. that you wear b. to wear c. wear) something nice, but I
4.

guess it doesn't have to be anything special.

Speaking of good restaurants, do you remember that I was planning to try that place China

Palace for dinner last weekend? Well, my boss _____ (a. tells me that the service had been bad there
5.

b. told me that the service was bad there c. said that "the service was bad there), so I wasn't sure what to

expect. But I went anyway, and _____ (a. I'm telling you b. I tell c. I told) that it's the best Chinese
6.

restaurant I've ever been to. The service was great. When I asked the waitress _____ (a. please
7.

describe b. that she describes c. to describe) a few of the dishes, she explained them in detail. I decided

to try the beef with noodles. I had never learned to eat with chopsticks, so when she brought my

food, I asked her, "Could you show me _____ (a. how to use b. how should I use c. how I had used)
8.

my chopsticks?" She did, and I used them to eat most of my meal. And the food was excellent! I

can't remember _____ (a. when I last had b. when had I last had c. when did I last have) such delicious
9.

hot and sour soup. I wonder _____ (a. why don't more people eat b. why don't more people to eat
10.

c. why more people don't eat) at China Palace. I thought it was great!

Oh well. I'd better go now. See you tonight!

Paula

5 | WRONG DIRECTIONS

Read this story about what happened when Jon forgot how to get to Bianca's house. Complete the direct and indirect speech sentences with the correct forms of the words in parentheses.

Last night I almost got lost when I was trying to get to my friend Bianca's house. Bianca

_____ *told me to take the bus* _____ from my office to her place after work. I thought I
        0. (tell / me / take the bus)

had to take bus number 170. But I wasn't sure where to get it. So I asked a man standing at the

bus stop in front of my office. He _____ the street to
        1. (say / I have to cross)

another bus stop to get bus number 170. He _____ there
        2. (tell / me / the bus should be)

in a few minutes.

But then I started to doubt myself. I remembered that Bianca told me

_____ to get the bus. So I called Bianca on my
        3. (not / cross the street)

cell phone and _____ some help. She
        4. (tell / her / I need)

_____ to her place. She
        5. (say / bus number 170 / won't go)

_____ bus number 107, which passes right in front of my
        6. (tell / me / take)

office. I waited a few minutes, and the bus came. It took me straight to her house. Thank

goodness I called Bianca before I got on the wrong bus!

6 | EDITING: MISUNDERSTANDING WITH PARENTS

Read this diary entry about Jen's misunderstanding with her parents. There are 10 mistakes in the use of direct and indirect speech and embedded questions. The first mistake is already corrected. Find and correct nine more. (Note: There may be errors in punctuation. There can be more than one way to correct a mistake.)

June 5

My parents ruin everything! I can't believe what they did today. Well, to be fair, I guess it was a misunderstanding, and it wasn't really their fault. But I'm still mad! OK, here's what happened:

Yesterday Sara asked me ~~did I want~~ *if I wanted* to meet her and some friends at the lake today. I was so excited! I told her that "I would love to go," but I said that I had to talk to Mom and Dad first. I needed to ask if I could use their car. Last night I told them that I had wanted to go to the lake, and Mom told that it sounded like a good idea. Dad asked who did think of it. They told me they would use the car to run some errands in the morning, and I asked them be home by 2:00.

Well, when they got home at 2:00, I was ready to leave. They got out of the car and told me wait for them. I wondered why they keep me waiting for 15 minutes. It turned out they were getting ready to go to the lake, too! They looked so excited that I didn't want to tell them they weren't invited. So I called Sara on the phone. "You'll never guess who I'm bringing with me," I say. In the end it wasn't so bad, but I'd still like to know why did they think I invited them to go with me!

Audioscript

PART I Diagnostic Test

Radio News International proudly announces the addition of its newest correspondent, Wesley Hammond. Mr. Hammond received his journalism degree from Wimbley College and began his journalism career in Los Angeles in 1979. He had worked briefly as a local sports announcer there before he started reporting news internationally with Urban News Systems in 1982. In 1985, he won an award for the stories he had written the previous year about teachers who were making a difference in Rio de Janeiro schools. He was working in China when the Tiananmen Square protests took place in 1989. In 1990, he was honored with the Arnold Gutman award for the stories he had produced about this event.

Mr. Hammond has contributed to Radio News International as a guest correspondent throughout his career, but he now joins us as a permanent senior correspondent. This week he has been covering the elections in India, and he will return to our studios on Monday.

Mr. Hammond is currently finishing a book called *From Where I Stand*. In his book, he shares some of the stories that have made him one of the most recognized names in broadcast journalism. He lives in New York and has one daughter, Samantha, who is currently acting in a Broadway production.

Unit 1 Achievement Test

Madison. Paula. Sarah. Each of these names creates an impression and carries certain cultural meanings, according to social scientist Dr. Paul Sellers, author of the book *The Power of Names*. Sellers suggests that our names influence not only how others feel about us, but how we feel about ourselves. He claims that names shape our careers, personalities, and relationships. For example, when most people hear the name Madison, they think of a woman who is hardworking and professional, most likely a businesswoman. The name Paula, on the other hand, sometimes brings to mind a woman who is always taking charge and doesn't take "no" for an answer. Finally, people often imagine a woman named Sarah to be nice, sweet, and youthful. In addition to providing people's impressions of thousands of names, Sellers summarizes dozens of studies that look at how names impact our lives. The author investigates the politics and cultures that have influenced naming America's babies over the past two hundred years.

Unit 2 Achievement Test

DONNA: Welcome to *Love Affair*. I'm your host, Donna Wright. Today on our show we're talking to Nancy Powers, who founded the highly successful dating and matchmaking service MatchRight. Nancy, welcome to the show.

NANCY: Thank you, Donna.

DONNA: Nancy, why did you start up MatchRight?

NANCY: Well, Donna, I get that question a lot. Some people think I started MatchRight because I was looking for my true love, but actually I set up the company after I was already married. I just love being a matchmaker. In fact, in college I introduced three of my best friends to the men who became their husbands. Matchmaking just comes naturally to me.

DONNA: I understand that you consider a person's dating history to be very important when making a match. Why's that?

NANCY: I look for patterns that either help or hurt a person in finding a good match. For example, one woman walked into my office after she broke up with her boyfriend. I found out that when they were dating, she was working 60 hours a week, which didn't leave much time for her relationship. While we were working together over the next couple of weeks, she realized that if she wanted to have a healthy relationship, she would need to slow down a bit.

DONNA: You're listening to *Love Affair* with our guest Nancy Powers of MatchRight. We'll be right back.

Unit 3 Achievement Test

ANNA: Wow! I've always loved Italian food, but I haven't had lasagna as delicious as this before! Where did you learn to cook so well?

ELIO: I grew up in an Italian family, and I've been cooking all my life.

ANNA: Did you live in Italy when you were a child?

ELIO: Yes, I did. I lived there for twenty-five years and studied at a cooking school. I moved here last year, and I've cooked at a couple of Italian restaurants in town since then.

ANNA: No wonder you're such a good cook! Have you thought about opening your own restaurant?

ELIO: I've considered it, of course, and I really want to, but I haven't saved enough money yet.

Unit 4 Achievement Test

INTERVIEWER: We return now to our interview with Amy Wang, author of *Gardening for Life,* and host of the popular television program by the same name. Amy, before our break you had mentioned that you moved to Chicago in 2002. Had you ever been to Chicago before that?

AMY: Actually, I had come once to visit the Chicago Botanical Gardens—a beautiful place! But I moved here much later—after I had finished my book.

INTERVIEWER: And what finally brought you here to live?

AMY: Well, my book had already been selling really well when I was invited to be the host of *Gardening for Life.* I had never planned to work in television before then, but I've been on the show for a year now, and I love it!

INTERVIEWER: So how did you get into gardening? I mean, had you worked as a gardener before writing the book?

AMY: Yes, I had. I was working in a greenhouse for a long time before I started writing. I had often thought about sharing my gardening ideas. So I decided to write a book.

PART I Achievement Test

Empire Publishers proudly welcomes its newest editor-in-chief Ramona Gibbons. Ms. Gibbons grew up in Baltimore and started her editing career there in 1981. After she had written as a leisure columnist at the *Baltimore Daily* for a few years, she moved to Los Angeles in 1984. In 1985, she earned popularity from a series of articles she had published earlier about gifted children and how L.A. schools were failing them.

She was working in Berlin when the Wall fell in 1989. In fact, she had been living there for five years, so she wrote about the event from direct experience. In 1990, she was honored with the Gretta Eisner award for articles she had written the previous year about the fall of the Iron Curtain.

Ms. Gibbons had been serving as president of the Editing Standards Association for three years when she agreed to join Empire Publishers. She strives for excellence in editing and has been writing essays on the topics of standards and quality for the past 10 years. She has edited 22 books.

Ms. Gibbons is currently living in England, and she intends to work from home. She has one son, Anthony, who also works in publishing. Together, they are working on a book. Please join me now in welcoming Ramona Gibbons.

PART II Diagnostic Test

Technology is improving all the time and changing our lives as a result. In the future, how will you be communicating? How will you travel and work? How are you going to see society change as a result?

A typical day in the future will go something like this: While you're sleeping, you'll be learning through a miniature computer in your brain. You'll put on clothes that will have been washed by your robot. You'll ride to work in a flying car. But you won't be driving; the car will drive itself. When you come home, you'll eat a delicious meal that will have already been prepared for you.

By the time you celebrate your 120th birthday, you will be living with about 10 billion people on the earth, but you will have been breathing cleaner air your whole life. You will have experienced 80 percent less stress during your life than people do today, and you won't have gotten sick once. You will never have been lonely with all the technological improvements in communication. You will have learned 600 percent more than people do today. You will have enjoyed many foods that you can't even imagine today. You will even have visited Mars on vacation. These are just some of the ways technology will change the future. This is only half of what is possible!

Unit 5 Achievement Test

The Mars Vacation Group will launch its first commercial flight to Mars next week. Eight civilian, non-military passengers will be on the spaceship. The group will be traveling 60 million kilometers in 208 days. When the flight arrives, some people will take an extended hiking and camping trip and learn about the Red Planet firsthand. While this group is exploring, other travelers will be enjoying different activities that the Mars Vacation Group will plan. These include a variety of classes such as Gardening on Mars and Mars in Literature. The whole group will spend a total of six months on Mars before returning home. Crew members have promised that they will be sending us digital photos throughout the trip.

Unit 6 Achievement Test

PATTY: We're returning now to live coverage of Ted Johnson, who is trying to break two world records at the same time.

DOUG: That's right Patty. Ted has been walking for about a day and a half. Two days from now, when he arrives in Chicago, Ted will have traveled nearly 200 miles—or 322 kilometers. He will have been walking for 82 hours straight, breaking the previous world record by 10 hours. Twenty-four hours into his walk, he began singing, and in two days, he will have been singing for 58 hours, breaking that record by 18 hours. Another amazing fact, Patty, is that he will have taken about 3,520,000 steps by the time he finishes. Doctors, of course, will be watching him carefully, since he will have burned about 20,000 calories during his adventure. He will not have slept for about three and a half days. In addition, he will have sung the song he is singing about 1,560 times.

PATTY: Doug, have you had a chance to speak with Ted?

DOUG: Yes, just a few minutes ago Ted sang to me that, by next year, he hopes he will have broken two more records, for a total of four world records. But, he said he still won't have broken enough to satisfy himself. He believes that by the time he is 30, he will have already earned 10 world records for a variety of activities. How much satisfaction will he have found by then? We can only imagine.

PART II Achievement Test

Are you single and trying to date the old-fashioned way? In the next 100 years, how will people be dating? How will they meet their spouses? What kind of dates will they go on? How is society going to change as a result?

Imagine that you're dating in the future. Your search will go something like this: You'll register with a website where people can read about you and your interests. When you come home each day, you'll have received e-mails from people who are interested in dating you. You'll choose the ones who interest you, and you'll have online "dates" with them. It's possible that you'll be dating many people at the same time.

By the time you finally meet your true love, you'll have been spending about five hours a week getting to know people, but you won't have spoken face to face with any of them. You'll have saved lots of money because you will never have gone out to a restaurant. You will have experienced 80 percent less stress about dating than you do today, and if things don't work out with someone, you won't have felt as rejected. You'll never have been bored because you will have met 300 percent more people than you do today. You will have enjoyed many conversations with people. You will even have visited exotic places like Hawaii on virtual vacations with your dates. In short, you will have had many more dating opportunities than you have today. Will such virtual romances result in fewer divorces? Only time will tell.

PART III Diagnostic Test

JONATHAN: This is a great Japanese restaurant, isn't it?

SARA: Yes, it is. I love the food here.

JONATHAN: So do I . . . I also like the way they've decorated the restaurant. It's like you're really in Japan!

SARA: I feel that way too! I love to come and have a relaxing dinner here when I get the chance.

JONATHAN: Me too. If I remember correctly . . . You've been to Japan once, haven't you?

SARA: Yes, I have. I spent last summer there, working on my Japanese.

JONATHAN: That's great! Learning Japanese is quite a challenge, isn't it?

SARA: It really is. Everything in Japan is so different, but I enjoyed it.

JONATHAN: Sounds great! Hey, I don't really have a plan for tonight. Do you have anything that you'd like to do?

SARA: Hmmm . . . I heard there's going to be a jazz concert over at the Union Garden. Do you like jazz?

JONATHAN: Well, I'm not really into it. But we can certainly check it out, if you like.

SARA: Well, I'm not that into jazz either. I'm just trying to come up with something fun to do.

JONATHAN: I know . . . well, we could go to the movies, but I'm really not in the mood to do that.

SARA: Me neither. I'd like to do something else instead. We've been watching movies like crazy lately. Don't you think we should be able to come up with something better to do?

JONATHAN: Yes, we should! . . . Well, here comes our food! Maybe we can come up with something interesting to do after we eat.

Unit 7 Achievement Test

DAVID: You're with Globe Enterprises, aren't you?

WOMAN: Yeah. Have we met?

DAVID: No, not exactly. I saw a presentation you gave at a conference in San Francisco last year. Globe is headquartered in San Francisco, isn't it?

WOMAN: Yes, that's right. I guess that was last summer. So, how did you like San Francisco?

DAVID: Oh, it was very nice, but to be honest, I thought the weather would be better. Maybe the winters there are pleasant, though. It doesn't snow in San Francisco during the winter, does it?

WOMAN: No, it doesn't, except in the mountains. The winter's pretty mild, compared to here in Toronto. It snows a lot in the winter here, doesn't it?

DAVID: Uh-huh. You'd better buy yourself a really heavy winter jacket to survive the snow and cold!

WOMAN: Don't you get tired of the winter here?

DAVID: No way. I love skiing and snowboarding. This is a great place for me to live!

Unit 8 Achievement Test

JASON: This shopping mall is great. I really love shopping.

DIANA: So do I. How often do you go shopping?

JASON: At least once a week.

DIANA: Me too. Sometimes when I really can't find any time to go shopping at the mall, I shop online instead.

JASON: I do too. But I prefer going to the mall. When I shop at the mall, I love to go out to eat at the same time. Like at that Japanese restaurant in the Galleria.

DIANA: I do too. I love combining eating and shopping. I also like to go to movies afterwards.

JASON: So do I. Nothing is better than a good movie, good food, and some new clothes!

DIANA: Exactly. When you're not shopping, what else do you do for fun? Do you like to read?

JASON: Uh-huh. Especially novels or mysteries.

DIANA: I do too. What about biographies?

JASON: I don't read those very much . . . they're kinda boring.

DIANA: I don't either . . . what about sports?

JASON: I don't really play any sports. What about you?

DIANA: I do. I play table tennis and basketball. But I never watch sports on TV.

JASON: Me neither. I watch a lot of reality TV shows, though.

DIANA: Me too.

PART III Achievement Test

ROSS: This is a great Indian restaurant, isn't it?

CAROL: Yes, it is. I think the food and the service are first-rate.

ROSS: So do I. The food is so good, and the waitresses are wonderful. I also like the way they dress.

CAROL: I do too! It's like you're really in India!

ROSS: Exactly! Hey, you've been to India, haven't you?

CAROL: Yeah. I spent my senior year of college there as an exchange student.

ROSS: Wow! Living abroad is quite an experience, isn't it?

CAROL: It is. Everything is so different, but I enjoyed it a lot.

ROSS: Sounds like you had fun! So . . . is there anything that you'd like to do tonight? I've run out of ideas.

CAROL: Hmmm . . . There's a rock concert over at the State stadium. Do you like rock music?

ROSS: It's not my favorite, but it's OK. But we can certainly try to check it out if you like.

CAROL: Well, it's not my favorite either. I just heard that it's the biggest thing happening this weekend.

ROSS: Maybe we should check it out. I'm certainly not planning to stay home again.

CAROL: Me neither. I'm tired of staying home. Don't you feel like you're missing out on all the action when you stay home?

ROSS: Totally. Well, our food is coming! We can figure out our plans later.

PART IV Diagnostic Test

REPORTER: Tell us about your start as a fitness trainer.

BRIAN: Starting a career in fitness is not an easy task. I began with a plan of opening my own fitness training center. My father sold some of his land to help me financially. One month later he asked me to help him work out. He was my first long-term client. So I created a specialized program to meet my father's needs. I started out slowly; then I added extra time and weights to my father's exercise routine. Adding time and weights gradually helped my father's body get used to the exercises. I let my father decide when to work out, but I tell him to try to do something every day. Now, he loves it.

Unit 9 Achievement Test

LISA: Hi, Jane. Where are you going?

JANE: To the store. I need to buy some groceries.

LISA: Oh! I usually eat in the cafeteria. But next semester, I'll be in an apartment, so I'll need to go to the grocery store. Where do you usually go to shop?

JANE: There's a supermarket near my house that I like. It's a great place for buying fresh fruit and vegetables, and they have an ethnic foods section if you need to find something special.

LISA: Sounds great. Do you share the food expenses with your roommates?

JANE: Yes. We've found that by sharing the expenses, we can save a lot. We each pay $15 or $20 for groceries and take turns shopping.

LISA: That's a good idea.

JANE: Oh, I wanted to remind you to come to our dinner party tomorrow night.

LISA: I'll be there. Do you need some help with the cooking?

JANE: Actually, we're asking everyone to pay $10 for the food. We're planning on cooking the meal together.

LISA: Oh, no problem. Sounds fun. See you tomorrow.

JANE: See you. Bye.

Unit 10 Achievement Test

FRANK: So, how was the movie?

DEBBI: I really liked it.

FRANK: What was it about?

DEBBI: It was a documentary film about endangered wildlife for my environmental biology class. Professor Thompson wants to help us learn as much as possible about the subject.

FRANK: So, what were you supposed to get out of it?

DEBBI: Um . . . mostly background information. In this class, we have to do a presentation, but he lets us choose a kind of endangered species to report about. The film gave us some background for the presentation.

FRANK: Cool. What kind of animals are you interested in?

DEBBI: I'm not sure yet. Let me read some more, and then I'll decide. The professor's letting us search for information for two more weeks before we have to decide on our endangered animal.

FRANK: Oh, you have plenty of time.

DEBBI: Well, not really . . . I've got a lot of work in my other classes.

FRANK: Yeah, me too.

DEBBI: But I'm not too worried because he made us watch the movie first. Having some background information makes me feel better before starting my project.

FRANK: Yeah, the movie can help you get a rough idea before you start.

DEBBI: Right. I'm a visual person, so films really get me to think more clearly.

FRANK: Let me know how it goes, OK?

DEBBI: I will.

PART IV Achievement Test

INTERVIEWER: Hi, George. We're glad to have you with us. Can you tell us about your new book?

GEORGE: Well, this book is for consumers who have been tricked into believing that they're feeding their pets healthy foods. Actually, they're giving them food that is not healthy at all, and that contains cheap grains and dangerous chemicals. This book will tell you how to help your pets achieve a balanced diet so their bodies can operate at maximum efficiency. The food should provide all of the nutrition that is important for a pet's body to function properly. A body that is working properly does an amazing job of preventing disease and healing itself. However, good health requires the nutrients of a well-balanced diet. In terms of finding the proper diet for our pets, we must learn to look beyond our own beliefs and needs, so we can begin to care for the animals that are so important to us in a proper way.

INTERVIEWER: That's very interesting . . .

PART V Diagnostic Test

Now that I'm in college, I'm a good student. But when I was younger I almost dropped out of school. I thought the teachers gave out too much homework, and then I'd put off doing the homework until the last minute. I also found it difficult to turn down my friends. If they wanted to make trouble, I usually went along with them. Worst of all, I let my parents down with my poor grades. But after high school, I guess I grew up a little. Now I set up a study schedule for myself every week and stick to it. I show up to all my classes and keep up with my homework. I sure wish I had figured out these study skills in high school!

Unit 11 Achievement Test

HELEN: Hi, Tim! Have you found out about any jobs yet?

TIM: No, and I'm about to give up. Maybe I'll just have to stay at my old job.

HELEN: I wish I could cheer you up. Let's talk it over. Have you looked into working with your brother?

TIM: I thought it over, but I don't think it would work out. His restaurant has really been struggling lately.

HELEN: OK, well, have you set up an appointment with that job agency that I told you about?

TIM: I left a message on their answering machine, but they haven't called back yet.

HELEN: Keep trying. If you try hard to find a job, I'm sure your efforts will pay off.

Unit 12 Achievement Test

DONNA: Hey, Franco, can you help me out?

FRANCO: Sure. What's up?

DONNA: I'm trying to figure out how to fill out this form to enter this vacation contest. It sounds great, and I don't want to leave anything out. For example, what does "timeshare" mean?

FRANCO: Let me look it over . . . Donna, this isn't a form to enter a vacation contest. You're signing up to buy a house somewhere with people you don't even know! Where did you get this?

DONNA: In the mail.

FRANCO: Donna, you shouldn't fall for these ads. You should throw that paper out.

[phone rings]

DONNA: Hello? . . . uh-huh. Sure! Sign me up! Yes, I can hold on a minute.

FRANCO: Who's that?

DONNA: I won a vacation to Florida!

FRANCO: Donna! Tell whoever is calling never to call back, then hang the phone up, please!

PART V Achievement Test

JEAN: You sure look tired. What have you been doing?

SAM: Housework! First, I picked up a ton of garbage from my yard and cut down some bushes. Then I folded clothes and put them away. I had to turn over my living room rug to cover up a big spot on it. Then I threw away some old food in the refrigerator and took out the trash. Finally, I straightened up my bedroom. And I just finished putting some shelves up.

JEAN: Wow! You *have* been busy! Can I help out with anything?

SAM: If you don't mind, you could help me turn this couch around. Then I think I'll sit down and rest!

PART VI Diagnostic Test

New Zealand is a small country that has geographic, political, economic, and cultural features that make it unique. The two islands of New Zealand, which resulted from volcanic activity in the South Pacific Ocean, have lush farmland and beautiful landscapes.

Despite its relatively small size, New Zealand has established its own position in global affairs. For example, New Zealand doesn't allow any ships that carry nuclear weapons to visit its ports. Ships that use nuclear energy are not welcome either.

In addition, New Zealand has been a strong advocate of the United Nations, which is an organization that tries to resolve conflicts around the world. New Zealand also supports the World Trade Organization, which works to break down international trade barriers. The products which New Zealand sells in international markets are primarily agricultural ones such as milk, lamb, and beef.

Unit 13 Achievement Test

PROFESSOR
WAHAL: Good morning, class. Today we have a guest speaker who comes from Heights University. This lecturer is a person whose research on world governments is widely known. Our guest, who teaches courses in the history of government, will explain some basic principles of democracies and dictatorships. Please welcome Professor Marilyn Feinberg.

PROFESSOR
FEINBERG: Thank you, Professor Wahal. It's a pleasure to be here. I'll start today by talking about governments. Governments are institutions which make decisions about the lives of people in a particular area. Some governments promote values and beliefs that are acceptable to the people. These governments try to make policies that benefit citizens and society as a whole. People who can see the benefits of the government's policies will follow its wishes. When people obey the government, one can say that it has legitimacy. Yet any government must be able to enforce its decisions against those who do not

obey its wishes. This is the power of coercion.

Political scientists differentiate among types of governments by considering the degree of legitimacy and the degree of coercion that they use to make and enforce decisions. Governments which are democracies have a high sense of legitimacy and a low level of coercion. In this type of government, people elect their leaders in periodic elections, and leaders pass laws that people normally accept and follow. If leaders fail to pass laws and make decisions which people accept, citizens will elect new leaders in the next election.

Unit 14 Achievement Test

Have you ever read a novel that took place in Canada? If you have, then there's a good chance that it wasn't written until the mid 1900s. This is because until that time, many people thought that Canada was only a place where people went to get away from Europe. Some people even considered it the absence of civilization. This was a time when few people wrote books or stories about Canada.

But one writer did a lot to change that. Hugh MacLennan, who many people consider among the greatest Canadian writers, was one of the first authors to write about the country. Before him, most Canadian authors wrote novels about the United States, Europe, or traveling the world. They thought that people wanted to read about these important and interesting places—not about the forests, snow, and wind of Canada. This was the opinion that most people held until Hugh MacLennan published his first novel in 1941. *Barometer Rising,* which he set in his hometown of Halifax, Nova Scotia, was one of the first Canadian novels. In this and his other works, MacLennan wrote about situations and themes that he felt were uniquely Canadian.

PART VI Achievement Test

Many people think that Canada and the United States are very similar, perhaps partly because of how close they are. In fact, Canada, which is the second largest country after Russia in terms of area, is similar to the United States in many ways. However, important differences that set Canada apart from the United States exist as well. Canada, which is a democratic country like the United States, has a style of democracy called a parliamentary system. This is a system that is different from the American one in several ways. For example, in a parliamentary system, members of parliament in the political party that is the largest select a prime minister to lead the nation. The United States has a presidential system of government that allows each citizen to vote for a president. The candidate who wins the most votes from a sufficient number of states becomes president. A team of leaders which the president chooses work with him or her at the highest levels of government.

PART VII Diagnostic Test

JANE: Hey, Eric. Where do you think we should go on vacation this year?

ERIC: I've been thinking about it, but I haven't been able to come up with a good idea yet. Last year we went to the beach, and that was a disaster! The beach must not be our ideal vacation spot!

JANE: This year we should go somewhere really exotic! Last year we couldn't pay for a big vacation, but this year we can!

ERIC: How about Egypt? There must be a lot of really interesting sites to see there, like the Pyramids.

JANE: OK, let's consider Egypt. We should also consider England. I've always wanted to see Stonehenge. Do you know what I've always wondered? Why might the ancient Britons have built Stonehenge? I have questions about a lot of ancient places. I'm sure the tourists who visit them are able to learn about their histories while they're there.

ERIC: I'm sure they are. But remember that we don't have to decide between Egypt and England right now. In fact, we had better research both places before deciding.

JANE: You're right. We should find out about the history of each place before we decide because we might discover that we're really more interested in one place than the other. Shouldn't we have done that last year?

ERIC: I think so. Last year we made our decision too fast.

JANE: Oh well, that was last year. Now we can learn from our past mistakes. We can take our time and do some research first. We might make a better decision this year if we do that.

ERIC: Travel guides might have helpful information. They're full of both history and useful travel tips. Do you want to meet at the bookstore tomorrow to research Egypt and England? I might be free at noon, but I've got to check my schedule first.

JANE: OK. The bookstore might be busy then, so let's plan on being there for two hours.

Unit 15 Achievement Test

BEN: Ann, I read a story yesterday that you have got to read. It said the city might build a new park right next to your house next year.

ANN: Really? What else did it say?

BEN: Well, I can't remember much more. I think it said the city could make citizens pay extra money to help build the park.

ANN: Really? I haven't heard anything yet. My neighbors might know something about it, though. I'll ask around.

BEN: That's a good idea. Somebody must have some information about it.

ANN: You know, the city can't make citizens pay more money without a city-wide vote. That story can't be right. Good reporters always consider all the facts, but irresponsible reporters often leave out important information. That's why it's important to read articles carefully, and remember, don't assume everything you read is true!

Unit 16 Achievement Test

DAN: We're really going to miss you, Mark, when you move to Costa Rica.

MARK: I'll miss you too, Dan, but I am excited to move to Marisa's country—excited but really unprepared!

DAN: What do you mean? What could you have done to prepare better?

MARK: Well for one thing, I should have studied Spanish for more than the past five months.

DAN: Oh, yeah. That could have helped.

MARK: I could have started taking Spanish in elementary school. I should have taken it in high school and college, too.

DAN: But at least you have your Master's degree in Business Administration from New York University!

MARK: That's another thing. I should have studied international business. I could have learned about international currencies and trade at NYU. I shouldn't have focused on U.S. business so much. We studied a little about international markets, but really focusing on them might have helped me a lot in Costa Rica.

Unit 17 Achievement Test

Plato, an ancient philosopher, wrote about the city of Atlantis. Atlantis may have been an ancient city located on an island in the Atlantic Ocean. The legend says that Atlantis might have been a paradise where a great empire existed. Because of the stories, many people believe that the people of Atlantis must have been brilliant engineers who built palaces, temples, and waterways.

Then, around 9500 B.C.E., the whole island disappeared. Some think that a series of earthquakes could have caused Atlantis to sink to the bottom of the ocean. Despite the fact that many explorers have tried to find the ancient city under water, they must not have found much because we don't have any physical evidence that the city of Atlantis actually existed.

Could Atlantis have existed? Many people think that Atlantis couldn't have existed because humans at that time couldn't have had the technology the legends describe. Some believe that Atlantis did exist, and that it may have been located in the Americas, the Canary Islands, or even Antarctica. Due to some recent archaeological findings, others are convinced that Atlantis must have been a city on the Greek island called Thera. If Thera and Atlantis were the same place, Plato may have been wrong about where, how, and when the island was destroyed. Or, Plato might have based his stories about Atlantis on ancient Eqyptian stories about the island of Thera.

Perhaps we will never know if the lost city of Atlantis ever really existed. But one thing is for sure—the myth of Atlantis could not have survived this long without Plato's stories.

PART VII Achievement Test

HARRY: Jason, here are our seats. Look, there might be room for our bags either underneath the seat or in these compartments above the seats. Where should we put them?

JASON: I think we ought to put them underneath our seats. My bag is pretty heavy, and I can't lift it high enough to get it into the overhead bins.

HARRY: OK. Wow, it's really a tight fit. My bag must be too big!

JASON: You have to put yours in the overhead compartment. Look, the train conductor is coming around to collect our tickets.

HARRY: Where could I have put mine? Oh, I remember. I thought the bottom of my bag might be the safest place for it. Should I have kept my passport out too?

JASON: Yes. You had better get it out.

HARRY: I didn't know I needed my passport on the train.

JASON: The conductor has to make sure you have a ticket and a passport.

HARRY: This must be a long train ride. I see a lot of people who brought meals along.

JASON: Well, everyone might not be going to the same place. People will come and go with each stop.

HARRY: Each stop? Do you mean this train isn't going straight from here to Barcelona?

JASON: That's right. The train could stop at as many as 10 or 15 other cities along the way. And Barcelona may not be the last stop either. That means we have to pay attention to where we are and remember to get off.

HARRY: But all the announcements are made in Spanish! We can't speak Spanish. We might not know when to get off.

JASON: I can understand some Spanish even though I can't speak it.

HARRY: That's a relief! That means you shouldn't sleep during the trip.

JASON: I can't ever sleep on the train anyway. It's too noisy.

HARRY: Well, it's not too noisy for me! Wake me up when we get there!

PART VIII Diagnostic Test

Hybrid cars are powered by two sources: gasoline and a rechargeable electric battery. These cars were first made available to consumers in the late 1990s. They quickly became very popular, and now companies are introducing new models, including trucks and SUVs. In the future, even hybrid sports cars may be sold.

The primary reason for hybrid cars' popularity is their energy efficiency. Hybrid cars produce less pollution than regular gas cars. This can be accomplished in a few ways. When a hybrid car speeds up, energy is taken from the battery, not gas, so less gas is used. Also, when a hybrid car stops, even at a traffic light, the gas motors shut off, and the car is powered by electricity. A hybrid car's battery recharges each time the driver steps on the brakes. When a car is moving, it has energy. When the brakes are applied, this energy is removed. Some of this energy can be captured by hybrid cars and stored in the battery to use later.

Energy-efficient cars are a trend of the future. This can be seen in changing laws. In some countries, strict laws have been established to limit the amount of pollution that cars can produce. The requirements of these laws can be met by hybrid cars. With hybrid cars, drivers save money on gas, and our earth's environment may be saved, too. Yes, it looks like the days of buying regular gas-powered cars may be numbered.

Unit 18 Achievement Test

The 1936 Berlin Olympic Games are remembered for several historical reasons. Forty-nine nations were represented at these Olympics, and 3,963 athletes (331 women and 3,632 men) participated in 129 events. More than 4 million tickets were sold to people from all over the world to attend the different events.

These Games are best known for disproving Adolf Hitler's theory of the superiority of the Aryan race. In fact, the most famous athlete of these Games was Jesse Owens, an African-American who broke 11 Olympic records and won four gold medals.

The torch relay was introduced in these Olympic Games. A torch is a long stick that is lit on fire. This relay is now an important Olympic tradition. In the relay, a torch is carried from Olympia, Greece, the site of the first Olympics, to the location of the current Games by athletes or other famous people.

The 1936 Summer Games were the first ones on television. Twenty-five large TVs were installed around Berlin. At this time most people didn't have televisions in their homes, so the Games were watched by local people on these televisions.

Basketball, canoeing, and team handball competitions were held for the first time in these Games, and the sport of polo was included for the last time.

Unit 19 Achievement Test

Many things must be considered as you prepare for a job interview. In order to demonstrate to the interviewer that you can meet the company's needs, your knowledge about the company ought to be made apparent. How can you do that? Well, first of all, your knowledge of the company can be expanded by reading annual reports, doing research on the Internet, and speaking with employees of the company. Then make sure to mention this information during the interview.

Also, you should plan for some of the questions you might hear. You can easily find frequently asked interview questions on the Internet. Answers to these questions might be prepared and practiced ahead of time. But be careful! Memorized answers from interview books or websites had better not be used. Interviewers are familiar with these standard answers and will not be impressed by them.

In order to become comfortable in an interview situation, mock interviews might be completed, even if they are with friends or family members. The more you practice, the more comfortable you'll become with interviewing.

Unit 20 Achievement Test

SUZY: Hi, Jess! What are you doing at the mall?

JESS: I'm getting my nails painted for a party tonight.

SUZY: Oh yeah? Where are you going to get them done?

JESS: At Nell's Nails.

SUZY: Really? I need to find a nail place for my wedding. Have you had them done by anyone there before?

JESS: Yeah, they're really good. So, how are the wedding plans going?

SUZY: Very well! I decided that I'm going to have my cake decorated by Carla's Cake Shop, and I'm going to have my flowers arranged by my neighbor. She owns a flower shop.

JESS: And what about your hair? Are you going to get it styled by a professional stylist?

SUZY: Yeah, at the Beauty Spot. And I think I'll have it cut by the stylist about a week before the wedding so it will be really healthy.

JESS: That's a great idea. Have you had your dress fitted yet?

SUZY: No, not yet. I'll do that next week. Oh, I have to meet my sister in a half hour. I had better get going. See you soon!

JESS: See you!

PART VIII Achievement Test

The Beatles, a musical group originally formed in 1959, was made up of four young men from Liverpool, England. Although their music is over 30 years old, they still might be defined as the best rock group ever. The four musicians, John Lennon, Paul McCartney, George Harrison, and Ringo Starr hold several records in the music industry that some say will never be broken. They are the only group in history to have 20 number-one songs. They have sold more albums than any other group, with global sales totaling more than 1.1 billion records.

Many of the Beatles' songs were written by John Lennon and Paul McCartney. Early on, it was decided that the Lennon-McCartney team should be given credit for all songs written by either of them. In reality, many of their songs were mainly written by just one of them with a little help from the other. Despite this fact, Lennon-McCartney may be considered the most successful popular songwriting duo in the world.

In addition to making music, the Beatles made five movies. The band can be seen starring in *A Hard Day's Night, Help!,* and *Magical Mystery Tour.* They were shown in animation in the movie *Yellow Submarine.* Their last movie, *Let It Be,* was a documentary which was filmed as the band recorded the album of the same title.

The Beatles played together in a recording studio for the last time in 1969. In 1970, it was announced that Paul McCartney had left the Beatles. The group officially broke up on December 31, 1970. But the Beatles will not be forgotten. In fact, when a CD of all their number one songs was released in 2000, 31 years after the release of their previous album, it became the fastest-selling CD of all time. Their music will be listened to and appreciated by fans of all ages for years to come.

PART IX Diagnostic Test

How long does it take you to plan a vacation? Buying plane tickets, finding a rental car, looking for activities for the kids. . . . It's a lot of work! What would you say if someone offered to do all that work for you? Because that's what Easy Travel does. It's so easy! If you come to our agency, we will ask you a few simple questions about the kind of vacation you want. Then we do all the work. We'll research all the options, and we'll offer you several packages to choose from. If you want a low-cost vacation, we'll give you *three* low-cost options! If you're looking for a romantic getaway, we will suggest at least *three* possibilities. All you do is pick the one that's best for you. So, if you don't want to spend another minute planning your next vacation, then we are the travel agency for you!

Unit 21 Achievement Test

These days many people are becoming very conscious of what they eat. Are you joining the trend? If you want to eat more healthfully, then I have the website for you! I can show you many ways to cook healthy, delicious dishes! If you eat healthy foods, you can improve more than your physical fitness. When you pay attention to what you eat, your energy level should also go up.

So what's your reason for wanting to change your eating habits? Many people go on diets when they want to lose weight or have a health problem. Different problems require different diets, so my website offers collections of recipes for a variety of health issues. But you don't have to start eating better because of a problem. You can actually prevent health and weight problems if you start eating well before they happen! If you want to learn how to cook healthy food in your own kitchen, then visit my website, www.eatrightforyourhealth.com. You'll find great meal ideas!

Unit 22 Achievement Test

CARLA: Betty, I'm glad you're here! I need help putting this new desk together. If you don't help me, I might never get it done!

BETTY: Well, if there are instructions, I'll be able to help you.

CARLA: There are instructions. But they're really difficult to understand! I've been looking at them for an hour! Here, take them.

BETTY: If you get frustrated, you'll never finish it.

CARLA: I know that. But I can't help it!

BETTY: Don't worry. We'll get it done if we work together.

CARLA: OK, what should I do?

BETTY: Here. If you hold this piece, I'll attach that one to it.

CARLA: Yeah, that looks right.

BETTY: Actually, this looks pretty easy. Unless we have a problem, it won't take long at all.

CARLA: Thank goodness. If you can really do this, I'll take you out to dinner.

BETTY: Well, then let's finish it up!

Unit 23 Achievement Test

SASHA: I wish we didn't have to work so much.

JOSEPH: I know. If I didn't have to work, I would take up some hobbies, like playing the piano. How about you?

SASHA: If I didn't work, I might travel the world. I've always wanted to see Turkey, Egypt, and Spain.

JOSEPH: If I had the chance to travel wherever I wanted, I would go to South America. I've always wanted to visit Peru to see Machu Picchu. Oh, and I would love to see the Nazca lines if I could.

SASHA: That would be so interesting! But if I were you, I wouldn't suggest any more places to visit. I might get too many ideas in my head. I wish I could quit my job right now!

JOSEPH: Believe me, I know. I wish I could take you to all those places. Maybe we can start to travel in a few years when we've saved some more money.

Unit 24 Achievement Test

BEN: Why do you think our band didn't get any jobs? Would we have succeeded if we had done something differently?

AMY: Well, if we had advertised the band, people might have known who we were. Or if we had hired a manager, he or she could have helped us find jobs.

BEN: You know what else would have helped? If we had recorded a sample of our music for potential clients, people would have known what kind of music we played.

AMY: That would have been a great idea if we had thought of it earlier. If our band had gotten a good reputation, people might have wanted to hire us.

BEN: If we had done some of these things before, our band might have become a success!

AMY: You know, maybe it's a *good* thing that the band didn't succeed. I mean, if it had been successful, I wouldn't have gone back to school.

BEN: That's true. I wouldn't have started dating Jennifer if we had had to work a lot of nights. I guess sometimes things just work out for the best, even if they don't turn out the way you expected.

AMY: That's so true. I'm glad we started the band even though it didn't work out. Although I wouldn't have bought a new guitar if I had known I wouldn't need it!

BEN: I guess sometimes lessons like that can be expensive.

PART IX Achievement Test

Do you want to challenge your mind? Would you like to win $5,000? You can do both if you come to the May Madness chess tournament next Saturday! Hundreds of chess players from all over come each year to play this tournament. When they get together, excitement fills the air! If you stop by to watch, you'll see the matches played in record time! If you come to compete, you'll play against some of the most talented players in the area. And if you win, you'll receive a prize of $5,000! What would you do with the money if you won?

PART X Diagnostic Test

YELENA: Hello?

MOM: Hi. It's Mom. What have you been up to?

YELENA: Well, I've been thinking that I should take a trip to Europe.

MOM: Really?

YELENA: Yeah. My friend Paul travels there all the time, so I asked him to help me plan a trip. I told him that I wanted to see something amazing.

MOM: Did he have any suggestions?

YELENA: Yeah. I asked him what his favorite places were. He told me that Italy and Greece were awesome. He asked me if I had considered going to one of those countries. I know he really loved Greece. In fact, he said, "Greece is the best place I've ever been."

MOM: Those sound like two pretty good options!

YELENA: Yeah, but he also told me not to forget about France. That would be pretty amazing, too.

MOM: I'm sure it would. Who do you think you'd go with?

YELENA: Well, I asked Paul who he had gone with last time. It turns out that he went alone on his last trip, and he really liked it. He said that he had met lots of people traveling by himself. So I think I want to go by myself, too.

MOM: How long are you going to be gone?

YELENA: Paul said to travel for at least three weeks. He usually stays at least that long. He said not to come home before that because I would regret not staying longer.

MOM: Oh, three weeks is a long time. Did you ask him when you should go?

YELENA: Yeah, I did. And he gave me some advice. He said, "You might not want to go in July because it can get really hot." He told me it would be best to go in May. The weather is milder, and there aren't so many tourists then.

Unit 25 Achievement Test

LAURA: Hey, Sue! Guess who I talked to yesterday?

SUE: Who?

LAURA: Greg. He told me about his date with Alice last Friday. He said he thought the date went well. It sounds like they had a great time.

SUE: Really? I talked to Alice and she said, "It was the worst date I've ever had."

LAURA: Oh, no! I wonder what happened. Greg told me dinner had been nice. They went to a new Korean restaurant downtown, and he said that the food was delicious.

SUE: Alice didn't think so. She said that it had given her heartburn because it was too spicy. In fact, when I talked to her, she said that she still didn't feel well.

LAURA: Well, Greg told me that they had had a great conversation during dinner and that they had really gotten to know each other.

SUE: Alice said that Greg had talked through the entire dinner and that she had suggested a movie so she wouldn't have to listen to him talk anymore. But she said he hadn't stopped talking during the movie, either.

LAURA: Oh . . . Wow. Poor Greg! He told me that he was going to ask her out again.

SUE: Oh, no. What a mess.

LAURA: I know. I think I should talk to Greg before he calls her.

Unit 26 Achievement Test

JULIE: Hi, Sean! I saw your mother yesterday, and she said you had moved into a new apartment.

SEAN: Yes, I did. One of my friends lives in an apartment in the same building, and she told me the apartments were really nice. But I'm having some problems.

JULIE: Really? Like what?

SEAN: Well, there are insects in my apartment. I called the apartment manager last week, and he said, "I'll take care of it." But he hasn't been there. Then I discovered the air conditioner didn't work, so I called the manager again. He told me, "We'll fix it

tomorrow." But that was four days ago, and no one has come. When I complained to my friend, she told me I was being too picky.

JULIE: That's ridiculous!

SEAN: I know! And I didn't sleep well last night because the neighbors were having a loud party. I asked them to be quiet, and they told me I could join them. Can you believe it? I told them, "I want to sleep, not have a party." When I asked them to be quiet the second time, they told me their party might last until the next morning. I was so mad! I said, "If you don't quiet down, I'll call the police."

JULIE: Why don't you move again?

SEAN: I can't. Before I moved in, the apartment manager told me that I had to sign a one-year lease. Well, really he convinced me to do it. He told me I had to rent the apartment soon because there weren't many left. So I decided to sign the lease and get the apartment before they were all rented.

JULIE: Maybe you should write a complaint letter to the management company.

SEAN: I think I will.

Unit 27 Achievement Test

ANA: Hello?

MOM: Hi Ana, it's Mom. Are you still sick in bed?

ANA: Yes. I'm feeling a little better, but the doctor advised me to stay in bed for a few days.

MOM: Will you be able to miss work?

ANA: I called my boss, and he said to take today and tomorrow off, so that's good. Hopefully, I can sleep a lot. But he asked me to go in on Thursday for the staff meeting. I have so much work to do, but the doctor told me not to do too much. He really recommends resting as much as possible. He also told me to stay away from others because I might be contagious.

MOM: Do you think you should go to work then?

ANA: Well, my boss instructed me to go in. I guess I'll just wait and see how I feel.

MOM: Are you taking any medicine?

ANA: The doctor told me to take aspirin, so I went to the pharmacy and got some, and I think it's helping a little. He also said to drink a lot of fluids, so I'm drinking a couple kinds of hot tea and plenty of water. He told me to eat lots of chicken soup, too.

MOM: I can bring you some soup for dinner.

ANA: That would be great! Oh, no! I just remembered that I'm supposed to eat dinner with Jennifer tonight. She invited me to go out for pizza. I'd better call her right now and tell her I can't go. I'll see you later, Mom.

MOM: OK, I'll be there around 7:00.

Unit 28 Achievement Test

SAM: How did your meeting with Dr. Gupta go?

ED: Well, he asked me some questions I didn't know the answers to.

SAM: Like what?

ED: He asked what I was planning to do after graduation. When I didn't respond right away, he asked if I would study for a higher degree.

SAM: I know you've been thinking about that. What did you say?

ED: I said I hadn't decided. Then he asked me why I was studying biology. I told him I had always wanted to be a doctor, but I wasn't sure I could. When he asked me why I thought that, I told him I wasn't sure my grades were high enough. But he said they were fine.

SAM: That's great!

ED: Yeah! He asked what I wanted to specialize in. When I told him I wanted to become a heart specialist, he seemed surprised.

SAM: Didn't he specialize in heart medicine?

ED: Yes, he did. He asked me who had interested me in the heart, and I told him that I had become interested in it after taking his course last semester. I think he was happy about that. I asked if he would write a letter of recommendation for me, and he said yes.

SAM: That's good news!

ED: Yeah. So I think I'll start applying to some medical schools.

Unit 29 Achievement Test

KATE: Lee, can you tell me how I know that man? I'm talking about the guy with the dark hair and beard. He looks so familiar, but I don't know what his name is.

LEE: He looks familiar to me, too. We must know him. But I can't remember where we've seen him.

KATE: Have we met him before, or have we just seen him somewhere? I'm not sure. Oh, I wonder if he's the owner of the new Italian restaurant downtown. It sort of looks like him.

LEE: It could be. But I'm not sure if the restaurant owner has a beard. I haven't been to that place in a while, though, so maybe he has one now.

KATE: Let's ask Paul who he is.

LEE: OK. Hey, Paul!

PAUL: What's up?

LEE: Well, I wonder how much you know about the people at this party.

PAUL: Why? Who do you want to know about?

LEE: Do you know who that man is?

PAUL: Yeah, that's Gino de Selva. He owns the Italian restaurant Gino's downtown.

KATE: I was right! Does he speak English? I'd like to talk with him, but my Italian isn't very good.

PAUL: No problem. He speaks English really well.

KATE: Good. I'm going to go introduce myself.

PART X Achievement Test

JAMAL: What a day!

SCOTT: What happened?

JAMAL: Well, my boss told me that we had a meeting at 12:00 with important clients. He wanted me there early. I clearly remember him saying, "You should be in the conference room at 11:45." So I arrived at the conference room at 11:40, but the meeting was already in progress. Afterwards, my boss told me that my behavior was unacceptable.

SCOTT: He really said that? Why? He told you to be there at 11:45! I guess he forgot what he'd said.

JAMAL: Apparently, because he insisted that he had said to arrive at 10:45! He really thought that he was right. I didn't want to argue with him, but I said he had told me 11:45. I didn't want him to think I was irresponsible, so I asked if maybe he had made a mistake. He got really mad at that comment. He asked me if I wanted to keep my job!

SCOTT: What? That's really ridiculous.

JAMAL: I know. At that point I asked myself why I was working for someone like that.

SCOTT: I believe it! So then what happened?

JAMAL: Well, he calmed down a little. He told me that I was one of the most responsible workers in the office. That made me feel better. Then he asked me how we were going to fix this problem.

SCOTT: Wow!

JAMAL: Yeah. I was really surprised. I told him that it might be a good idea to document all meeting times in e-mails to avoid these types of misunderstandings. He agreed and said, "We ought to keep an electronic schedule of all meetings." Then he talked to his assistant and asked her to organize the schedule.

SCOTT: Thank goodness!

JAMAL: I know! I was really stressed out for a while.

Answer Key

PART I Diagnostic test

1 | LISTENING: AN AWARD-WINNING NEWS CORRESPONDENT

A.
1. received U2
2. had worked U4
3. won U3
4. had written U4
5. were making U2
6. took U3
7. had produced U4
8. has contributed U3
9. joins U1
10. *Stand* U1
11. is . . . acting U1

B.
1. T U2
2. T U3
3. F U4
4. F U3
5. T U1
6. F U3
7. F U1
8. F U1

2 | A GROWING FAMILY

1. a U2
2. b U2
3. d U2
4. a U3
5. c U3
6. b U4
7. a U4
8. d U4
9. b U4
10. c U4
11. b U3
12. a U1
13. c U1
14. b U3
15. d U1
16. c U1
17. d U3
18. a U1

3 | A SMART DECISION

Note: Both contractions and noncontracted forms are acceptable.
1. 'm . . . going / was . . . going U1
2. Don't . . . have U1
3. decided U3
4. was paying / paid / had been paying U2
5. had had / had / had been having / was having U4
6. had been getting / got / was getting U4
7. sold U2
8. have been walking / have walked U3
9. have saved / have been saving / save / am saving U3
10. have started / started U3
11. do . . . get / are . . . getting / have . . . been getting U1
12. take U1

4 | WANTED: DRUMMER

Note: Both contracted and noncontracted forms are acceptable.
1. have been / was U3
2. played U2
3. recorded U3
4. had become / became U4
5. toured / had toured U3
6. were not making / did not make U2
7. had been stealing / had stolen / was stealing / stole U4
8. do . . . want U1
9. had seen / saw U4
10. need U1
11. work / are working / have been working U1
12. are making / have made / have been making / make U1

5 | EDITING: NEW BAND

A fresh sound is in the air, and it's ~~come~~ ^coming^ from Arizona. The first album from the Phoenix-based band Exile has ~~hitted~~ ^hit U3^ radios and stores. The band's singer, Tim Reeves, ~~is quickly become~~ ^is quickly becoming / has quickly become U1^ a superstar. Like most local bands, Exile ~~had struggling~~ ^had been struggling / had struggled U4^ since its members started playing together seven years ago. However, that ~~all changing~~ ^all changed U3^ after Reeves ~~had bring~~ ^brought U3^ some fresh talent to his group last year. Reeves ~~reorganize~~ ^reorganized / has reorganized U2^ his band, which included bringing on a sensational new drummer, Brian Fathera. Success came when a representative of Electra Records ~~had be visiting~~ ^had been visiting / was visiting / visited U4^ Phoenix and ~~attends~~ ^attended U2^ an Exile concert. Before the band members left the building that night, they ~~had sign~~ ^had signed / signed U4^ a contract to record with Electra, and the rest is music to our ears.

Unit 1 Achievement Test

A.
1. suggests `N4`
2. think `N2`
3. brings `N1`
4. doesn't take `N1`
5. summarizes `N4`
6. investigates `N4`

B.

The chart includes all possible answers. Students only need to find the number listed at the top of the column.

Simple present (7)	Present progressive (1)
influence `N1`	is . . . taking `N1`
feel `N2`	
claims `N1`	
shape `N1`	
hear `N2`	
is `N1`	
imagine `N1`	
look `N2`	
impact `N1`	

2   A FUTURE AUTHOR

1. am putting / 'm putting `N1`
2. weigh `N3`
3. do . . . figure out `N1`
4. make `N1`
5. do . . . know `N2`
6. destroy `N3`
7. turn `N3`
8. sounds `N2`
9. am always adding / 'm always adding `N5`
10. am not writing / 'm not writing `N1`

3   EDITING: E-MAIL TO MONSON BOOK PUBLISHERS

To Whom It May Concern:

    I ~~write~~ *am writing* this letter to introduce you to a book I have written, *Fun Facts of Science*. The book is for children ages 8 to 12 and ~~is including~~ *includes* `N1` color photographs. Parents and teachers often complain that their children are not interested in science, and I ~~am thinking~~ *think* `N2` this book can help motivate these children. As a teacher myself, I ~~always collects~~ *am always collecting / always collect* `N5` ideas to make science interesting. I printed a few copies of the book from my computer, and I am currently ~~give~~ *giving* `N5` them to small groups of children to read. These children say that they find the book very interesting. I ~~am believing~~ *believe* `N2` such a book could be a valuable reference in homes and school libraries. I ~~looks~~ *look* `N1` forward to hearing from you.

Sincerely,
Daniel Stoletta

Unit 2 Achievement Test

A.
1. did . . . start up `N1`
2. was looking `N2`
3. didn't leave `N1`
4. were working `N3`

B.
1. F `N3`
2. F `N1`
3. T `N5`
4. F `N4`
5. T `N3`

2   NEW MATCHRIGHT CLIENT

1. a `N1`
2. b `N1`
3. a `N2`
4. c `N3`
5. c `N3`
6. a `N1`
7. b `N3`
8. d `N5`
9. d `N4`

3   BAD DATE

1. was sitting `N3`
2. was talking `N3`
3. waited / was waiting `N1`
4. was playing / played `N4`
5. was locking `N3`
6. suggested `N1`
7. said `N5`
8. started `N1`

4   EDITING: GOOD NEWS

Hi Nancy,

    I'm writing to let you know that Melissa and I just celebrated seven months of dating, and she is so perfect for me. Thank you for matching us up!

    Last night, I ~~propose~~ *proposed* to Melissa, and she ~~says~~ *said* `N1` yes! My hand was shaking while I ~~holding~~ *held / was holding* `N3` out the ring, and Melissa was ~~cry~~ *crying* `N4`. We were both very emotional! When I woke up this morning, I ~~decide~~ *decided* `N5` to tell you the good news first. We are two very happy people because of you.

Thank you,
Pietro

Unit 3 Achievement Test

1 | LISTENING: ITALIAN COOK

A.
1. haven't had `N2`
2. did . . . learn `N1`
3. 've been cooking `N2`
4. Did . . . live `N1`
5. 've cooked `N2`
6. Have . . . thought `N5`

B.
1. F `N2`
2. F `N1`
3. T `N1`
4. T `N2`
5. T `N2`

2 | IRENE BARROW—AN ARTIST

1. T `N6`
2. F `N6`
3. F `N1`
4. T `N1`
5. T `N6`
6. F `N6`
7. T `N2`
8. F `N2`

3 | CAR LOVER

Note: Both contracted and noncontracted forms are acceptable.
1. has lived / has been living `N2`
2. has fixed `N5`
3. opened `N4`
4. have seen `N5`
5. expanded `N4`
6. has been doing / has done `N3`

4 | EDITING: POSTCARD FROM ISTANBUL

Note: Both contracted and noncontracted forms are acceptable.

Hi Roger,

I've ~~sightseed~~ *been sightseeing* in Istanbul for the past week, and it ~~was~~ *'s been* `N2` wonderful! On Saturday, I ~~have visited~~ *visited* `N1` the Hagia Sofia. Then on Monday, ~~I've been spending~~ *I spent* `N3` about three hours at the Rumeli Fortress. The food here is amazing! I ~~ate~~ *'ve been eating / 've eaten* `N2` dolma almost every day since I arrived. I ~~don't find~~ *haven't found / didn't find* `N2` a flying carpet for you yet, but I'm still looking!

Linda

Unit 4 Achievement Test

1 | LISTENING: GARDENING FOR LIFE

A.
1. Had . . . been `N1`
2. had come `N1`
3. had . . . been selling `N2`
4. had . . . planned `N5`
5. had . . . worked `N1`

B.
1. F `N1`
2. T `N6`
3. F `N7`
4. T `N4`

2 | NEW JOB

1. had shopped `N1`
2. had arrived `N1`
3. had . . . had `N5`
4. had . . . managed `N4`
5. had been working / had worked `N4`
6. had . . . relaxed `N7`
7. hadn't felt `N1`

3 | A MUSIC CAREER

Note: Both contracted and noncontracted forms are acceptable.
1. had not yet started `N5`
2. had not yet released `N5`
3. had already gotten `N5`
4. had already won `N5`
5. had not yet gone `N5`
6. had already starred `N5`
7. had already had `N5`
8. had not yet bought `N5`

4 | EDITING: A COMEDIAN'S START

   In 2004, moviegoers first enjoyed the unique humor of actor Steven Wall in the comedy hit *Farmland*. They were amazed to learn that Wall ^*had* actually been a high school math teacher before his first film role. His students already knew that he was a funny teacher, but they hadn't ~~imagine~~ *imagined* `N2` him as the next big name in comedy.

   Wall was born in Ontario, Canada, in 1974. His father was a mathematician, and by the time Wall was 10, his father ^*had* `N7` taught Wall most major mathematical formulas. But Wall never really liked math, even though he was good at it; he liked to make people laugh! At age 25, Wall began to write comedy and to appear in Ontario comedy clubs (by then, he had already been ~~teach~~ *teaching* `N7` for three years). In 2003, Wall starred in a local television commercial, which made him hugely popular in Ontario. Before the commercial, Wall had ~~struggling~~ *been struggling / struggled* `N4` to start his comedy career. A movie producer saw the commercial, and knew immediately that he *had* found the star for *Farmland*. **N1**

At that time, Wall's hopes had finally ~~being~~ *been* **N1** realized.

PART I Achievement test

1 | LISTENING: A NEW EDITOR IN CHIEF

A.
1. started **U3**
2. earned **U3**
3. had published **U4**
4. were failing **U2**
5. fell **U3**
6. wrote **U3**
7. had written **U4**
8. is . . . living **U1**
9. intends **U1**
10. has **U1**
11. works **U1**

B.
1. T **U4**
2. F **U3**
3. T **U4**
4. T **U4**
5. F **U3**
6. F **U1**
7. F **U3**
8. T **U1**

2 | A GROWING FAMILY

1. b **U2**
2. b **U2**
3. d **U2**
4. a **U3**
5. a **U4**
6. c **U3**
7. d **U4**
8. c **U3**
9. b **U4**
10. a **U4**
11. d **U3**
12. c **U1**
13. c **U1**
14. a **U3**
15. c **U1**
16. b **U1**
17. b **U1**
18. d **U3**

3 | MOTORCYCLE BLUES

Note: Both contracted and noncontracted forms are acceptable.
1. 'm . . . walking / was . . . walking **U1**
2. Don't . . . ride **U1**
3. took **U3**
4. was making / made / has been making / had been making **U2**
5. had broken / broke **U4**
6. 'd been struggling / have been struggling / was struggling / struggled **U4**
7. decided / had decided **U2**
8. 've been debating / have debated **U3**
9. haven't saved / haven't been saving **U3**
10. have tried / tried **U4**
11. have **U1**
12. want **U1**

4 | WANTED: GUITARIST

Note: Both contracted and noncontracted forms are acceptable.
1. 've played / played **U3**
2. helped **U2**
3. started **U3**
4. had released / released **U4**
5. traveled **U3**
6. weren't selling / didn't sell **U2**
7. had been taking / was taking / took **U4**
8. do . . . want **U1**
9. had read / read **U4**
10. liked **U2**
11. need **U1**
12. 're doing / do **U1**

5 | EDITING: OVERNIGHT SUCCESS

The first album by the band Spinal Column has been ~~rise~~ *rising* to the top of the charts. Their funky sound ~~had broken~~ *has broken / breaks / is breaking* **U3** the rules of contemporary pop music, and their distinctive style is quickly ~~makes~~ *making* **U1** Spinal Column a household name. The new album ~~is going~~ *went / had gone* **U2** on sale last month, it and ~~had selling~~ *had been selling / was selling / sold* **U4** poorly in the first two weeks until the band appeared on *The Nightly Show*. Their appearance ~~had been changed~~ *changed / has changed* **U3** the course of the band's success. It ~~happen~~ *happened* **U3** quickly: A talent scout from *The Nightly Show* ~~had be shopping~~ *had been shopping / was shopping* **U4** downtown when he ~~hears~~ *heard* **U2** music from the new album coming from one of the shops. Before the end of the day, he ~~had book~~ *had booked / booked* **U4** Spinal Column for their appearance on the show.

PART II Diagnostic Test

1 | LISTENING: DAILY LIFE IN THE FUTURE

A.
1. will you travel **U5**
2. are you going to see **U5**
3. 'll be learning **U5**
4. will have been washed **U6**
5. won't be driving **U5**
6. will have been breathing **U6**
7. will have experienced **U6**
8. will never have been **U6**
9. will have enjoyed **U6**
10. will change **U5**

B.

Note: Both contracted and noncontracted forms are acceptable.

Future verbs	Future perfect verbs
1. will go **U5**	6. will have . . . been
2. 'll put **U5**	prepared **U6**
3. 'll ride **U5**	7. won't have gotten **U6**
4. will drive **U5**	8. will have learned **U6**
5. 'll eat **U5**	9. will . . . have visited **U6**

2 | NEW TECHNOLOGY MUSEUM

1. b **U6**
2. d **U5**
3. a **U6**
4. c **U5**
5. a **U5**
6. c **U5**
7. d **U6**
8. b **U5**

3 | CLASS PRESENTATION

Note: Will or forms of be can be used instead of contractions in answers.

1. 're going to do / 'll do **U5**
2. 'll check out / 'm going to check out **U5**
3. 'll have read / 'll read / 'm going to read **U6**
4. 'll have written / 'll write / 'm going to write **U6**
5. 'll look for / 'm going to look for / 'll be looking for / 'm going to be looking for **U5**
6. 'll summarize / 'm going to summarize / 'll be summarizing / 'm going to be summarizing **U6**
7. 'll give / 'm going to give **U5**
8. meet **U5**
9. 'll have finished / 'll finish / 'm going to finish **U6**
10. 'll practice / 're going to practice **U5**
11. 'll practice / 're going to practice / 'll have practiced **U6**

4 | TODAY

Note: Both contracted and noncontracted forms are acceptable.

1. 'll have walked **U6**
2. 'll mow / 'll be mowing / 's going to mow / 's going to be mowing **U5**
3. will have been doing **U6**
4. 'll make / 'll be making / 's going to make / 's going to be making **U5**
5. 'll have gone shopping **U5**
6. 'll wash / 'll be washing / 's going to wash / 's going to be washing **U5**
7. 'll have been washing **U6**

8. 'll have washed **U6**
9. 'll have been reading **U6**
10. 'll have picked up **U6**
11. 'll eat / 'll be eating / 's going to eat / 's going to be eating **U5**
12. 'll have eaten **U6**

5 | EDITING: END-OF-SEMESTER EVENT

Comedian will ~~visits~~ *visit* campus!

By the end of the semester, you will have ~~study~~ *studied* **U6** too much and ~~laughs~~ *laughed* **U6** too little. Comedian Jeff Foster ~~had helped~~ *will help / is going to help* **U5** bring fun back into your life. Foster ~~will have gave~~ *will be giving / will give / is going to give / is going to be giving* **U5** a free show this coming Saturday at 6:00. After his comedy show, he'll ~~speaking~~ *speak / be speaking* **U5** about the benefits of humor. The first 50 people to arrive ~~received~~ *will receive / will be receiving / are going to receive* **U5** free tickets to City Comedy Club. Everyone ~~will be having~~ *will have / is going to have* **U5** a chance to win tickets to Foster's television show. We ~~have given~~ *will be giving / will give / are going to give / are going to be giving* **U5** away free hotdogs. Foster's performance ~~will be begin~~ *will begin / is going to begin/begins* **U5** the end-of-semester activities on campus. By the end of the week, we ~~have been having~~ *will have had* **U6** four other comedy performances, and you will have had an opportunity to relax.

Unit 5 Achievement Test

1 | LISTENING: A FUTURE NEWSCAST

1. will be traveling **N2**
2. arrives **chart**
3. will take **N3**
4. learn **N3**
5. will be enjoying **N2**
6. will plan **N1c**
7. will spend **N1c**
8. will be sending **N2**

2 | SPACE CARS

1. b **N1a**	6. c **N1a**
2. d **N2**	7. c **N1a**
3. a **N2**	8. a **N2**
4. b **N2**	9. d **N2**
5. a **chart**	

3 | COMET X

1. Will . . . be / Are . . . going to be (N1)
2. 'll be / 're going to be (N1)
3. won't come (N1) / isn't going to come (N1) / won't be coming (N2) / isn't going to be coming (N2)
4. will be watching / are going to be watching (N2)
5. Will . . . invite / Are . . . going to invite / Will . . . be inviting / Are . . . going to be inviting (N2)
6. won't, aren't (N1)
7. will be moving / is going to be moving (N2)
8. 'll be measuring / 're going to be measuring (N2)

4 | EDITING: COMET X MESSAGE BOARD

Note: Both contracted and noncontracted forms are acceptable.

    will be traveling
    I ~~travel~~ to Auckland next week, and I am concerned about the comet passing so close to
will be / is going to be (N1a)
Earth. I wonder if it ~~will being~~ safe to travel when
        is it (N3)
the comet passes by. How close ~~it is~~ going to get to Earth? With our current technology, are we
 to (N chart)
going ^ be able to get an exact measurement?
          will check / will be checking /
 will we (N1) *am going to be checking* (N1)
Where ~~we will~~ be safest? I ~~check~~ the message board later this week for any warnings or advice.

Joe

Unit 6 Achievement Test

1 | LISTENING: A NEWS REPORT

1. will have been walking (N2)
2. will have been singing (N2)
3. will have taken (N1)
4. will have burned (N1)
5. will not have slept (chart)
6. will have sung (N1)
7. will have broken (N3)
8. won't have broken (N1)
9. will have already earned (N4)
10. will he have found (N3)

2 | BIG DREAMS

Note: Both contracted and noncontracted forms are acceptable.

A.

1. He will not have sold 1,000 computers (N1)
2. he will have bought a sports car (N1)
3. he will have gone to the dentist (N1)
4. He will not have opened a computer store (N1)
5. he will have bought his first house (N1)

B.

1. T (N1)   4. F (N1)
2. T (N1)   5. F (N1)
3. F (N1)   6. T (N1)

3 | EDITING: A NEW CAREER

Note: Both contracted and noncontracted forms are acceptable.

          been
    By August, I will have ^ working as a janitor
      been earning / earned (N2)
for five years. I'll have ~~been earned~~ the same
               have (N1)
amount of money each year, and I won't ^ saved
    have (N2)
very much. I'll ^ been living in the same apartment for five years, too. So I've decided to become a
          arrives (N3)
mechanic instead! By the time spring ~~will arrive~~,
    decided (N1)
I will have ~~decide~~ where to apply, and I will
    applied (N1)
have ~~applies~~ to different auto shops. By summer,
will (N1)
I ^ have gotten job offers, and I will have
    started (N1)
~~been starting~~ my new career. But before doing
          have (N1)
anything, I have to ask myself, will I ^ made a change for the better?

PART II Achievement Test

1 | LISTENING: DATING IN THE FUTURE

A.

1. will they meet (U5)
2. going to change (U5)
3. 'll have received (U6)
4. 'll be dating (U5)
5. 'll have been spending (U6)
6. won't have spoken (U6)
7. will have experienced (U6)
8. won't have felt (U6)
9. 'll never have been (U6)
10. will have enjoyed (U6)
11. will have had (U6)

B.

The chart includes all possible answers. Students only need to find the number listed at the top of the column.

Future verbs (4)
will go [U5]
'll register [U5]
'll choose [U5]
'll have [U5]
will . . . result [U5]
will tell [U5]

Future perfect verbs (4)
'll have saved [U6]
will never have gone out [U6]
will have met [U6]
will . . . have visited [U6]

---

2 | A NEW SCHOOL

1. b [U6]
2. d [U5]
3. a [U6]
4. b [U5]
5. a [U5]
6. c [U5]
7. d [U6]
8. b [U5]
9. a [U6]

---

3 | BUSINESS PRESENTATION

Note: Both contracted and noncontracted forms are acceptable.

1. 're going to do / 'll do [U5]
2. 'll read / 'm going to read [U5]
3. 'll have finished / 'll finish / 'm going to finish [U6]
4. 'll have written / 'll write / 'm going to write [U6]
5. 'll call / 'm going to call [U5]
6. 'll have summarized / 'll summarize / 'm going to summarize [U6]
7. 'll give / 'm going to give [U5]
8. meet [U5]
9. 'll have completed / 'll complete / 'm going to complete [U6]
10. will . . . practice / are . . . going to practice [U5]
11. 'll have / 'll have had / 're going to have / have [U5]

---

4 | TOMORROW

Note: Both contracted and noncontracted forms are acceptable.

1. 'll be working / 's going to be working [U5]
2. 'll have met / 'll have been meeting [U6]
3. 'll have been shopping [U6]
4. 'll have / 'll be having / 's going to have / 's going to be having [U5]
5. 'll be writing / 's going to be writing [U5]
6. 'll talk / 'll be talking / 's going to talk / 's going to be talking [U6]
7. 'll have been talking / 'll have talked [U6]
8. 'll have talked [U6]
9. 'll be paying / 's going to be paying [U5]
10. 'll go / 'll be going / 's going to go / 's going to be going [U5]
11. 'll have eaten [U6]

---

5 | EDITING: EMPLOYEE APPRECIATION DAY

The company will ~~celebrates~~ *celebrate* employee appreciation day this Friday!

By the end of the week, you will have ~~work~~ *worked* [U6] too much and relaxed too little. Meditation expert James Clark ~~had helped~~ *will help / is going to help* [U5] to bring balance back into your life. Clark will ~~be lead~~ *lead / be leading* [U5] a free meditation workshop this coming Friday at 4:00 P.M. Before teaching us how to meditate, he'll ~~speaking~~ *speak / be speaking* [U5] about the benefits of relaxation. The first 10 people to arrive to the workshop ~~had received~~ *will receive / will be receiving / are going to receive* [U5] free tickets to a health spa. All employees will ~~be having~~ *have* [U5] a chance to win a certificate for a free massage. After Clark's workshop, we ~~began~~ *will begin / are going to begin / begin* [U5] the employee office party at 7:30. By then we will have been ~~sit~~ *sitting* [U6] for hours, so be prepared to dance. We will ~~offering~~ *be offering / offer* [U5] free sushi, and a band will ~~have played~~ *be playing / play* [U5] as well. Join us!

PART III Diagnostic Test

1 | LISTENING: DINNER WITH FRIENDS

1. c [U8]
2. a [U8]
3. b [U7]
4. b [U7]
5. a [U8]
6. c [U8]
7. c [U7]

---

2 | BEST FRIENDS

C.

1. F [U8]
2. F [U8]
3. T [U8]
4. T [U8]
5. F [U8]
6. F [U8]
7. F [U7]
8. T [U7]
9. F [U7]
10. T [U7]

D.

Negative tags	Affirmative tags
1. isn't it **U7**	3. can you **U7**
2. isn't he **U7**	4. would you **U7**

3 | MEETING A FRIEND

1. c **U8**
2. a **U8**
3. c **U8**
4. a **U8**
5. d **U8**
6. b **U8**
7. d **U8**

4 | DOING WELL

1. can I **U8**
2. did you **U7**
3. isn't it **U7**
4. isn't **U8**
5. I'm **U8**
6. are they **U7**
7. I do **U8**
8. haven't we **U7**
9. do **U7**

5 | CATHY AND NATALIE

1. but Natalie isn't **U8**
2. but Cathy doesn't **U8**
3. and so does Cathy OR and Cathy does too **U8**
4. and neither does Cathy OR and Cathy doesn't either **U8**
5. and neither has Natalie OR and Natalie hasn't either **U8**
6. but Natalie didn't **U8**
7. and so does Cathy OR and Cathy does too **U8**
8. but Natalie isn't **U8**
9. but Cathy doesn't **U8**

6 | LIFE OF A STAR

1. Haven't you been living / Haven't you lived in California since graduating from high school? **U7**
2. Didn't you grow up in Iowa? **U7**
3. Haven't you always loved R&B? **U7**
4. Wasn't your work too extreme for them / DreamField Studio? **U7**
5. Didn't you like *Adventureland* better? **U7**
6. Didn't you just start your own company? OR Haven't you just started your own company? **U7**
7. Aren't you opening an organic French restaurant? **U7**

7 | EDITING: SANDY'S DATE

Dear Diary,
    This evening I went on my first date with David. What a funny, handsome guy! It's funny how you sometimes "click" with someone, ~~is~~ isn't it? For the most part, I feel I really clicked with David. We have so much in common! For example, he likes classical music and so ~~am~~ do I. **U8** I love old movies, and he ~~is~~ does too. **U8** Both of us read every day, but I don't read fiction, and ~~either~~ neither does **U8** he. But although we are similar in many ways, in other ways we ~~are~~ aren't / are not. **U7** David likes fast food, but I ~~am~~ don't. **U8** (~~Isn't~~ Doesn't **U8** he realize how bad fast food is for him?) He doesn't work out regularly, but I work out every day. All in all, I feel pretty good about the date. I hope we go out again. I guess time will tell, ~~will~~ won't **U7** it?

Unit 7 Achievement Test

1 | LISTENING: NEW FRIENDS

1. c **N4**
2. a **N5**
3. a **N4**
4. b **N1**

2 | CITY LIVING

1. e **N1**
2. c **N1**
3. f **N1**
4. a **N1**
5. b **N1**
6. h **N1**
7. g **N1**

3 | A TV INTERVIEW

1. Didn't you **N1**
2. doesn't it **N3**
3. haven't you **N3**
4. don't they **N3**
5. they do **N6**
6. Yes, I do **N6**
7. isn't it **N1**

4 | LIFE OF A STAR

1. Didn't you grow up in Reno? **N2**
2. Haven't you always loved short stories? **N2**
3. Weren't the topics in the stories too controversial? **N2**
4. Didn't you like the book better? **N2**
5. Didn't you just open your own writing school? OR Haven't you just opened your own writing school? **N2**

5 | EDITING: BANK ROBBERY

NICK: You stole the money from the bank, ~~haven't~~ *didn't* you?

LEE: I don't think banks miss money. They have enough, don't ~~that~~ *they*? **N3**

NICK: If it's not yours, you can't take it. ~~Doesn't~~ *Don't* **N2** you know right from wrong?

LEE: Yes, I ~~don't~~ *do* **N2**. But I need the money and they will never notice, will they?

NICK: Of course they will. In fact, the missing money has already been reported on TV. ~~Doesn't~~ *Don't* **N2** you think you should turn yourself in?

LEE: No. But I'm leaving town tonight. I just need you to tell the police you haven't seen me.

NICK: I can't do that. I can't afford to get in trouble with the police. You know that, ~~do~~ *don't* **N5.3** you?

LEE: Yes, I guess that's true. You can't even help me hide, can you?

NICK: ~~Yes, I can.~~ *No, I can't* **N6**. There is no way for me to help you hide. Don't ~~I~~ *you* **N1** understand?

Unit 8 Achievement Test

1 | LISTENING: NEW FRIENDS

1. b **N1**   4. a **N1**
2. c **N1**   5. a **N6**
3. b **N1**

2 | A TRUE STORY

1. T **N4**   5. T **N2**
2. T **N1**   6. F **N2**
3. F **N2**   7. F **N5**
4. T **N2**   8. F **N4**

3 | THERE'S MY DINNER!

1. neither **N7**
2. can I **N5**
3. I do **N7**
4. you do **N7**
5. do I **N5**

4 | PARK AND KUMAR

1. and neither does Park OR and Park doesn't either **N2**
2. and so does Kumar OR and Kumar does too **N2**

3. but Park doesn't **N4**
4. but Park isn't **N4**
5. and so does Park OR and Park does too **N2**
6. and neither does Park OR and Park doesn't either **N1**
7. and neither has Kumar OR and Kumar hasn't either **N1**
8. but Kumar isn't **N4**

5 | EDITING: BEST FRIENDS

My Best Friend Lindsay

Lindsay is younger than I ~~is~~ *am*. However, we look alike. I have curly blonde hair and dark blue eyes, and so ~~have~~ *does/has* **N5** she. We share some of the same interests too. I love to talk and hang out with friends, and she does too. Both of us play piano, but I can't play guitar, and ~~either~~ *neither* **N3** can she. There are also some differences between my friend Lindsay and me. For example, she likes eating Chinese food, but I don't. She doesn't want to be a movie star, but I ~~don't~~ *do* **N4**. I am creative, but she ~~not~~ *is not/isn't* **N4**. Our appearance makes us seem similar, but once you get to know us, we seem quite different.

PART III Achievement Test

1 | LISTENING: DINNER WITH FRIENDS

1. c **U8**
2. b **U8**
3. c **U7**
4. b **U7**
5. a **U8**
6. b **U8**
7. a **U7**

2 | MEETING FRIENDS

A.

1. F **U8**   7. T **U8**
2. T **U8**   8. T **U8**
3. F **U8**   9. F **U7**
4. T **U8**   10. T **U7**
5. T **U8**   11. T **U7**
6. F **U8**

B.

Negative tag questions (2)
1. don't you **U7**
2. didn't you **U7**

Affirmative tag questions (2)
3. are you **U7**
4. can you **U7**

3 | PIANO SISTERS

1. b U8
2. a U8
3. d U8
4. b U8
5. a U8

4 | FRIENDS ARE TALKING

1. did you U7
2. wasn't it U7
3. haven't they U7
4. don't you U7
5. do I U8
6. too U8
7. I do U8
8. hasn't it U7
9. do U8

5 | BROOKE AND LORENA

1. but Lorena isn't U8
2. but Brooke doesn't U8
3. and so does Brooke OR and Brooke does too U8
4. and neither does Brooke OR and Brooke doesn't either U8
5. but Brooke isn't U8
6. and neither has Lorena OR and Lorena hasn't either U8
7. and so does Brooke OR and Brooke does too U8
8. but Lorena isn't U8
9. and so does Brooke OR and Brooke does too U8

6 | LIFE OF A DOCTOR

1. Weren't you named after a famous poet? OR Aren't you named after a famous poet? U7
2. Didn't you grow up in Minnesota? U7
3. Haven't you always loved science? U7
4. Wasn't your first interest children's medicine? U7
5. Didn't you dislike working in an emergency room? U7
6. Didn't you just open your own office? OR Haven't you just opened your own office? U7
7. Aren't you planning on publishing a book on family medicine? U7

7 | EDITING: MIMI'S FRIEND

Dear Diary,
Sometimes I forget about people from my past. That probably happens to everyone, ~~does~~ *doesn't* it? I don't want to forget people—especially my friend Debbie. She is just a year older than I am, and we look a lot alike. People sometimes confuse us, but our boyfriends ~~doesn't~~ *don't*. U8 I have straight, brown hair

and light blue eyes, and so ~~have~~ *has/does* U8 she. We share some of the same interests too. I love dancing and musicals, and she ~~did~~ *does* U8 too. Both of us cook every day, but I don't cook meat, and ~~either~~ *neither* U8 does she. Although there are a lot of similarities between us, there are also some differences. That's not too surprising, ~~isn't~~ *is* U7 it? For example, she likes shopping, but I ~~do~~ *don't*. U8 I like to talk on the phone, but she ~~did~~ *doesn't*. U8 Luckily, we both love writing e-mails. That'll make it easy for us to keep in touch, and I won't forget her, ~~won't~~ *will* U7 I?

PART IV Diagnostic Test

1 | LISTENING: A CAREER IN FITNESS

1. opening U9
2. to help U10
3. work out U10
4. to meet U10
5. Adding U9
6. get U10
7. let U10
8. decide U10

2 | FITNESS TRAINING

1. b U10
2. c U10
3. c U9
4. a U10
5. d U10
6. b U10
7. a U10
8. b U9
9. d U10

3 | TEEN ZONE

1. watching U9
2. talking U9
3. working U9
4. to learn U9
5. to be U9
6. to have U9
7. to pay / paying U9
8. to take / taking U9
9. Getting U9
10. to listen U9
11. to respect / respect U9

4 | AN AMBITION

1. interviewing U9
2. to spend / spending U9
3. Inventing U9
4. tasting U9
5. supervising U9
6. to make U9
7. become / to become U10
8. create U10

9. design **U10**
10. to print **U9**
11. achieve / to achieve **U9**

5 | AN ADVERTISEMENT

A.
1. exploring **U9**
2. walking **U9**
3. sharing **U9**
4. bringing **U9**
5. to help **U9**
6. to join **U9**
7. volunteering **U9**
8. to participate **U9**

B.
1. to meet **U10**
2. to find / find **U10**
3. participate **U10**

6 | EDITING: LEARNING TO DANCE

To the Editors,

Yesterday, my roommate persuaded me ~~joining~~ *to join* a dancing club. I didn't really want ~~going~~ *to go* **U9** because I thought a dancing club would make you ~~doing~~ *do* **U10** only aerobic dance. I am not good at ~~hear~~ *hearing* **U9** rhythm. However, ~~be~~ *being* **U9** at the club changed my mind. I learned other forms of dancing that I didn't know before. Many people, like me, think they can't dance because they have poor coordination, but anyone can dance. The main purpose is to enjoy moving to music, so ~~to~~ dancing **U9** is suitable for people of all ages. As with most activities, it's a matter of ~~start~~ *starting* **U9** gently and ~~to build~~ *building* **U9** up to the right level of activity. So I invite you all ~~finding~~ *to find* **U9** some some time ~~enjoy~~ *to enjoy* **U9** yourselves by ~~to dance~~ *dancing* **U9**.

Unit 9 Achievement Test

1 | LISTENING: FOOD MATTERS

1. to go **N2**
2. to shop **N8**
3. buying **N5**
4. to find **N2**
5. sharing **N5**
6. to come **N2**
7. cooking **N5**

2 | TO PLAN OR NOT TO PLAN

1. to buy **N3**
2. building / to build **N4**
3. Referring **N1**
4. to organize / organizing **N4**
5. to plan **N3**
6. arranging **N5**

3 | A PERSUASIVE TEACHER

1. urges me to write down **N3**
2. persuaded me to do **N3**
3. look forward to talking **N5**
4. asked my friend George to help **N3**
5. are happy about her suggesting **N2**

4 | A FOOD FAIR

1. to see **N3**
2. decorating **N5**
3. tasting **N2**
4. eating **N2**
5. to go **N3**

5 | EDITING: STAYING IN PLACE, STAYING FIT

You don't need ~~leaving~~ *to leave* the house to stay fit. With a bit of thought, everyday tasks can keep you trim. Here's our list of the top four tips for ~~stay~~ *staying* **N5** fit in your own home.

Tip 1: ~~To dry~~ *Drying* **N1** off after a hot shower is a great time ~~doing~~ *to do* **N7** some simple shoulder stretches. Begin by ~~to hold~~ *holding* **N5** the towel. Then, still holding the towel with both hands, place one hand behind your back and the other above your head. With the top arm, pull upwards so your other arm ends up between your shoulder blades. Hold for 10–15 seconds and then change arms.

Tip 2: If you're a tall person, you probably know that bending down to do the dishes isn't good for your back. Instead, simply stand with your legs wide apart to ~~lowering~~ *lower* **N8** your body and arms. This position keeps your back straighter. Unfortunately, it means you won't have an excuse to keep you from ~~wash~~ *washing* **N5** dishes!

Tip 3: Forget the gym. If you want strong leg muscles, then all you need are some stairs. Simply climb the stairs 10 times a day to work the muscles. After three weeks, you should start to notice a difference.

Tip 4: Keep ~~to do~~ *doing* **N2** your exercises. If you want to stay fit, don't give up.

Unit 10 Achievement Test

1 | LISTENING: A DOCUMENTARY

1. lets us choose **N1**
2. Let me read **N1**
3. letting us search for **N1**
4. made us watch **N1**
5. makes me feel **N1**
6. help you get **N1**
7. get me to think **N3**
8. Let me know **N1**

2 | AT THE ZOO

1. b N1
2. a N2
3. d N1
4. b N1
5. c N1

3 | AT AN ANIMAL CLINIC

1. helped her (to) describe N2
2. got another assistant to type N3
3. had her wait N1
4. had Dr. Banda explain N1
5. help her (to) find N2

4 | CAMPUS CONVERSATIONS

1. get our university to arrange / help our university (to) arrange / let our university arrange / have our university arrange N3
2. had us prepare / made us prepare N1
3. have my sister groom / make my sister groom / let my sister groom / get my sister to groom N1
4. get him to enter / make him enter / have him enter N3

5 | EDITING: A WILD VISITOR

Hey Dina,

   I have an exciting experience to share with you. Last week I saw a deer come into my

backyard. It made my daughter ~~yelling~~ *yell* when she saw it while she was playing in the yard. I hurried

to get my child to ~~coming~~ *come* N3 into the house and then called the police. Two policemen from Animal Control came right away. One policeman, Officer

Malloy, had his partner, Officer Perez, ~~to~~ chase the N1 deer into the corner of the yard. Then they helped

each other ~~catching~~ *to catch/catch* N2 the deer. Officer Malloy had

Officer Perez ~~threw~~ *throw* N1 a rope around the deer's neck.

Of course, this made the deer ~~to~~ try to run away. N1

But they held on to it and had it ~~walks~~ *walk* N1 to their

van. Officer Malloy helped Officer Perez ~~putting~~ N2 the deer in a cage. I don't know what they're

going to do with it. Hopefully, they'll let it ~~to~~ go N1 back to a national park.

Take care,
Susan

PART IV   Achievement Test

1 | LISTENING: PET'S HEALTH

1. believing U9
2. achieve U10
3. to function U9
4. preventing U9
5. healing U9
6. finding U9
7. to look U9
8. to care U10

2 | DOG FOOD

1. d U9
2. b U9
3. c U10
4. b U9
5. a U9
6. a U9
7. c U9
8. a U9
9. d U9

3 | A TEEN CONCERT

1. to get U9
2. to see U9
3. to help U9
4. to be U9
5. (to) sing U10
6. performing U9
7. sing / singing U10
8. to believe U9
9. claiming U9
10. to stay U9
11. change U10

4 | A COOL CAREER

1. listening / to listen U9
2. stopping U9
3. fighting U9
4. do U9
5. to become U9
6. to help U9
7. find / to find U10
8. (to) track U10
9. (to) locate U10
10. to have U9
11. to consider U9

5 | AN ADVERTISEMENT

A.
1. to create U9
2. smile U10
3. gaining U9
4. listening U9
5. trying U9
6. Bringing U9
7. to locate U9
8. to make U9

B.
1. (to) keep U10
2. to buy U10
3. produce U10

6 | EDITING: JOB INTERVIEW ADVICE

Dear Editor,

   My name is Carole Ford. I would like *to* ^share my experience about job interviews. I've interviewed for many jobs and most companies offered me the positions I wanted. Interviewing well is not difficult ~~achieving~~ *to achieve* **U9**. I have many useful

stories and tips ∧*to* **U10** pass along. First, did you know that some companies are looking for people

~~solving~~ *to solve* **U9** their problems? They will hire you if they

truly believe that you have the skills ~~helping~~ *to help* **U9** them. In an interview, if your answer is too brief, you

may leave your interviewer unsatisfied. ~~Talk~~ *Talking* **U9** too much during an interview will make your

interviewer ~~wanting~~ *want* **U10** to get rid of you, even if you

ARE the best candidate for the job. ~~Give~~ *Giving* **U9** answers

that you think the interviewer wants ~~hearing~~ *to hear* **U9** may cause a stressful and unsatisfying interview. A job interview is an intimidating process, and even the most self-confident, outgoing, and friendly person

can easily give the impression of ~~to be~~ *being* **U9** tongue-tied and incompetent. The best solution to this

common problem is ~~come~~ *to come/coming* **U9** to the interview prepared, knowing exactly what to expect.

PART V Diagnostic Test

1 | LISTENING: STUDY HABITS

A.
1. off **U11/U12**
2. along **U11/U12**
3. up **U11/U12**
4. to **U11/U12**
5. up with **U11/U12**

B.
1. set up **U11/U12**
2. figure out **U11/U12**
3. let down **U11/U12**
4. show up **U11/U12**
5. turn down **U11/U12**

2 | FRIENDSHIP

Phrasal verb
1. tears down **U11/U12**
2. cut off **U11/U12**
3. brings down **U11/U12**
4. cheers up **U11/U12**
5. pick out **U11/U12**
6. run into **U11/U12**
7. light up **U11/U12**
8. find out **U11/U12**

Direct object
1. people **U11/U12**
2. all contact **U11/U12**
3. people **U11/U12**
4. them **U11/U12**
5. good qualities **U11/U12**
6. them **U11/U12**
7. (no d.o.) **U11/U12**
8. the importance of your friendships **U11/U12**

3 | A ROBBERY

1. I **U11/U12**
2. I **U11/U12**
3. S **U11/U12**
4. S **U11/U12**
5. S **U11/U12**
6. I **U11/U12**
7. I **U11/U12**
8. I **U11/U12**

4 | A DREAM COME TRUE

1. go after / take on **U11/U12**
2. grew up **U11/U12**
3. put . . . off **U11/U12**
4. take on / go after **U11/U12**
5. found out **U11/U12**
6. fight off **U11/U12**
7. took off **U11/U12**
8. set up **U11/U12**
9. put on **U11/U12**
10. keep . . . on **U11/U12**
11. give up **U11/U12**
12. looked up **U11/U12**
13. took in **U11/U12**
14. paid off **U11/U12**
15. ended up with **U11/U12**
16. came down **U11/U12**
17. go back **U11/U12**
18. thought . . . over **U11/U12**

5 | PREPARING FOR A PARTY

1. picked them up **U11/U12**
2. cut them down **U11/U12**
3. put them away **U11/U12**
4. turned it over **U11/U12**
5. covered it up **U11/U12**
6. took it out **U11/U12**
7. threw it out **U11/U12**
8. straightened it up **U11/U12**
9. put them up **U11/U12**

6 | EDITING: NEW TV

DIEGO: Did the TV arrive today?

LUISA: Yes, and I tried ~~out it~~ *it out* **U11/U12**. I turned it ~~in~~ *on* **U11/U12**, but I couldn't hear anything. So I turned ~~away~~ *up* **U11/U12** the volume as high as it would go, but I still couldn't hear anything. So I called the company. I was on hold for an hour, so I hung ~~off~~ *up* **U11/U12**. I even tried to look ~~out~~ *up* **U11/U12** information on the Internet, but I couldn't come up ∧*with* **U11/U12** any reason ~~with~~ why the sound didn't work. So I turned ~~off it~~ *it off* **U11/U12**, and I'm planning to send ~~back it~~ *it back* **U11/U12** today.

DIEGO: That's too bad!

Unit 11　Achievement Test

1 | LISTENING: JOB HUNTING

A.
1. up N5
2. up N4
3. over N4
4. into N5
5. over N4
6. out N5
7. up N4
8. back N4
9. off N5

B.
1. T N2
2. F N2
3. F N2
4. T N2
5. F N2
6. F N2

2 | JOB HUNTING MESSAGE BOARD

1. down N1
2. over N3
3. out N3
4. out N3
5. together N3
6. on N3
7. on N5
8. down N1
9. ahead N2
10. down N5
11. out N3

3 | EDITING: A NEW JOB

Now that I've moved into my new office, I

                                     up
have so much to do! First, I need to straighten ~~away~~
my old office. Second, I have to clean up all my

               them away N4
papers and throw ~~away them~~. Also, I should take

out the garbage / the garbage out N1
~~over the garbage~~. Then, I need to take down my

                       it up N4
picture in the old office and hang ~~up it~~ in the new

                    up N1
one. Finally, I need to put ~~around~~ some shelves.

Unit 12　Achievement Test

1 | LISTENING: A FAKE CONTEST

1. F N1
2. F N1
3. T N1
4. F N4
5. F N4
6. T N1
7. T N1
8. F N5
9. T N1

2 | DIET AND EXERCISE

1. watch out for N4
2. end up with N4
3. write down N1
4. turn up N1
5. get off N2
6. stick to N2
7. come up with N4
8. turn down N1
9. fill up on N4

3 | IN THE BOOKSTORE

1. pass it up N1
2. put it down N1
3. take them off N1
4. keep them on N3
5. write it down N1
6. throw it away N1

4 | EDITING: CAR DEALERSHIP AD

               in on
    Cash ~~on in~~ this sale of a lifetime! Come to Car

                  out N1
World and check ~~up~~ our new line of cards. Keep

  with N4
up ~~to~~ the newest technology and buy a new model.

           you back N1
We'll give ~~back you~~ $1,000 in cash. We'll even

    up N1
fill ~~on~~ your gas tank for the first month, FREE!

                 on us N2
You can always count ~~us on~~ for good deals. You

                    down N1
can't turn this opportunity ~~up~~!

PART V　Achievement Test

1 | LISTENING: TOO MUCH HOUSEWORK

A.
1. away U11/U12
2. up U11/U12
3. out U11/U12
4. up U11/U12
5. around U11/U12

B.
1. threw away U11/U12
2. help out U11/U12
3. sit down U11/U12
4. turn over U11/U12
5. straightened up U11/U12

2 | BROKEN RADIO

Phrasal verb		Direct object	
1. turn up	U11/U12	1. the volume	U11/U12
2. figure out	U11/U12	2. any way	U11/U12
3. look over	U11/U12	3. it	U11/U12
4. gone away	U11/U12	4. (no d.o.)	U11/U12
5. took in	U11/U12	5. it	U11/U12
6. send back	U11/U12	6. it	U11/U12
7. check out	U11/U12	7. it	U11/U12
8. got back	U11/U12	8. it	U11/U12

3 | AN ACTOR'S STORY

1. I `U11/U12`
2. I `U11/U12`
3. S `U11/U12`
4. S `U11/U12`
5. I `U11/U12`
6. S `U11/U12`
7. I `U11/U12`
8. I `U11/U12`

4 | BUGS!

1. figure out `U11/U12`
2. go away `U11/U12`
3. show up `U11/U12`
4. build up `U11/U12`
5. throw out `U11/U12`
6. put off `U11/U12`
7. take away `U11/U12`
8. put down `U11/U12`
9. light up `U11/U12`
10. leave . . . on `U11/U12`
11. call in / look into `U11/U12`
12. call in / look into `U11/U12`
13. sign up for `U11/U12`
14. look up `U11/U12`
15. protecting . . . from `U11/U12`
16. pay off `U11/U12`
17. go back `U11/U12`
18. keep out `U11/U12`

5 | PREPARING FOR A BUSINESS TRIP

1. check it out `U11/U12`
2. fill them out `U11/U12`
3. give them back `U11/U12`
4. look them over `U11/U12`
5. put it up `U11/U12`
6. leave it out `U11/U12`
7. fill it up `U11/U12`
8. keep it on `U11/U12`
9. drop it off `U11/U12`

6 | EDITING: A MISLEADING AD

I saw a TV ad that said to call ~~on~~ *up* this

company and cash ~~on~~ *in on* `U11/U12` a great opportunity to
own my own business. I thought I should check

it ~~up~~ *out* `U11/U12` and find ~~off~~ *out* `U11/U12` more about it. When I called,

the guy I talked to wanted to sign me ~~out~~ *up* `U11/U12` to sell a
product I had never heard of. He said he could set

~~up me~~ *me up* `U11/U12` to start earning thousands of dollars a
week. All he needed was $50 to send me my kit.

It didn't take me long after that to hang ~~off~~ *up* `U11/U12` the

phone. I can't believe I fall ~~in~~ *for* `U11/U12` those kinds of ads.

PART VI Diagnostic Test

1 | LISTENING: AN INTRODUCTION TO NEW ZEALAND

A.

1. that make it `U13`
2. which resulted `U13`
3. that carry `U13`
4. that use `U13`
5. which is `U13`
6. which works `U13`
7. which New Zealand sells `U14`

B.

1. b `U14`
2. a `U13`
3. c `U13`
4. a `U13`
5. a `U13`
6. c `U13`
7. c `U13`
8. d `U13`
9. b `U13`
10. a `U13`

2 | A NEW ZEALAND VACATION DIARY

January 5

I flew into Auckland this morning. The city,
which is surrounded by volcanic hills, harbors, `U13`
bays, beaches, and islands, is absolutely beautiful!
A New Zealand native who I met on the plane `U13`
told me that Auckland used to be the capital of
New Zealand. But now the capital is Wellington,
which I will visit the day after tomorrow. After `U14`
checking into my hotel, which is clean and not too `U13`
crowded, I spent all day at the beach.

January 7

Yesterday I went to Mount Eden and One
Tree Hill, where I enjoyed amazing views. I also `U14`
spent some time at the Auckland Domain, which `U13/U14`
is a huge park. Then I went to the Auckland
Museum, where many Polynesian artifacts are on `U14`
display. I saw a 150-year-old Maori war canoe
that was 30 meters long! I spent the rest of the day `U13`
at the beach. Some Australians who needed `U13`
another player for a game of volleyball asked me
to play. I did, and I had a lot of fun!
This morning I drove to Wellington, which is `U13/U14`
on the southern coast of the North Island. I rode a
cable car that took me all over the city. The cable `U14`
car driver, who had lived in Wellington his whole `U13`
life, told me to eat at Cuba Mall, which is a `U14`
popular place for street performers. My meal,
which was inexpensive, was delicious. `U13`

January 8

This morning I took the InterIslander Ferry to
Picton, which is on the South Island. On the ferry `U14`
I met a girl named Jill who works in Nelson, and `U14`
we drove to Nelson together. My destination was
Abel Tasman National Park, where they offer `U14`
guided walks. Surprisingly, that was Jill's
workplace! I took her guided walk. On the walk,
which was two miles long, I saw a baby penguin! `U14`
My trip to New Zealand, which I've been looking `U13`
forward to all year, has been amazing so far!

3 | FUN FACTS ABOUT NEW ZEALAND

1. New Zealand is a country which / that consists of two islands, the North Island and the South Island. **U13**
2. Eighty percent of New Zealand's population, which is a mixture of many different ethnic groups, lives in cities. **U13**
3. In A.D. 800, the Polynesian Maori arrived in New Zealand, where they were the first inhabitants. OR **U14** In A.D. 800, the Polynesian Maori, who were the first inhabitants there, arrived in New Zealand. **U13**
4. The Maori, who lived along the coast, survived by hunting and fishing. **U13**
5. The first European traveler to see New Zealand was Abel Tasman, who(m) the Dutch had sent to explore the area. **U14**
6. The first Europeans in New Zealand, with whom the Maori traded extensively, were whalers and missionaries. OR **U14** The first Europeans in New Zealand, who(m) the Maori traded with extensively, were whalers and missionaries. **U14**
7. In 1840, New Zealand and Great Britain signed The Treaty of Waitangi, which gave power over the islands to Queen Victoria. **U13**
8. People that / who were citizens of Great Britain established new cities in New Zealand after the Waitangi Treaty. **U14**
9. The British citizens and the native Maori had conflicts which / that turned into a war during the 1940s. **U13**
10. The capital of New Zealand is Wellington, which is the southernmost capital in the world. **U13**

4 | FOOD FRENZY: AN INTERVIEW ABOUT NEW ZEALAND DAIRY PRODUCTS

1. which happens / is happening **U13**
2. where . . . sell **U14**
3. where . . . live **U14**
4. which sends **U13**
5. where . . . work **U14**
6. which processes **U13**
7. which . . . make **U14**
8. who / that . . . know **U14**
9. where . . . buy **U14**
10. that / which . . . love **U14**

5 | EDITING: A BUSINESS OPPORTUNITY IN NEW ZEALAND

Dear Mr. Higgins:

I am the Chief Executive Officer for Michigan
Wood Designers, ~~that~~ *which* is a small company in the northern part of the United States. We design and produce wooden souvenirs for the tourist industry. Through market research I have discovered that the Bay of Islands region of New Zealand, which *attracts* **U13** ~~it attracts~~ many tourists, has few souvenir shops. *that/where they* **U13** In addition, there are no souvenir shops ~~that they~~ sell natural wood products. We believe that our *has* **U13** experience in wood design, which ~~have~~ led to great success in the northern Michigan tourist region, could help increase sales of souvenirs in the Bay of Islands. We hope to work directly with *that/who* **U13** people ~~which~~ live in the Bay of Islands. Our business plan offers both Michigan Wood Designers and the Bay of Islands area a valuable opportunity for development.

I am planning a trip to New Zealand at the end of the month, and I would like to schedule a meeting at your convenience. At that time, we can *that/which* **U14** discuss any issues ~~what~~ you are concerned about. Thank you for your kind consideration.

Sincerely,
James F. Dalley
President and CEO of Michigan Wood Designers

Unit 13 Achievement Test

1 | LISTENING: TYPES OF GOVERNMENT

1. person whose **N3**
2. who teaches **N6**
3. which make **N3**
4. that are **N3**
5. that benefit **N3**
6. who can see **N3**
7. those who **N1**
8. that they **N3**
9. which are **N3b**
10. that people **N3**
11. which people **N3**

2 | DICTATORSHIPS

Identifying adjective clauses

1. that operate with a low level of legitimacy and a high level of coercion **N6**
2. who live under a dictatorship **N6**
3. which dominates a political system **N6**

Nonidentifying adjective clauses

4. who usually seize power through military force `N6`

5. who ruled in Iraq `N6`

6. which have the Communist party in power `N6`

7. whose government consisted of members of about 13 families `N6`

3 PARLIAMENTARY AND PRESIDENTIAL DEMOCRACIES

1. a `N3`
2. b `N1`
3. b `N5`
4. c `N3`
5. b `N3`
6. c `N6`
7. a `N1`
8. a `N6`

4 EDITING: ASKING FOR INFORMATION

Dear Ian,

I'm hoping that you can help me with some homework for my world government class, which ~~It~~ is due on Friday. I need to answer a question about the Canadian government. I already asked

live `N5`

one of my friends whose grandparents ~~lives~~ in Canada, but she didn't know the answer.

I think that your country has a parliamentary system of government, right? I don't understand the timing of the elections for a new prime minister there. As you know, the system in the United States is different. Every four years there is

`N3c`

an election for a new president, who ~~he~~ will then serve for the following four years. But in Canada,

which `N3`

~~who~~ seems very similar to the United States in some ways, I can never predict when the next

who `N3`

election will be. My friends Josh and Tim, ~~which~~ I'm doing the homework with, think that there is no set day that everyone recognizes as election day in Canada. Are they right?

Thanks for any help you can give me on this.

Steve

Unit 14 Achievement Test

1 LISTENING: AN INFLUENTIAL CANADIAN AUTHOR

A.

1. when few people wrote `N5`
2. who many people consider `N1`
3. that most people held `N3`
4. which he set `N2`
5. that he felt `N1`

B.

One Canadian theme that MacLennan wrote `N2` about in his book, *Two Solitudes,* is the tension between English-speaking and French-speaking Canadians. This book was also set in an environment with which MacLennan had a lot of `N4` experience. MacLennan grew up in Halifax, Nova Scotia, the son of English-speaking Scottish immigrants. However, he lived most of his life in the province of Quebec, where French is the `N5` official language. *Two Solitudes* describes how the French and English languages meet in daily life in Quebec.

Another of MacLennan's Canadian themes is the magnificence of the country's geographical features. MacLennan developed this theme, which `N2` he made clear throughout his novels, by focusing on features of Canada's landscape. For example, *Rivers of Canada* is a book in which MacLennan `N4` discussed important rivers in Canada's history. Immigrants from Europe traveled down the St. Lawrence River on which Quebec City and `N4` Montreal are located. From there they continued westward on the Ottawa River to the place where `N5` the capital of Canada sits today. He wrote stories about the people who made those voyages and `N3` asked readers to think about the times when these `N5` people lived and the hardships that they endured. `N3` MacLennan attempted to show the relationship between the geography of Canada and the character of Canadians.

2 MACLENNAN'S LIFE

1. MacLennan, who(m) many people supported, won a men's doubles tennis championship in 1928. `N3`
2. In 1928, MacLennan went on a trip to England with his only sister, who(m) their parents had named Frances. `N2`
3. In 1931, MacLennan wrote a book of poetry that/which three London publishers rejected. `N2`
4. Dorothy Duncan, who(m) he met in 1932, became his wife in 1936. `N3`
5. The Lower Canada College, where MacLennan taught from 1935 to 1945, is in Montreal, Canada. `N5`
6. *Two Solitudes,* which Canadians and Americans made a best seller, reflected MacLennan's own experiences living in Quebec. `N3`
7. The MacLennans bought a house that/which they called Stone Hedge. `N2`
8. In 1954, MacLennan published a collection of essays that / which Dorothy Duncan edited for him. `N1`
9. In 1951, MacLennan started working at McGill University, where he taught in the Department of English. `N5`

10. MacLennan published a second version of *Two Solitudes* in 1963, when he translated it into French. **N5**

11. In 1968, MacLennan became a full professor at McGill University, where he had taught since 1951. **N5**

12. In 1980, MacLennan published his seventh novel, which he called *Voices in Time*. **N2**

3 | EDITING: AN E-MAIL TO A FRIEND

Peichi,

What do you think about a trip to Canada
                          where
this summer? There are a lot of places ~~which~~ we could have a great vacation. In fact, I've been

reading a wonderful book that I found **N4** it at the library last week. It's called *Rivers of Canada,* and it describes places like Niagara Falls and tells interesting historical stories. It's by the author
whose **N4**
~~his~~ stories I already told you about. I like all the
                  writes **N1**
stories that this particular author ~~write~~ because they are based on facts about Canada's history.
                  who(m) / that **N3**
Another Canadian author ~~which~~ I saw on TV the other day will be at The Corner Bookstore tomorrow for a book signing. Do you want to go? We could find out a lot more about Canada while we're there. Let me know!

Sally

PART VI Achievement Test

1 | LISTENING: SOME DIFFERENCES BETWEEN CANADA AND THE UNITED STATES

A.
1. that set **U13**
2. which is **U13**
3. that is different **U13**
4. that is **U13**
5. that allows **U13**
6. who wins **U13**
7. which the president chooses **U14**

B.
1. a **U13**   6. c **U13**
2. c **U14**   7. a **U13**
3. b **U13**   8. a **U13**
4. d **U13**   9. d **U13**
5. b **U13**   10. b **U13**

2 | CULTURAL DIFFERENCES BETWEEN CANADA AND THE UNITED STATES

Canada and the United States are countries that people often think have very similar cultures. **U13** However, social scientists point out significant cultural differences between them. These differences, which partly result from their **U13** histories, make the countries very interesting. For example, today's Canadians include people whose **U13** ancestors wanted to remain a British colony during the American Revolution. (The American Revolution, which took place in the late 1700s, **U13** was a war to separate the United States from British rule.) Other Canadians come from families whose ancestors were French immigrants. **U14** Many of these immigrants settled in eastern Canada, where **U14** they established the province of Quebec. Canada, where French and English are both official **U14** languages, is a bilingual nation. The country is an example of a mosaic society in which citizens **U14** preserve the ethnic and cultural traditions of its immigrant populations.

By contrast, social scientists describe the United States as a melting pot society. Citizens who came from many different cultures have **U13** joined their ethnic and cultural traditions and created a larger American culture. Many of the first immigrants, who came from England, Ireland, **U13** Italy, Germany, Poland, Scotland, and other European countries, began to create one culture that combined elements from all of their cultures. **U14** These early immigrants, who often spoke their **U13** native languages in their homes, communicated with each other in English. Today, the United States is a country that has only one official **U13** language: English.

American media and entertainment that reflect **U13** the cultural values of the United States are popular and widely available in Canada. As people who **U13** are concerned with preserving their culture, some Canadians worry that the things which they see **U14** will influence their culture. During the 1930s, Canada created a national public broadcast system that citizens can watch and listen to as an **U14** alternative to American media.

Above all, it's important to remember that Canada and the United States are countries with distinct cultures that represent their people. These **U14** cultures, which many people value, are influenced **U13** by the histories of the countries.

3 | FUN FACTS ABOUT CANADA

1. The first Europeans in Canada, who arrived there about 1,000 years ago, were probably Vikings from Iceland. **U13**

2. The French, who first claimed the land of Canada, gave it to Great Britain in 1763. **U13**

3. The government of Great Britain, which controlled the area, divided it into four colonies. **U14**

4. On July 1, 1867, the four colonies became one country that / which people called Canada. U13

5. The first prime minister was John A. Macdonald, who many people know as the founding father of Canada. U14

6. Canada covers about 10 million square kilometers, which is an area slightly larger than the United States. U14

7. The Canadian flag pictures a maple leaf, which the government named the national symbol. U14

8. Canada's two official languages, which are French and English, have caused problems in the past. U13

9. Each year 12 million tourists that / who want to see the second-largest waterfall in the world visit Niagara Falls. U13

10. Canada has a population of almost 30 million people who are mostly of British, French, other European, American Indian, and mixed backgrounds. U13

4 | AN INTERVIEW ABOUT CANADA'S NATIVE PEOPLE

1. who lived U13
2. which is U13
3. who / that . . . trusts U14
4. that / which . . . saw U14
5. that / which . . . encounter / are encountering / have encountered U14
6. which . . . viewed U14
7. which . . . promote U14
8. that / which . . . don't know U14
9. who / that are U13
10. that / which . . . mentioned U14

5 | EDITING: A BUSINESS OPPORTUNITY IN CANADA

Dear Mr. Bothham:

I am the president and chief executive officer
                                                    which
of Wisconsin Sign Makers, ~~that~~ is a small
                                makes U13
American company that ~~make~~ all kinds of signs for businesses. I am seeking to expand our business into the province of Ontario. We believe
                                        are U13
that Toronto and Ottawa are areas that ~~is~~ particularly good markets for our products. In
                                        which U13
those areas, there aren't any companies ~~that they~~ offer services as extensive as ours. We believe that
                            which U13
Wisconsin Sign Makers, ~~that~~ offers more services than any other sign-making business, can serve the area well.

In order to proceed, I am writing to request any information that you can give us. Is there a
                        whom U14
particular person with ~~which~~ I should work to carry out these plans? Thank you for your consideration. I look forward to hearing from you.

Sincerely,
Joseph A. McDuffie
President and CEO of Wisconsin Sign Makers

PART VII Diagnostic Test

1 | LISTENING: PLANNING A VACATION

A.
1. must not be U15
2. couldn't pay U15
3. might the ancient Britons have built U17
4. don't have to decide U15
5. Shouldn't we have done U16
6. can take U15
7. might be U15

B.

Ability
1. can U15
2. can learn U15
3. are able to learn U15

Advice
4. should go U15
5. should also consider U15
6. should find out U15

Necessity
7. had better research U15
8. 've got to check U15

Assumption
9. must be U15
10. might have U15

Future possibility
11. might discover U15
12. might make U15
13. might be U15

2 | THE MYSTERY OF STONEHENGE

1. have U17
2. could U17
3. must U17
4. can't U15
5. have stopped U16
6. ought to U16
7. have U16
8. could U17
9. moved U17
10. may U17
11. have U16
12. aren't able to U15
13. must U15
14. must U15
15. can't U15

3 | EGYPTIAN PYRAMIDS

A.

1. They had to have been. `U17`
2. They might have been. `U17`
3. They must not have. `U17`
4. He may have been. `U17`

B.

1. The Egyptians may have brought the huge stones from 500 miles away. `U17`
2. The Egyptians must have also built the Sphinx, a giant statue. `U17`
3. The Sphinx might have guarded the pyramids and the treasure they held. `U17`
4. The Egyptians had to have had many tools for cutting stones. `U17`
5. The Egyptians couldn't / could not have built the pyramids quickly. `U17`

C.

Note: Both contracted and noncontracted forms are acceptable.

1. We should have visited the pyramids at Giza. `U16`
2. We should not have only visited the pyramids at Giza. `U16`
3. We could have checked out the Sphinx while we were at Giza. `U16`
4. We ought to have hired a personal tour guide when we explored the pyramids. `U16`
5. We should not have forgotten our cameras in the hotel. `U16`

4 | EDITING: MAKING A DECISION

Note: Both contracted and noncontracted forms are acceptable.

Dear Seema,

Well, it's time for Eric and I to decide for sure where we should ~~go~~ go on our vacation this year. It's getting kind of late. Remember when you asked me if we should've already gotten tickets? Well, we should ~~of~~ *have* `U15` `U16`. We should ~~decide~~ decide where we're going tonight because the travel agent who's helping us arrange the trip says we should buy plane tickets by next week. I guess that ~~should~~ *must/might/may* `U15` be when ticket prices start to really go up for the summer.

What should we ~~had~~ *have* `U16` spent less time on? I guess we ought ~~×~~ *to* `U16` have spent less time researching the different places, but it was so interesting! I enjoyed learning why ancient people might *have* `U17` built magnificent structures like Stonehenge and the pyramids. I still can't believe these people could `U17` ~~not~~ have built them without today's machines.

These ancient structures ~~has~~ *had* `U17` to have taken a long time to build and a lot of people must ~~work~~ *have worked* `U17` on them before they were finished!

The problem is that both places sound so interesting! England ~~musts~~ *must* `U15` have better weather in the summer because that's when most tourists go there. Perhaps we ~~are able to~~ *could* `U15` go to England this summer and then to Egypt next winter. What do you think?

Jane

Unit 15 Achievement Test

1 | LISTENING: READING NEWS AND MAGAZINE STORIES

1. might build `N6`
2. can't remember `N2`
3. could make `N6`
4. might know `N5`
5. must have `N5`
6. can't make `N2`

2 | A JOURNALIST'S DILEMMA

1. may `N5`
2. have to `N4`
3. might `N5`
4. should `N1`
5. have to `N4`
6. should `N3`
7. could `N6`
8. might not `N5`
9. had to `N4`
10. had better `N3`
11. were able to `N2`
12. couldn't `N2`
13. was able to `N2`
14. may `N6`
15. must `N4`
16. ought to `N3`

3 | RESPONSIBLE REPORTERS

1. AS `N5`
2. AB `N2`
3. AD `N3`
4. AB `N2`

4 | EDITING: A LETTER TO THE EDITOR

Dear Editor in Chief,

I was very disturbed last week when a friend showed me an article published in your newspaper. The article reported that the city ~~mights~~ *might* force citizens to pay extra money next year in order to build a new park in the downtown area. ~~Might~~ *Will* `N6` the city really build this park without asking the citizens what they want? Of course it won't!

The reporter who wrote that article ~~musts~~ *must* `N1` not know very much about city affairs, because the city can't ~~×~~ `N2` make these types of decisions without making a formal proposal and holding a public vote on the issue. The city knows this, and any good reporter should too! As the editor of this newspaper, you should take responsibility for the quality of reporting that you print. You *must not/should not/shouldn't* **N4** ~~don't have to~~ allow irresponsible reporters to leave out these details that make citizens worry. If you monitor your reporters more carefully in the future, your readers will be much happier.

Sincerely,
Ann Matthews

Unit 16 Achievement Test

| **1** | **LISTENING: MOVING TO COSTA RICA** |

A.

1. should have studied **N3**
2. could have helped **N3**
3. could have started **N3**
4. could have learned **N3**
5. shouldn't have focused **N2**
6. might have helped **N3**

B.

1. a **N1**		6. b **N2**
2. a **N1**		7. b **N1**
3. b **N2**		8. a **N1**
4. b **N1**		9. b **N1**
5. a **N2**		10. b **N2**

| **2** | **MARK'S UNFORTUNATE EXPERIENCE TRAVELING** |

Note: Both contracted and noncontracted forms are acceptable.

1. I could have gotten to the airport early enough. **N1**
2. I should not have brought only credit cards on the trip. **N2**
3. I could have packed extra clothes in my carry-on bag. **N1**
4. My sister might have told me that luggage often gets lost. **N1**

| **3** | **A DISCUSSION BETWEEN MARISA AND MARK** |

1. should . . . have refused **N2**
2. shouldn't / should not have **N2**
3. should . . . have told **N2**
4. could've / could have **N1**
5. should . . . have done **N2**

| **4** | **EDITING: A LETTER TO A FRIEND** |

Dear Dan,
    Well, Marisa and I are all settled in our new home. We could *'ve / have* ~~of~~ bought a house right on the beach, but we decided on a house in San Juan instead.

I finally found a new job working for a Costa Rican company that sells coffee beans all over the world. Like I told you before, I *should* **N2** ~~might~~ not have studied only U.S. business while I was in college. It was hard to find a job. It shouldn't have been so hard. In fact, I really ought *to* **N3** ~~a~~ have found a job before Marisa and I got married and we moved down here. Didn't you have trouble finding a job when you moved to another state? You might *'ve/have* **N1** ~~had~~ reminded me how difficult it would be! Just kidding! I know that I *should/ought to* **N1** ʌhave started looking much earlier. I should have known it would be more time consuming in a foreign country.
    Oh, I wanted to ask you a question. Should we *have* **N3** ~~of~~ sent you that coffee? I sent it, and then remembered that you don't like coffee all that much. Hopefully you can enjoy it. Talk to you soon.
Mark

Unit 17 Achievement Test

| **1** | **LISTENING: THE LOST CITY OF ATLANTIS** |

A.

1. might have been **N6**
2. could have caused **N6**
3. must not have found **N2**
4. Could . . . have existed **N4**
5. couldn't have had **N3**
6. may have been located **N6**
7. must have been **N2**
8. could not have survived **N3**

B.

Modal of impossibility	Modal of speculation
1. couldn't have existed **N3**	2. may have been **N1**
	3. might have based **N1**

| **2** | **PLATO AND THE LOST CITY OF ATLANTIS** |

1. g **N2**	5. b **N2**
2. i **N2**	6. j **N2**
3. d **N2**	7. e **N2**
4. h **N1**	

3 | WHAT HAPPENED AT POMPEII?

A.

Note: Both contracted and noncontracted forms are acceptable.

1. It might have been too late to flee once they realized what was happening. **N1**
2. Since the volcano erupted very early in the morning, everyone must have been sleeping. **N2**
3. The people of Pompeii couldn't have recognized the signs that the volcano would erupt. **N3**
4. The people of Pompeii may not have had a safe place to go to. **N1**

B.

Note: Both contracted and noncontracted forms are acceptable.

1. It must've. **N5**
2. They couldn't have. **N5**
3. It might've been. **N5**

4 | EDITING: SHARING KNOWLEDGE

Dear Tom,

    In my history class we've been discussing whether or not Atlantis may ~~had~~ *'ve/have* been a real city. We've read a translation of Plato's story about Atlantis, and it must ~~of~~ *'ve/have* **N6** been a magnificent city because Plato describes grand temples and palaces and complicated waterways. What kind of people ~~might~~ *could* **N4** have built this advanced technology such a long time ago? I imagine they had to ~~had~~ *have* **N2** been very intelligent to be capable of this. It had to have been hard to build without modern machines.

    The legend says Atlantis must have disappeared under the ocean. How could this really ʌ*have* **N4** happened? I think it ~~might~~ *could* **N3** not have really disappeared completely, because if the city were really at the bottom of the ocean, we would have found it by now. Don't you think so? Please write me back and tell me what you think!

Manuel

PART VII | Achievement Test

1 | LISTENING: TRAVELING BY TRAIN

A.

1. can't lift **U15**
2. must be **U15**
3. could I have put **U17**
4. Should I have kept **U16**
5. has to make **U15**
6. could stop **U15**
7. can't speak **U15**

B.

Ability
1. can't speak **U15**
2. can understand **U15**
3. can't ever sleep **U15**

Advice
4. ought to put **U15**
5. had better get **U15**
6. shouldn't sleep **U15**

Necessity
7. have to put **U15**
8. have to pay **U15**

Assumption
9. might be **U15**
10. must be **U15**

Future possibility
11. might not be going **U15**
12. may not be **U15**
13. might not know **U15**

2 | A WALK THROUGH BARCELONA

1. have taken **U16**
2. don't have to **U15**
3. can **U15**
4. have read **U16**
5. have **U17**
6. been **U17**
7. might **U17**
8. were able to **U15**
9. had to **U17**
10. have been **U17**
11. might **U15**
12. could **U17**
13. should **U16**
14. have **U16**
15. were able to **U15**

3 | ANTONIO GAUDI: THE FAMOUS ARCHITECT

A.

1. He might've / might have been. **U17**
2. He must not have. **U17**
3. He must've / must have. **U17**
4. He may've / may have. **U17**

B.

Note: Both contracted and noncontracted forms are acceptable.

1. Gaudi might have been Spain's most famous architect. `U17`
2. Gaudi had to have had both natural talent and excellent training. `U17`
3. Gaudi must have spent all his time designing and building his masterpieces. `U17`
4. Gaudi couldn't have used computers to help him design his buildings. `U17`
5. People may have wanted Gaudi to design buildings in other parts of the world as well. `U17`

C.

Note: Both contracted and noncontracted forms are acceptable.

1. I could've climbed the 340 steps to the top of one of the Sagrada Familia's towers. `U16`
2. I should've bought a poster of Park Guell. `U16`
3. I should've taken pictures of the Sagrada Familia at night. `U16`
4. I ought to have gone to Park Guell. `U16`
5. I shouldn't have thrown away our entrance tickets to the Sagrada Familia. `U16`

---

4 | EDITING: A POSTCARD FROM BARCELONA

Note: Both contracted and noncontracted forms are acceptable.

Dear Mom and Dad,

Yesterday we visited Park Guell, which is a city park designed by Antonio Gaudi. To get there, we had to climb up a large hill. It was so high that we could ~~of~~ *have* seen the whole city if it hadn't been cloudy. The park is very beautiful, with lots of curving structures. Gaudi must ‸*have* `U17` liked using mosaics, because everything is decorated with a mosaic. Artists make mosaics by setting small colored tiles into a surface to make an image. There are so many tiny little pieces that it ~~couldn't~~ *had to/must* `U17` have taken a really long time to build the park, and the builders must ~~be~~ *have been* `U17` very skillful. We only got to stay at the park for two hours because it closed. We ~~must~~ *should / ought to* `U16` have checked to see when the park closed. `U19`

Barcelona was great! It's such a beautiful and busy city. It ~~musts~~ *must* `U15` be a popular vacation spot. I feel like we missed so many interesting sights. You've been to Barcelona. Where else should we ~~had~~ *have* `U16` gone?

Jason and I are on the train going to Paris from Barcelona now. Remember when you asked me if we should have made train reservations so early? Well, we shouldn't ~~of~~ *have* `U16`! We might ~~stay~~ *have stayed* `U17` for two weeks instead of one, but we had to keep our train reservations.

We'll be visiting Paris for the next week. We must not forget to visit the Eiffel Tower and the Louvre, which is the world's largest museum. I'm sure Paris must ✗ *be* `U15` be a great city to visit too. I'm worried that we ~~should~~ *may* `U15` not have time to see everything there either. I guess I'll just have to come back again next year! Hey, you guys ought ✗ *to* `U15` come with me!

Love,
Harry

PART VIII Diagnostic Test

1 | LISTENING: HYBRID CARS

1. may be sold `U19`
2. can be accomplished `U19`
3. is taken `U18`
4. is used `U18`
5. are applied `U18`
6. can be captured `U19`
7. can be seen `U19`
8. have been established `U18`
9. can be met `U19`
10. may be saved `U19`
11. may be numbered `U19`

2 | BICYCLE: THE TRIP

June 1
We biked 20 miles today in warm weather. I was challenged by the trip, and now I'm exhausted. My body hasn't been trained to `U18` perform in such warm weather. But I will be rested `U19` after a good night's sleep. I hope I can go faster tomorrow, or I might not be taken seriously by Ari `U19` and Tomas.

June 2
Today we biked into the redwood forests around Big Sur. The trees were awesome! I hope that these trees are never cut down so that their beauty `U18` may be respected forever. They should be enjoyed `U19` by many future generations. We decided to camp overlooking the ocean. Less than 30 minutes after we had stopped, the tent was set up and `U18` the fire was built. I prepared the meal, and it `U18` was eaten very quickly! I don't know who the `U18` meal will be prepared by tomorrow night, but I `U19` doubt it will be as good as mine!

June 3

It was so hot today! The back of my neck (U18) (was burned) by the sun. Although I had considered shaving my head to be cooler, I won't cut my hair now that I've seen Ari's sunburned head! He (U18) (had his hair shaved) before we went on the trip, but I think he regrets it now.

June 4

What a morning! My bike broke after only 10 (U19) miles. I realized that all bikers (ought to be taught) how to fix their bikes! Ari, Tomas, and five other bikers examined it, and they all said that it (U19) (had to be fixed) by a bike mechanic. We had to walk (U20) three miles to a bike shop where I (had my bike) (U20) (taken apart) by a mechanic. I (got a tire replaced), (U20) too, and I (got my brakes checked).

---

3 | PLANES: *THE AVIATOR*

1. was directed (U18)
2. was released (U18)
3. is / was portrayed (U18)
4. is / was considered (U18)
5. was transformed (U18)
6. was raised (U18)
7. was attracted (U18)
8. is / was portrayed (U18)
9. is / was included (U18)
10. was obsessed (U18)
11. was awarded (U18)
12. was given (U18)
13. was recognized (U18)

---

4 | BOATS: A CRUISE

1. have them done (U20)
2. get your back massaged (U20)
3. had my feet rubbed (U20)
4. got my hair done (U20)
5. had drinks and snacks delivered (U20)
6. were you served (U18)
7. were you impressed (U18)
8. Were you taken (U18)
9. must be considered (U19)
10. Was the tour included (U18)
11. ought to be taken care of (U19)
12. will be treated (U19)

---

5 | EDITING: TRAIN COMPLAINT

Dear Deluxe Train representative,

I am writing to complain about the service I received on a recent trip with Deluxe Train. I

decided
~~was decided~~ to travel with Deluxe Train after friends told me of its excellent service and reliability. On my trip, however, I was extremely disappointed. When I got on the train, I had one

(U20)
of the attendants ~~to~~ carry my bag. But he wasn't careful with it, and he threw it on a shelf. A

broken (U18)
bottle of perfume in my bag was ~~breaking~~ by him.

(U18)
Then, I ~~was~~ asked a train attendant for a second blanket, and he told me that only one blanket was allowed per person. But I saw extra blankets in a

brought (U20)
closet! Later I had some coffee ~~bringing~~ to me. But it took over half an hour to arrive, and by then it was cold.

informed (U19)
I thought you should be ~~informing~~ of my terrible experience. Passengers ought to be

respected (U19)
~~respect~~ by Deluxe Train employees. Your

be (U19)
company's service had better ~~been~~ improved if you want more business from the Smith family.

Sincerely,
Cynthia Smith

Unit 18 Achievement Test

1 | LISTENING: 1936 BERLIN OLYMPICS

1. were represented (N1)
2. were sold (N1)
3. are . . . known (N1)
4. was introduced (N1)
5. is lit (N1)
6. is carried (N4)
7. were installed (N1)
8. were watched (N4)
9. were held (N1)
10. was included (N1)

2 | THE ANCIENT OLYMPIC GAMES

1. A (N1)   4. A (N1)
2. P (N1)   5. P (N1)
3. P (N1)   6. P (N1)

3 | INTERVIEW: *SPORTS SPECIAL*

1. is pushed (N2)
2. Is . . . played (N2)
3. is (N2)
4. was . . . developed (N2)
5. were reported (N2)
6. were . . . played (N2)
7. were (N2)
8. were held (N2)
9. was . . . made (N2)
10. was added (N2)

4 | EDITING: OLYMPIC CHAMPION

          was
Nadia Comaneci ~~is~~ born on November 12,
         introduced N2
1961, in Onesti, Romania. She was ~~introduce~~ to
gymnastics at the age of six. She began competing
in 1972, and she accomplished a lot during her
career. She was the first gymnast in Olympic
history to be awarded a perfect score of 10.0. She
was N2
~~were~~ given this score for her routine on the uneven
parallel bars at the 1976 Summer Games in
Montreal, Canada. Six more 10.0s were
presented N2
~~presenting~~ to her during those Games. In the 1976
and 1980 Games she was decorated with nine
medals in total. She retired from competition in
the early 1980s and left Romania in 1989. Now
she lives in the United States. Nadia's incredible
    are / were / have been admired N2
performances ~~admire~~ by athletes and fans as
triumphant moments in Olympic history.

Unit 19 Achievement Test

1 | LISTENING: JOB INTERVIEW PREPARATION

1. ought to be made N5
2. can be expanded N3
3. might be prepared . . . practiced N4
4. had better not be used N5
5. might be completed N4

2 | JOB INTERVIEW

    Interviewers will pay a lot of attention to
how you act during an interview. Certain behavior
N2 (will be expected) of you. In fact, whether you are a
N2 good fit with the company (will be decided) within
your first five minutes there! So here are few more
things to consider before you arrive.
N2   First, you (will be expected) to arrive on time.
Make sure you know how to get to the interview
location. Any problems with directions (must be)
N5 (discovered) ahead of time.
N3   Second, your appearance (can't be forgotten).
N5 Your clothing (should be cleaned and pressed) so
you look professional.
    Several copies of your resume (had better be)
N5 (made) ahead of time. If someone asks you for it,
you'll want to have it ready.
    Next, greet the interviewer appropriately. This
includes a firm handshake, a smile, and
introducing yourself. The interviewer (should be)
N5 (greeted) in the way that you would want someone
to greet you.
    When you answer questions, look the
interviewer in the eye. Eye contact (should be)
N5 (maintained) while you talk.

    And this is important! Your positive qualities
(must be highlighted) for the interviewer; how will N5
the interviewer know about your skills if you don't
tell him or her? Although it's sometimes difficult,
you must stay calm during the interview so that
you can sell yourself. Act professionally, or you
(may not be taken seriously). N4

3 | INTERVIEW QUESTIONS AND ADVICE

1. has (got) to be cut N5
2. have to be shaved N5
3. Can . . . be seen N3
4. will be hired N2
5. have to be changed N5
6. can . . . be considered N3
7. can't be ignored N4
8. had better be taken N5
9. can't be shown N4
10. may be considered N4
11. could be offered N3

4 | EDITING: SUMMER JOB INQUIRY

Dear Mr. Myers,
    I am writing to request additional information
about the summer job you advertised in *The Town
Chronicle* this week for a flower delivery person.
You stated that the job requires 25 hours per
week, Monday through Friday. Will the delivery
    be allowed
person ~~allow~~ to work more hours on certain days
and fewer hours on others? Or will the person
be required N2
~~require~~ to work five hours each day? Also, I am
planning to go on vacation for a week in June. If I
      be N3
get the job, can I ~~been~~ excused for that week and
make up the time another week? Also, money was
not mentioned in the advertisement. Is the new
        paid N2
employee going to be ~~pay~~ minimum wage? Since
the employee has to provide his or her own car,
    N2
will he or she ̶b̶e̶ be given additional gas money?
Thank you for your time.

Jenny Pantella

Unit 20 Achievement Test

1 | LISTENING: WEDDING PREPARATIONS

1. get them done N1
2. had them done N3
3. have my cake decorated N3
4. have my flowers arranged N3
5. get it styled N3
6. have it cut N3
7. had your dress fitted N1

2 | WEDDING ADVICE

In many places, it's becoming more common for brides and grooms to pay for their own weddings. And they're learning that weddings can be expensive! Here is some advice on how to save money on a wedding.

Some people (get their flowers delivered) from an expensive flower store. But there are other

N3 options. You can (have your flowers arranged) by a
N1 friend. Or you can (have the wedding located) in a
N2 beautiful outdoor area and (have the flowers provided) as part of the scenery! If you choose a location that has more than one wedding per day, schedule your wedding after someone else's. Maybe you can use the flowers from the previous ceremony for free!

N2/N3 Some people (have their wedding photographed) by a professional photographer. To save money,
N2/N3 (have only formal pictures taken) by a professional. Put disposable cameras on the tables at the wedding
N2/N3 reception, and (have the reception captured) on film by friends and relatives. You can also try to (get
N2/N3 your pictures taken) by a photography student. This will cost less than a professional photographer.

N2/N3 Many people (have a large meal catered) by a restaurant or catering service. Instead of this,
N1 you can (have the wedding scheduled) for a time
N2 between meals. Then you can (have appetizers served) instead of a meal, which will save you
N1/N3 money. If you really want to save money, you can (have food brought) to the reception by the guests. This is very informal, but it can be a lot of fun!

3 | THINGS TO BE DONE

1. Suzy is going to have the bridesmaids' lunch prepared. **N1**
2. Suzy is going to have the bridal party's presents wrapped. **N1**
3. Suzy is going to have her wedding dress adjusted. **N1**
4. Suzy is going to get her wedding dress pressed. **N1**
5. Suzy is going to get her hair colored. **N1**
6. Suzy is going to have extra flowers ordered. **N1**

4 | EDITING: HONEYMOON

Dear Jess,

Hi! How are you? Our honeymoon is wonderful! Sam is a great husband, and we're

my hair braided
having a great time. Today I got ~~braided my hair~~ on the beach. Sam laughed when he saw me! But

drawn **N1**
he got a bad fake tattoo ~~draw~~ on his shoulder, so he can't laugh too much. Yesterday we got our

developed **N1**
pictures ~~developing~~ from the first few days here. We got some really good pictures. We're enjoying all the hotel services. Every day I have a tropical

made **N1**
fruit drink ~~made it~~ for me. Yesterday I got my

massaged **N1**
whole body ~~massage~~. We had our breakfast

brought **N1**
~~bringed~~ to us this morning. And last night

got / had **N1**
we ^champagne and strawberries delivered to us on ^the beach! Anyway, I'll call you when I get back! Take care!

Suzy

PART VIII Achievement Test

1 | LISTENING: ROCK 'N ROLL: THE BEATLES

1. might be defined **U19**
2. will never be broken **U19**
3. were written **U18**
4. should be given **U19**
5. may be considered **U19**
6. can be seen **U19**
7. were shown **U18**
8. was filmed **U18**
9. was announced **U18**
10. will not be forgotten **U19**
11. will be listened to **U19**

2 | A MUSICAL TOUR

July 4
My destination of Austria (was chosen) because of its importance in classical music. I started in Salzburg because it was the home of the famous classical composer Wolfgang Amadeus Mozart. Today I visited the place where Mozart (was born) **U18** in 1756. It (has been converted) into a museum. His **U18** childhood violin and other musical instruments (can be seen) there, and letters he and his family **U19** wrote to each other (can be read). I learned that **U19** Mozart (had his first music published) before he **U20** was 10 years old! That's amazing!

July 5
Today I went on the *Sound of Music* tour and saw the original home of the Von Trapp family. I didn't know much about them. So I (got their story **U20** explained) to me by a tour guide, and I learned a lot. After his wife died, Georg Von Trapp (had his **U20** nine children looked after) by a woman named Maria Kutschera. Maria taught the children to sing and love music. Eventually Maria and Georg fell in love, and they (were married). When Austria **U18** (was taken over) by the Nazis in 1938, the family **U18** escaped to mountains, leaving their possessions behind. They sang to make money. Eventually they arrived in the United States, where they (could be **U19** heard) singing in performances around the country. Their story (was made) into a Broadway musical **U18** and a very well-known movie. The tour was a lot of fun. Well, it's late, and I should figure out my schedule for tomorrow. Each day's activities (must be planned) so I get the most out of my trip! **U19**

July 6

U18 Today I traveled to Vienna. I saw the Vienna State Opera where (audiences have been treated) to some of the best opera music in the world since the 1860s. Tomorrow some of the waltzes of Johann **U19** Strauss (will be played) there, including some pieces **U19** that (may be considered) his best. I got a ticket, and I can't wait. I also visited the House of Music. It's a museum where you interact with music. I conducted a virtual Vienna Philharmonic Orchestra, and I sang and played instruments and **U20** (had my music recorded). It was awesome! I have learned a lot about music on this trip that I didn't study in my music classes. I think all music **U19** students (should be encouraged) to visit Vienna!

3 | BLUES: RAY

1. was directed **U18**
2. was released **U18**
3. is / was considered **U18**
4. was raised **U18**
5. was introduced **U18**
6. was discovered **U18**
7. was treated **U18**
8. was not discouraged **U18**
9. was heard **U18**
10. was complicated **U18**
11. was controlled **U18**
12. is / was portrayed **U18**
13. was awarded **U18**

4 | A NEW CD

1. was offered **U18**
2. couldn't / could not be made **U19**
3. have their other songs recorded **U20**
4. the CD be released **U19**
5. get the cover done **U20**
6. had their pictures taken **U20**
7. got the other art created **U20**
8. have the songs written **U20**
9. were they paid **U18**
10. the band was given **U18**
11. Have they been / Were they interviewed **U18**
12. may be featured **U19**

5 | EDITING: RECORD LABELING

Dear Music Mania representative,
   I am writing to complain about your store's practice of not labeling CDs that contain mature content. I ~~was~~ recently bought a CD from your **U18** store for my son. I ~~was~~ listened to it, and I was shocked by the obscene language. These types of
be **U19**
CDs had better ~~been~~ labeled so parents can be alerted to the material they contain.
   There is another thing that concerns me. My **U18**
13-year-old son ~~was~~ purchased CDs with mature content in your store without parental consent. A

13-year-old child should not be allowed to buy something like this if his or her parents aren't present. CDs with adult content had better not **U19**
~~be~~ be sold to children without their parents' approval.
labeled **U20**
   Your store should have its CDs ~~label~~ if they contain mature content, and children should have
approved **U20**
their purchases ~~to approve~~ by a parent or a responsible adult. If you don't make these changes,
be **U19**
your customers may ~~being~~ tempted to shop at other music stores.

Sincerely,
Vonetta Hood

PART IX Diagnostic Test

1 | LISTENING: EASY TRAVEL

1. if someone offered **U23**
2. If you come **U22**
3. we'll give **U22**
4. we will suggest **U22**
5. if you don't want **U21**

2 | MAKING DECISIONS

   Every day we are faced with decisions. Some decisions are very important while others are not. If a decision has long-term effects, (that decision is) (usually important). (A decision is also important) if **U21** it affects many people. If a decision is important, (you should consider all the possible consequences) **U21** (before making a choice). Decisions made without careful consideration can often result in bad choices and regrets.
   (If you consider all the possible consequences, (will you make the right choice)? Even if you try to **U22** consider all the possibilities, (you can't always) **U22** (think of everything). But there are some ways to improve your decision-making skills, (Consider) **U21** (these tips) (when you make decisions).

1. Make a list of the positive and negative consequences of each choice.
2. Consider the people who the decision will affect. What is best for them?
3. Try to think of similar situations. What decisions did you make in the past, and what happened as a result?
4. Avoid rushing into a decision. Take time to think it over.
5. Recognize any biases you may have about the choices you are considering.

(I follow these guidelines) when I'm faced with **U21** an important decision, and I have learned to make good choices. If you use these tips, (you might) **U21** (improve your decision-making skills). And if you (improve your decision-making skills, (you'll lead a) **U22** (happier life with fewer regrets)!

B.

1. a. F
   b. T U23
2. a. F
   b. T U23
3. a. F
   b. F U24
4. a. F
   b. T U24

5. a. T
   b. T U23
6. a. F
   b. F U24
7. a. T
   b. F U23
8. a. T
   b. T U24

3 | PLANNING A VACATION

A.

1. It's much faster and easier if you use a travel agent. U21
2. I have a lot of patience if I'm interested in the topic. U21
3. If you don't know any good websites, try www.planyourvacation.com. U21
4. We should reserve plane tickets early if we want to pay low fares. U21
5. If you travel near a holiday, plane tickets always cost more. U21

B.

Note: Both the contracted and noncontracted forms are acceptable.

1. charges, will stay U22
2. is, will not go U22
3. can share, visit U22
4. do not find, will save U22

4 | PACKING FOR A VACATION

A.

1. Unless U22
2. if U22
3. If U22
4. unless U22

B.

1. If I didn't get motion sickness on airplanes, I wouldn't take this medicine. OR I wouldn't take this medicine if I didn't get motion sickness on airplanes. U23
2. If I knew how to get to the hotel from the airport, this map wouldn't be so important. OR This map wouldn't be so important if I knew how to get to the hotel from the airport. U23
3. If I were familiar with the tourist attractions in Mexico City, I wouldn't have to take this travel guide. OR I wouldn't have to take this travel guide if I were familiar with the tourist attractions in Mexico City. U23
4. If I didn't love taking good pictures, I wouldn't take this expensive camera. OR I wouldn't take this expensive camera if I didn't love taking good pictures. U23

5. If I knew how much money to take, I wouldn't put this credit card in my purse. OR I wouldn't put this credit card in my purse if I knew how much money to take. U23
6. If I didn't hate traveling without something to read, I wouldn't take this book. OR I wouldn't take this book if I didn't hate traveling without something to read. U23
7. If the hotel didn't have a swimming pool, I could leave my swimsuit at home. OR I could leave my swimsuit at home if the hotel didn't have a swimming pool. U23
8. If I could buy this medication there, I wouldn't need to take it with me. OR I wouldn't need to take it/this medication with me if I could buy this medication/it there. U23
9. If my parents didn't want me to call them, I wouldn't pack this phone card. OR I wouldn't pack this phone card if my parents didn't want me to call them. U23
10. If airplanes weren't always cold, I wouldn't need this sweater. OR I wouldn't need this sweater if airplanes weren't always cold. U23

C.

Note: Both contracted and noncontracted forms are acceptable.

1. hadn't, wouldn't have gotten U24
2. hadn't carried, wouldn't have seemed U24
3. wouldn't have had, 'd mailed U24
4. wouldn't have been, hadn't bought U24
5. wouldn't have brought, hadn't been U24
6. 'd spent U24
7. 'd gone U24
8. 'd known, would've invited U24

5 | EDITING: A POSTCARD FROM MEXICO

Dear Molly,

    Mexico City is warm and sunny! If I ~~knew~~ *had known* that, I wouldn't have packed two sweaters and a jacket! Tomorrow I'm going shopping. If I ~~will~~ find something nice, I'll get it for you. U22 I'm so glad you suggested Mexico for my vacation. I wouldn't ~~think~~ *have thought* U24 of it if you hadn't mentioned it.

    Yesterday I visited the pyramids at Teotihuacan. ~~Unless~~ *If* U22 you're scared of heights, you might not want to climb to the top. Some of the pyramids are over 60 meters tall! I was there all day, but I wish I ~~can~~ *could* U24 have spent a week there! You know me. If a place is full of history, I ~~would love~~ *will love/love* U21 it!

When I ~~would~~ [U21] travel, I always make a list of places to visit again, and Mexico is definitely on

moved/could move [U23]

it! If I ~~would move~~ next month, I would buy a house in Mexico. That's how much I love it here.

[U23]

Will you come with me if I ~~had~~ come again next year? If I get the chance, I'll definitely be back!

See you soon,

Tanya

Unit 21 Achievement Test

1 LISTENING: LET'S COOK!

A.

1. you can improve [N3]
2. should also go up [N3]
3. when they want [N1, N2]
4. if you start [N3]
5. then visit [N4]

B.

If you eat a lot of dairy products like milk, cheese, and yogurt, you should buy low-fat versions of them. These low-fat products usually cost the same as the higher-fat versions, and they generally taste pretty similar. [N2] If you're trying to avoid fat, then eat leaner meats. Fish, seafood, and chicken have much less fat than red meat. When [N4] you purchase any meat, try to choose pieces that are well-trimmed. Another way you can eat healthier meals at home is to buy lots of fresh [N2] fruits and vegetables. When you eat these, you get lots of important vitamins and nutrients. [N3] You should always read the nutrition facts on food containers when you're at the grocery store. [N1/N5] If you pay attention to what you buy, then you also pay attention to what you eat! When I go to [N2] the grocery store, I usually start in the health foods section. Even if your store doesn't have a [N3] section just for health foods, you can still find healthy foods. Look for fresh fruits and vegetables, lean meats, low-fat dairy products, and whole grains.
And finally, if you eat out often, try to cut [N4] down on that habit. If you cook at home, then you have more control over what you eat. And [N3] you can save a lot of money if you eat at home, too. These are all ways you can change your eating habits to better your health and energy [N3] levels. So if you like these tips, explore the rest of the website for more!

2 HEALTHY EATING TIPS

1. If you want to fix a healthy meal for a friend, you should check my website for great meal ideas. [N3]
2. If your friend likes low-fat desserts, she ought to make something with fresh fruit. [N3]
3. If you like to cook with the freshest food, shop at a market that gets food delivered each day. [N4]
4. If your children need healthier snacks, give them plenty of fresh fruit and vegetables. [N4]
5. If you want to start eating better, remember to eat a variety of foods. [N4]

3 A SEAFOOD MARKET

1. You can tell it's fresh if the fish doesn't have a strong smell. [N5]
2. And you know it's good if the fish is firm, not too soft. [N5]
3. If you know about the products, you can serve customers better. [N5]
4. If you do that, it comes out great every time. [N5]
5. Most people eat a lot of seafood if they know how to prepare it. [N5]

4 EDITING: MAKING DINNER PLANS

Darren,
I went to the seafood market on Lincoln

want

Avenue today. When I walk by it, I always ~~wanted~~ to stop in. So today I did, and I bought some salmon for dinner. The woman who works there is a seafood expert. If she tells me something, I

believe [N2]

~~will believe~~ it. She told me to cook the salmon with just a little salt and pepper. She said that

is [N2]

when fish ~~will be~~ fresh, it doesn't need a lot of seasoning. I think it'll be so good. If we like this

[N5]

fish, I can get more next week.
I'm also planning to fix a salad and some fresh

let [N4]

fruit. If you want anything else, just ~~letting~~ me know.

Love,
Marla

Unit 22 Achievement Test

1 LISTENING: PUTTING TOGETHER A NEW DESK

1. if there are [N1]
2. you'll never finish [N1]
3. We'll get [N1]
4. I'll attach [N1]
5. Unless we have [N4]
6. I'll take [N1]

2 CONDITIONS AND RESULTS

1. d [N2]   4. b [N1]
2. g [N1]   5. a [N2]
3. c [N2]   6. i [N1]

3 | MAKING A SCHEDULE

1. if **N4**
2. If **N4**
3. Unless **N4**
4. unless **N4**
5. If **N4**
6. Unless **N4**

4 | A CO-WORKER'S ADVICE

1. will get **N1**
2. 'll / will be **N1**
3. follow **N1**
4. will see **N1**
5. finish **N1**
6. get **N1**
7. will reward **N1**
8. do **N1**
9. will be **N1**

5 | EDITING: A MOTIVATIONAL E-MAIL

Hey Thomas,

I know you're giving a big presentation

tomorrow. Are you nervous? If you ~~practiced~~ *practice* a lot, I'm sure you'll do well. I always used to get nervous before presentations. But I learned how to

N2

deal with it. If you ~~will~~ relax for 15 minutes before the presentation starts, you'll do much

N3

better. You won't be able to concentrate ʌ unless

'll / will **N1**

you're calm. Remember, you ʌ do well if you prepare yourself and relax. Good luck tomorrow! I know you'll do just fine.

Byron

Unit 23 Achievement Test

1 | LISTENING: WISHFUL THINKING

1. I would take **N3**
2. I might travel **N3**
3. If I had **N2**
4. I would love **N3**
5. I were you **N5**
6. I could quit **N6**
7. I could take **N6**

2 | MORE WISHES

1. a. T
   b. F **N6**
2. a. F
   b. T **N6**
3. a. T
   b. F **N6**
4. a. F
   b. T **N6**
5. a. F
   b. F **N2**
6. a. F
   b. F **N2**
7. a. T
   b. F **N2**

3 | WHAT IF . . .

1. What would you do if you never had to worry about money? **N1**
2. If you could work anywhere, where would you want to work? **N1**
3. If you could buy any car, what would it be? **N1**
4. Who would you like to have dinner with if you could eat with anyone in the world? **N1**

4 | EXCUSES, EXCUSES

1. If I had a book to read, I would stop watching TV. OR I would stop watching TV if I had a book to read. **N1**
2. If I were good at sports, I would play basketball with my friends. OR I would play basketball with my friends if I were good at sports. **N2**
3. If I were hungry, I would eat supper. OR I would eat supper if I were hungry. **N3**
4. If I didn't like my room dirty, I would clean my room/it. OR I would clean my room if I didn't like my room/it dirty. **N1**
5. If I weren't afraid of water, I could take a bath. OR I could take a bath if I weren't afraid of water. **N3**
6. If the knob on the radio weren't broken, I could turn down the music. OR I could turn down the music if the knob on the radio weren't broken. **N2**
7. If my favorite TV show wasn't on, I would wash the dishes. OR I would wash the dishes if my favorite TV show wasn't on. **N2**
8. If my sister wanted help, I could help her with her homework. OR I could help her/my sister with her homework if my sister/she wanted help. **N2**
9. If I were tired, I would go to bed. OR I would go to bed if I were tired. **N1**

5 | EDITING: E-MAIL CHAIN LETTERS

If you have e-mail, you may have received a message like this:

you had

"What would you do if ~~you'll have~~ three wishes? Now you do! Make your wishes and send this

were **N5**

message to 10 more people. If I ~~was~~ you, I'd hurry and send the message on before you forget!"

People all around the world receive e-mails like this frequently. The messages usually come with instructions to make a wish and then send the message on to other people. The messages often warn that if you don't send the e-mail to more people, your wish won't come true.

received **N2**

If you ~~would receive~~ a message like this, what would you do? Would you delete it, or would you send it to other people? If you decided to send it

would **N6**

on, what would you wish for? Many people ~~will~~ wish for health, happiness, and wealth if they had the opportunity.

Unit 24 Achievement Test

1 | LISTENING: AN UNSUCCESSFUL BAND

A.
1. if we had hired **N1**
2. would have known **N1**
3. if we had thought **N2**
4. might have become **N3**
5. if it had been **N2**
6. if we had had **N3**

B.
1. F **N1**
2. T **N1**
3. F **N1**
4. F **N5**
5. T **N1**
6. F **N1**
7. T **N1**
8. T **N5**
9. F **N1**

2 | SOME THOUGHTS ABOUT WORK

Note: Both contracted and noncontracted forms are acceptable.
1. would not have known, had not taught me **N2**
2. had not driven, would have had **N2**
3. had been, might have been **N3**
4. had gone, would have studied **N2**
5. could have gone, had not broken **N5**
6. had known, would have become **N5**
7. might have traveled, had worked **N3**
8. had chosen **N6**
9. had taken **N6**
10. had told **N6**

3 | EDITING: LOSING A JOB

Dear Isabel,
 I have some bad news. The supermarket where I work is going out of business, and now I don't have a job. I don't know what I'll do! It has
been a great job for me. I never would ~~meet~~ *have met* my
boyfriend Mark if I ~~wouldn't have~~ *hadn't* **N2** worked there.
And if I ~~haven't~~ *hadn't* **N2** worked there at night, I ~~can't~~ *couldn't* **N3** have attended college during the day.
 I guess the situation isn't all that bad. I can
always find another job. But if I ~~knew~~ *had known* **N2** the store
was closing sooner, I ~~may~~ *might* **N3** have found a new job already! I really wish I had heard about this sooner. Anyway, I'll keep you updated on my job hunt.

Sunny

1 | LISTENING: LET'S PLAY CHESS!

1. When they get **U21**
2. you'll see **U22**
3. you'll play **U22**
4. if you win **U22**
5. if you won **U23**

2 | COMPETITIONS

A.
 If you enjoy testing your skills against other people, you should participate in a competition. A competition is a contest in which individuals or teams test their abilities against others'. If the result of the competition is very important, we call **U21** it a high-stakes competition. Professional sports are one example of high-stakes competition. In some professional sports, athletes earn a living by **U22** winning competitions. If they never win, they will **U22** not make very much money. Other competitions do not have such important results. We call these low-stakes competitions. A chess game between friends is one example of a low-stakes competition. If you want to take part in an activity for fun, you should participate in a low-stakes **U22** competition.
 When you participate in a competition, you **U21** become part of a community. Even if it's an individual competition, you are still a part of the **U21** community of people who compete in that type of contest. If you love challenging yourself and want to be part of a community, then you'll really enjoy **U22** competitions!
 Competitors are often superstitious. Regardless of the superstition, all competitors who believe in superstitions believe one thing. If they perform a certain ritual before the competition, **U21** they have a better chance at winning. What do you think? If competitors follow a ritual, will they **U22** increase their chances of success?

B.
1. a. F
 b. F **U23**
2. a. F
 b. T **U23**
3. a. T
 b. F **U24**
4. a. F
 b. F **U24**
5. a. T
 b. T **U23**
6. a. F
 b. T **U24**
7. a. T
 b. F **U24**
8. a. F
 b. T **U23**

3 | MAKING A TEAM FOR THE QUIZ BOWL

A.

1. If I have enough people to make a team, I compete each year. `U21`
2. You push your buzzer if you know the answer to the question. `U21`
3. If you're right, the judge gives your team points. `U21`
4. The other team has a chance to answer correctly if you say the wrong answer. `U21`
5. If your team wins, you advance to the next round of the tournament. `U21`

B.

Note: Both contracted and noncontracted forms are acceptable.

1. will answer, does not know `U22`
2. will not push, asks `U22`
3. concentrates, can win `U22`
4. will not respond, are `U22`

C.

Note: Both contracted and noncontracted forms are acceptable.

1. had known, would have won `U24`
2. would have studied, had realized `U24`
3. could have answered, had not pressed `U24`
4. had not stayed, would not have been `U24`
5. had practiced `U24`
6. might have contributed, had had `U24`
7. had known `U24`
8. had won, would have celebrated `U24`

4 | A CANOE RACE

A.

1. Unless `U22`   3. unless `U22`
2. If `U22`   4. if `U22`

B.

1. If I had a lot of free time, I would help organize the competition. OR I would help organize the competition if I had a lot of free time. `U23`
2. If I weren't helping with a tennis tournament this year, I would have free time. OR I would have free time if I weren't helping with a tennis tournament this year. `U23`
3. If I weren't too old, I could get up early to watch the race. OR I could get up early to watch the race if I weren't too old. `U23`
4. If I didn't have to work that day, I could go to the race. OR I could go to the race if I didn't have to work that day. `U23`
5. If I didn't have a meeting that day, I would take a vacation day from work. OR I would take a vacation day from work if I didn't have a meeting that day. `U23`
6. If my wife weren't afraid of water, she would be my racing partner. OR My wife / she would be my racing partner if my wife / she weren't afraid of water. `U23`
7. If my canoe didn't have a leak, I could race. OR I could race if my canoe didn't have a leak. `U23`
8. If I knew how to cook, I could prepare food for the picnic after the race. OR I could prepare food for the picnic after the race if I knew how to cook. `U23`
9. If my children could swim, they would compete in the kids' competition. OR They / My children would compete in the kids' competition if my children / they could swim. `U23`
10. If I were rich, I could give money for a prize. OR I could give money for a prize if I were rich. `U23`

5 | EDITING: CELEBRATING A VICTORY

Dear Mom and Dad,
        The canoe race was yesterday, and Tamara
                    hadn't practiced
and I won! If we ~~didn't practice~~ so much, we wouldn't have beaten Nancy and Shawna. I guess all the hard work paid off! Tamara and I always
        buy `U21`
~~bought~~ each other ice cream when we win a race, so afterwards we went to the Ice Cream Shoppe. We saw Nancy and Shawna there. I wish we
    've/have bought `U24`
could ~~buy~~ them ice cream too, but we didn't have
                    `U22`
enough money. If we ~~will~~ win next year, we'll buy them ice cream then. We have them to thank for our success. If we hadn't met them, we
        have trained `U24`
wouldn't ~~train~~ for yesterday's race so much.
        We might go to a new competition next month in Rochester, but I doubt we could win.
                    `U23`
But if we ~~would~~ won the race, we would get $500! Then we could afford a new canoe. What would
        won `U23`
you buy if you ~~win~~ $500?
        Well, I've go to run. I'm meeting Tamara at
            Unless we practice / If we don't `U22`
the river in an hour. ~~If we practice~~, we won't stay in shape for next week's race in New Town. And
                's / is `U21`
you know us! If it ~~was~~ nice outside, you can find us on the river! Are you coming to visit next week? If you come, you can get a canoe and race us for practice!

Love,
Connie

PART X Diagnostic Test

1 | LISTENING: TRIP TO EUROPE

1. I wanted to see **U25**
2. what his favorite places were **U28**
3. were **U26**
4. if I had considered **U28**
5. I've ever been **U26**
6. not to forget **U27**
7. who he had gone **U28**
8. said that he had met **U25**
9. to travel **U27**
10. not to come **U27**
11. you should go **U28**
12. might not want **U26**
13. it would be **U26**

2 | MOTHER'S QUESTIONS

1. how much the plane ticket will cost **U29**
2. when you will book your ticket **U29**
3. if / whether if you are still planning to go alone **U29**
4. if / whether your luggage is sturdy enough **U29**
5. if / whether you should change some money before you leave **U29**

3 | RESORT VACATION

In July, Rick decided to take a vacation to the beach. He asked his well-traveled friend Tim where he should go. Tim said he had gone to a place called Sea Breeze Resort a few years earlier, **U25** and he said it was a lot of fun. He advised Rick **U27** to go there, too. Rick asked him if he had any **U28** information about the place, but Tim told him to **U25** call the resort for the most accurate information. **U27**
Rick called Sea Breeze Resort and asked the **U28** receptionist how much a room cost. She told him **U25** that a package trip for seven days/six nights was only $750. He asked her what he could do at the **U28** resort, and she said, "We have so many activities **U25** you won't be able to do them all!" Rick was excited, and he told the receptionist to book him **U27** the package.
Rick left for Sea Breeze Resort the next week. When he arrived at the resort and tried to check in, the receptionist told him his name was not in **U25** the registry. He told her to check again. She **U27** checked and told him, "I'm sorry, sir, but your **U25** name is not registered." He told her he could get **U26** the registration information from his backpack. Suddenly he realized that he had left his backpack in the taxi that brought him to the resort. So he asked the receptionist if he could use the phone. **U26** He called the taxi service, and two hours later the taxi arrived with his backpack. He found the registration information and was finally able to

check in. "Now may I please have the keys to my room?" he requested. She replied, "I'm sorry, sir, **U27** but we don't have any clean rooms right now." **U26** Rick had to wait two more hours for his room to be ready!

4 | RESORT VACATION DIARY

1. a **U28**
2. c **U26**
3. c **U27**
4. c **U27**
5. b **U29**
6. b **U27**
7. c **U25**
8. a **U29**
9. b **U29**
10. b **U29**

5 | PACKING ADVICE

1. said, "Don't pack too much." **U27**
2. said that a combination of cash, traveler's checks, and credit cards is / was / would be best **U25**
3. told me that I should take euros **U26**
4. said, "Don't bring too many clothes." **U27**
5. told me, "You should travel with old clothes **U26**
6. told me, "You ought to take **U26**

6 | EDITING: TRAVEL DIARY

May 31
Today was my first full day in Florence, and it was great! I got up and ate breakfast at a little café down the street from my hotel. I asked my waiter what ~~did~~ he recommended doing during the day. He told me that I ~~will~~ *would* **U26** enjoy everything in Florence. He ~~said me~~ *told me / said* **U25** he had lived there his whole life, and he said ~~that~~ *said,* **U26** "I don't want to live anywhere else." I asked him what things ~~were there~~ *there were* **U28** to see. He said that the Uffizi Gallery ~~had been~~ *was* **U25** wonderful. It's one of the most famous art galleries in the world. He also told me to visit the Duomo, one of Italy's most beautiful cathedrals. I wondered what ~~did he think~~ *he thought* **U29** of the Piazza Della Signoria, or central square of the city, and he told me ~~don't~~ *not to* **U27** miss it. He told me ^ *to* take a boat ride down the River Arno, too. Then he invited me to eat supper at the restaurant with his family. I don't know if ~~have I~~ *I have* **U29** ever met such a nice waiter before. And I can't remember when I've had such a lovely vacation!

Unit 25 Achievement Test

1 | LISTENING: HE SAID, SHE SAID

1. was **N1**
2. had been **N4**
3. was **N4**
4. had given **N4**
5. didn't feel **N2**
6. had had **N4**
7. had talked **N4**
8. hadn't stopped **N4**
9. was going **N2**

2 | DATING ADVICE

Dr. Date,

    Last weekend I went on a date with a woman named Alice. I had a great time, and I thought she did, too. She (said) she liked Asian food, so I took
U27 her to a Korean restaurant. She also (told) me she wanted to see a movie, so we went to see a show that she picked. I enjoyed being with her, and at
U27 the end of the night, she (told) me that she had had
U25 a good time, too. She even (said), "We should do this again." But when I talked to my best friend
U27 Laura, she (told) me that her friend had talked with Alice about the date too. But she got a different
U26 story. Laura (said) Alice hadn't enjoyed the date as much as I had. I wanted to know what Alice had
U25 said. But Laura just (told) me, "Alice is very picky
U25 when it comes to men." She (said) that Alice liked
U25 me only as a friend. Then she (told) me "You're too
U25 good for Alice. You can do better." She (said) Alice was lucky to go out with me once.
U25   Laura always (tells) me I'm handsome, kind, and considerate. I'm confused. If I'm so great, then why doesn't Alice want to date me? What did I do wrong, and what should I do next?

Sincerely,
Clueless in Memphis

Dear Clueless in Memphis,
    Women often use nonverbal communication
U27 instead of verbal communication. You (said) that Alice had had a good time. Think back to your date. Did she look like she was having a good
U25 time? You (said) she liked Asian food, but did she
U27 seem to enjoy the Korean food? You (said) she had wanted to see a movie, but did she appear to like
U27 it or did she look bored? She (told) you she had enjoyed herself, but what did her body language suggest?
    I'm actually very interested in your
U25 relationship with Laura. You (say) she's your best
U26 friend. She (says) you are handsome, kind, and considerate. Is it possible that this relationship could develop into something more than a friendship? As far as what to do next, I suggest this: Forget about Alice and consider dating Laura. She's the winner.
    Good luck!

Dr. Date

3 | EDITING: A BLIND DATE

    Chris had not been on a date for a long time.
                    knew
His friend Tom said that he ~~knows~~ the perfect girl for Chris. Her name was Megan. In fact, Tom also said that he had already talked to Megan about **N4**
Chris. Megan said she ~~had~~ wanted to meet him.
                        said **N3**
During that conversation, Megan even ~~says~~ that she was excited about the date. The night of the date, Chris arrived at the restaurant a little early. He looked around for Megan. Tom had
told Chris / told him / said **N3**
~~said Chris~~ that Megan had long black hair and blue eyes. Finally, Chris saw a beautiful woman sitting at a table by the window. He went over and
                      was **N4**
introduced himself. She said she ~~had been~~ Megan. They had a wonderful dinner together. When Chris suggested having dinner again later that
           said **N3**
week, Megan ~~says~~, "I think that's a great idea."

Unit 26 Achievement Test

1 | LISTENING: APARTMENT PROBLEMS

1. were **N1**
2. 'll take **N2**
3. 'll fix **N2**
4. was being **N1**
5. could join **N3**
6. want to sleep **N1**
7. might last **N3**
8. 'll call **N2**
9. had to sign **N1**
10. had to rent **N2**

2 | CHOOSING AN APARTMENT

1. a **N4**
2. c **N4**
3. b **N3**
4. a **N3**
5. b **N2**
6. a **N3**
7. c **N2**
8. a **N3**

3 | HOW TO DECORATE AN APARTMENT

1. He said (that) I should evaluate my apartment's good points and bad points. **N3**
2. He said (that) I had to decide on a theme for my apartment. **N2**
3. He said (that) that old living room furniture could be mixed with new items. **N5**
4. He said (that) a color scheme would make a visual impact in the main room. **N2**
5. He said (that) warm colors could create an intimate, welcoming feeling, while cool colors could make a room feel elegant. **N2**
6. He said (that) if I decided to keep white walls, I could use curtains, pillows, and rugs to add color. **N2**

7. He said (that) I might want to shop at second-hand stores to save money. **N2**

8. He said (that) if I wanted to spend less on furniture, I should buy self-assembled furniture. **N3**

---

4 | EDITING: COMPLAINT LETTER

To Whom It May Concern:
    I am writing to complain about the poor service I have received over the past month from the manager at Grand Street Apartments. When I signed my lease, the apartment manager told me

that if I had any problems, ~~you~~ *I* should call him. Well, I've had to call about a few things. I recently had a problem with the air conditioning. He said, "I will take care of it." When I called again two

was **N1**
weeks later, he said that he ~~is~~ very busy right then.

that **N4**
He said he would fix the problem ~~this~~ week. The next day I saw him relaxing by the swimming pool for two hours. When I said that he could take a look at my apartment then, he said that

couldn't **N2**
he ~~can't~~ help me then. He was busy. When I told him that it was very important, he said, "I may do

tomorrow **N4**
it ~~the next day.~~" This behavior is unacceptable. If someone doesn't fix my air conditioning by next Saturday, I will move out and expect a full refund of this month's rent.

Sincerely,
Sarah Jones

Unit 27 Achievement Test

1 | LISTENING: SICK IN BED

1. said to take **N1**
2. asked me to go **N1**
3. told me not to do **N2**
4. told me to stay **N1**
5. instructed me to go **N1**
6. told me to take **N1**
7. said to drink **N1**
8. told me to eat **N1**
9. invited me to go **N1**

2 | SICK AT HEART

Dear Dr. Manners,
    One of my good friends (invited) me to go to her house for dinner last week because I had gotten a promotion at work. She (said) to arrive about 7:00, and she (told) me not to bring anything. When I arrived, she (told) me to come in and she (said) to sit down and relax. I sat down in the living room, but after ten minutes, I went into the **N1 N1 N2 N1 N1**

kitchen. She was busy preparing the food. I (told) her to let me help, but she (told) me not to touch anything. She (said) to wait in the living room. About half an hour later, she (asked) me to sit at the table. We ate the meal, and to be honest, it was terrible. She didn't say anything about the food, and she even (invited) me to eat a second helping. After dinner, she (said) not to clear the table. I (have invited) her to eat dinner at my place, and when she comes over we always enjoy cooking together. Why didn't she let me help, and why didn't she say anything when the food was so bad? I don't know what's going on or what to do. **N1 N2 N1 N1 N1 N2 N1**

Sincerely,
Sick at Heart

3 | DR. MANNERS' ADVICE

1. a **N2**   4. a **N1**
2. c **N2**   5. b **N1**
3. c **N2**   6. b **N1**

4 | EDITING: A TOUGH BOSS

November 9
    I'm sick and tired of my boss! I arrive to work early every day, but today I got caught in traffic so I was a few minutes late. When my boss saw me

make **N1**
walking in, he advised me to ~~making~~ sure I'm on

to **N1**
time every day. I was so mad! Then he said ^ finish the quarterly report by tomorrow when yesterday he told me to have it done by next week. Now I have to stay up all night to finish it. But it gets worse! This afternoon he advised me

not to **N2**
~~to don't~~ take such long coffee breaks. But I hadn't even taken a break—I had been working in another room! The absolute worst part of the day

to rewrite **N1**
was when he said ~~rewriting~~ an entire report because he had changed his mind about a few

N1
things. My friend told me ~~that~~ to quit my job, but my parents told me to keep trying. I don't know what to do.

Unit 28 Achievement Test

1 | LISTENING: MEETING WITH A PROFESSOR

1. if I would study **N1**
2. why I was studying **N2**
3. why I thought **N2**
4. what I wanted **N2**
5. who had interested **N3**
6. if he would write **N1**

2 | LOOKING FOR A ROOMMATE

March 5

Today I met with a guy named Patrick to see if he would be a good roommate. I asked <u>whether he would spend</u> a lot of time at the apartment, and he said no because he works a lot. I asked him <u>where he worked</u>. **N2** He told me he had a full-time job with Fisher Corporation. I asked <u>what had happened</u> **N2** with his last living situation, and he said his two roommates had moved away. He wants to rent for a full year. He seems very reliable.

March 7

Today I met with another guy, Jonathan. Before I could ask my questions, he asked, "What **N1** happened to your last roommate?" After I answered, he asked, "Do you mind if I smoke in **N1** the apartment?" I told him no smoking was allowed, and then he asked, "Do parties in the **N1** apartment bother you?" I told him that I needed eight hours of sleep each night but that I didn't mind a small gathering of friends. Then he asked, "Do you make a lot of money?" **N1** I told him that it was no concern of his and that I had a few questions to ask. I asked him <u>how much he worked each week</u>, **N2** and he said his dad would pay the rent. I was not impressed.

3 | ANOTHER MEETING

1. X **N1**   5. X **N1**
2. ✓ **N1**   6. ✓ **N1**
3. X **N1**   7. X **N1**
4. ✓ **N1**

4 | TALKING TO THE PARENTS

1. Ed asked his parents how they had been. OR Ed asked how his parents had been. **N4**
2. Ed's mom asked (him) if / whether he had met with the professor yet. **N4**
3. Ed's dad asked (him) when he would start applying to medical schools. **N4**
4. Ed asked his parents if / whether he had ever introduced them to Dr. Gupta. OR Ed asked if / whether he had ever introduced his parents to Dr. Gupta. **N4**
5. Ed's mom asked (him) if / whether he had decided on a roommate yet. **N4**
6. Ed's dad asked (him) when he was coming to visit them. **N4**

5 | EDITING: E-MAIL TO GRANDMA

Dear Grandma,

This has been a busy week. I met with one of my professors, and we talked about my future.
                                         I wanted
He asked me what ~~wanted I~~ to do with my life, and I told him I wanted to become a heart

                                       if / whether **N1**
specialist. When I asked him ~~if whether~~ he would help me with my medical school applications, he said yes. This week I also interviewed some guys who are interested in being my roommate. One
        whether I minded if the rent was late. /
        , "Do you mind if the rent is late?" **N4**
guy asked~~, "whether I minded if the rent was late."~~

                I could **N4**
Another guy asked if ~~could I~~ wait for his rent money until he got a job. I did have one good applicant, though, and he'll move in next week. Mom and Dad called yesterday. They asked me if I
                               visit. **N4**
could come home sometime soon for a ~~visit?~~ I think I'll go next weekend. Hope to see you then.

Love,
Ed

Unit 29 Achievement Test

1 | LISTENING: PUTTING A NAME WITH A FACE

1. what his name is **N4**
2. where we've seen **N4**
3. if he's **N3**
4. if the restaurant owner has **N3**
5. who he is **N4**
6. how much you know **N2**
7. who that man is **N2**

2 | MAKING AN ACQUAINTANCE

1. what you ordered **N1**
2. how I could forget **N1**
3. what you thought of the stuffed mushrooms **N2**
4. how it compares to the old one **N2**
5. how they could taste any better **N1**
6. where you got the recipes for your dishes **N2**
7. what your first dish was **N2**
8. how to cook macaroni and cheese **N5**
9. if you can help me improve my cooking skills **N3**

3 | TALKING ABOUT A PROBLEM

1. if / whether I should support her or not **N3**
2. if / whether I can encourage her not to perform **N3**
3. if / whether she's talented enough **N3**
4. if / whether she can handle losing **N3**
5. how I can tell her that OR how to tell her that **N5**
6. what the problem would be **N4**
7. how she felt **N4**
8. if / whether I've ever seen her so disappointed **N3**

4 | EDITING: FORGETTING A NAME

Dear Dr. Manners,

    I've gotten myself into an uncomfortable situation, and I don't know what ~~doing~~ *to do*. I wonder ~~*if/whether*~~ **N3** you can help me out. Yesterday I was shopping downtown when a familiar-looking woman greeted me by name. I wasn't sure who *she was* **N4** ~~was she~~, but instead of asking her name, I just said hello and talked to her for a few minutes. Then she invited me to lunch next week. I couldn't think of an excuse quickly enough, so now I'm supposed to meet her next week! Can you tell me what *I should* **N4** ~~should I~~ say? Should I simply ask her what *her name is* **N4** ~~is her name~~? I'd like to find out who she is, but I don't want to embarrass her or myself. I can't imagine what *she will* **N4** ~~will she~~ think. I'm not sure *how* **N5** to approach the situation politely.

Sincerely,
Please help!

PART X Achievement Test

1 | LISTENING: MISUNDERSTANDING AT WORK

1. You should be **U26**
2. told me that **U25**
3. you to be **U27**
4. had said to arrive **U27**
5. said he had told **U26**
6. he had made **U28**
7. if I wanted **U28**
8. why I was working **U28**
9. told me that I was **U26**
10. how we were **U28**
11. that it might be **U26**
12. ought to keep **U26**
13. her to organize **U27**

2 | STRESS AT WORK

1. what the cause of your anxiety is **U29**
2. if / whether you take any medicines on regular basis **U29**
3. if / whether you have had any nightmares lately **U29**
4. how you would rate your ability to concentrate **U29**
5. when you last felt completely at ease **U29**

3 | MISUNDERSTANDING WITH FRIENDS

    Josie had plans to meet her friends Carrie and Paula at an Italian restaurant downtown. Carrie *told* her *to be* at the restaurant at 8:00. She *said* *to* **U27** *get there on time because it got very busy*. Josie *asked* Carrie *to give her directions*, but Carrie just **U27** *said*, "You'll see it. It's right on Main Street." **U26** Paula *said* *the restaurant had just opened*, and she **U25** also *told* them *that most people dressed formally*. **U25** She *asked* them *to wear nice clothes*. **U27** **U27**

    That evening Josie got a taxi and she *said* to the driver, "Please take me to the new Italian restaurant downtown. It's on Main Street." She *asked* *if it would take long to get there*, and he **U28** *said* *it would take about 20 minutes*. When they **U26** stopped in front of the restaurant, Josie got out and paid the driver.

    She entered the restaurant and looked around for her friends, but she didn't see them. She *told* **U25** the host, "We have a reservation for Carrie Smith." He checked, but he couldn't find the reservation. Josie was confused, but she decided to wait. After 10 minutes, she called Carrie's cell phone. When Carrie answered, she *asked* Josie, **U28** "Where are you?" Josie *said* *she was at Rico's*. **U25** **U25** Carrie laughed and *said*, "That restaurant has **U25** been open for years." Carrie *said* *that she and* **U25** *Paula were at Gino's, the* new *Italian restaurant across the street*. She *told* Josie *to go there*. **U27**

    Josie walked across the street to Gino's and saw her friends. Both of them were wearing T-shirts and jeans. Josie *asked* them why *they hadn't* dressed **U28** up. Paula *asked* her *if she had checked her e-mail* **U28** *that day*. Josie hadn't. It turned out that Paula had learned that the restaurant wasn't fancy and that they didn't need to dress up after all. She had written an e-mail to let Carrie and Josie know, but Josie didn't get the message. Josie decided that she didn't care if she was overdressed, and they all sat down to eat.

4 | E-MAIL

1. b **U29**
2. a **U27**
3. c **U28**
4. b **U27**
5. b **U26**
6. a **U25**
7. c **U27**
8. a **U29**
9. a **U29**
10. c **U29**

5 | WRONG DIRECTIONS

1. said (that) I had to cross **U26**
2. told me (that) the bus should be **U26**
3. not to cross the street **U27**
4. told her (that) I needed **U25**
5. said (that) bus number 170 wouldn't go **U26**
6. told me to take **U27**

June 5

My parents ruin everything! I can't believe what they did today. Well, to be fair, I guess it was a misunderstanding, and it wasn't really their fault. But I'm still mad! OK, here's what happened:

Yesterday Sara asked me ~~did I want~~ *if I wanted* to meet her and some friends at the lake today. I was so excited! I told her ~~that "I would love to go,"~~ *that I would love to go / , "I would love to go,"* **U25** but I said that I had to talk to Mom and Dad first. I needed to ask if I could use their car. Last night I told them that I ~~had~~ wanted to go to the lake, and **U26** Mom ~~told~~ *said / told me* **U25** that it sounded like a good idea. Dad asked who ~~did think~~ *had thought* **U28** of it. They told me they would use the car to run some errands in the morning, and I asked them *to* **U27** ^be home by 2:00.

Well, when they got home at 2:00, I was ready to leave. They got out of the car and told me ~~wait for them~~ *to wait for them / , "Wait for us."* **U27**. I wondered why they ~~keep~~ *kept* **U29** me waiting for 15 minutes. It turned out they were getting ready to go to the lake, too! They looked so excited that I didn't want to tell them they weren't invited. So I called Sara on the phone. "You'll never guess who I'm bringing with me," I ~~say~~ *said* **U26**. In the end it wasn't so bad, but I'd still like to know why ~~did they think~~ *they thought / they think* **U29** I invited them to go with me!

ETS Grammar Proficiency Tests

General Information

This section of the *Focus on Grammar Assessment Pack* includes two Grammar Proficiency Tests (Form A and Form B) that were developed by Educational Testing Service (ETS). Each test includes 40 questions and takes 25 minutes. The tests were originally developed and administered by ETS as part of TOEFL®.

Because ETS has extensive data about the range of grammar proficiency of academic English learners, these tests can be used as independent benchmarks of students' general grammar proficiency. That is, students' scores on these tests indicate how their knowledge of English grammar compares with that of other academic English learners. The tests should NOT be used to draw any conclusions about students' performance on actual TOEFL exams.

ETS has determined the statistical difficulty of each test question by counting the number of TOEFL test-takers who answered the question correctly. A question that nearly everyone answers correctly is considered "easy;" one that only 75 or 80 percent of the population answers correctly is considered "difficult." (If it seems illogical to call an item "difficult" when 80 percent of the test-takers answered correctly, remember that in a 4-choice question, 25 percent of the people who guess at random will select the correct answer.) Form A and Form B include items of the same general difficulty level, so the overall difficulty of Form A is the same as the overall difficulty of Form B. This means that you can expect students to receive the same (or a similar) score regardless of which form they use on a particular testing day. Over time, students' scores on these tests should improve as their knowledge of English grammar increases.

The two ETS Grammar Proficiency tests can be administered to students at any point during their course of study, and in any order, depending on how you want to use the test results. They can be used for a variety of purposes:

Purpose	When to Administer
1) to identify students who may need more support during the course of instruction	• Form A: before students begin their course • Form B: halfway through the course
2) to give students an idea of how their knowledge of English grammar compares to that of the TOEFL® population (see "Scoring the Tests" below for further explanation)	• Form A: before students begin their course OR halfway through the course • Form B: after students have completed their course
3) to provide a measure of student progress in their general grammar proficiency	• Form A: before students begin their course • Form B: after students have completed their course

Administering the Tests

Before administering each test, let students know that they will have 25 minutes to complete it. Hand out copies of the test and ask students to write their names at the top. Go over the directions and examples for both sections of the test, and ask students if they have any questions before they begin. Then start the time and tell students to begin.

After 20 minutes, let students know they have 5 minutes to complete the test. After 25 minutes, ask students to stop working and collect the tests.

Scoring the Tests

Use the Answer Keys on page 308 to add up the number of questions the student answered correctly. This number is the student's raw score. To calculate the student's TOEFL® percentile ranking, use the Score Conversion Charts on page 293.

For example, if a student answers 35 questions correctly on Form A, that student's percentile ranking is 77. This means that the student's score is higher than 77 percent of the students who have taken the Structure and Written Expression section of the TOEFL.

When you give students their test scores, tell them that these scores reflect their *general grammar proficiency* in comparison with other academic English language learners, not their knowledge of the specific content taught in *Focus on Grammar*.

Score Conversion Charts

The following tables are for informational purposes only.

Form A

RAW SCORE	PERCENTILE RANK
38–40	99
36–37	96
35	77
33–34	64
31–32	51
29–30	38
26–28	28
24–25	19
22–23	13
20–21	8
18–19	5
16–17	3
14–15	2
12–13	1
<12*	0*

Form B

RAW SCORE	PERCENTILE RANK
38–40	99
37	96
34–36	88
32–33	64
30–31	51
28–29	38
25–27	28
23–24	19
21–22	13
19–20	8
17–18	5
15–16	3
13–14	2
12	1
<12*	0*

* NOTE: Because the items on the ETS Grammar Proficiency Tests are multiple choice, most students will answer at least 11–12 items correctly, even if they are guessing.

ETS Grammar Proficiency Test

Form A

This test is designed to measure your ability to recognize language that is appropriate for standard written English. There are two types of questions on this test, with special directions for each type.

PART 1

Directions: *Questions 1–15 are incomplete sentences. Beneath each sentence you will see four words or phrases, marked (A), (B), (C), and (D). Circle the letter of the ONE word or phrase that best completes the sentence.*

Example I

Geysers have often been compared to volcanoes _____ they both emit hot liquids from below the Earth's surface.

A Ⓑ C D

(**A**) due to
(**B**) because

(**C**) in spite of
(**D**) regardless of

The sentence should read, "Geysers have often been compared to volcanoes because they both emit hot liquids from below the Earth's surface." Therefore, you should choose (**B**).

Example II

During the early period of ocean navigation, _____ any need for sophisticated instruments and techniques.

A B C Ⓓ

(**A**) so that hardly
(**B**) when there hardly was

(**C**) hardly was
(**D**) there was hardly

The sentence should read, "During the early period of ocean navigation, there was hardly any need for sophisticated instruments and techniques." Therefore, you should choose (**D**).

Now begin work on the questions.

Go on to the next page ➤

1. No spectacle in the universe is _____ than an exploding star.   **A B C D**

   (**A**) impressive   (**C**) more impressive
   (**B**) as impressive   (**D**) the most impressive

2. The Allegheny and Monongahela rivers _____ in Pittsburgh,   **A B C D**
   Pennsylvania, to form the Ohio River.

   (**A**) meet   (**C**) for meeting
   (**B**) meeting   (**D**) which meet

3. The horns of a rhinoceros continue _____ throughout its entire   **A B C D**
   lifetime.

   (**A**) it grows   (**C**) they grow
   (**B**) to grow   (**D**) grow

4. Mathematics helps meteorologists to predict the weather more   **A B C D**
   accurately, to calculate the speed of storms, and _____ .

   (**A**) for the wind to blow determines   (**C**) to determine what causes
                                                     the wind to blow

   (**B**) causes the wind blowing to determine (**D**) determine the wind's
                                                     blowing

5. _____ position of Earth in relation to the Sun is always   **A B C D**
   slightly changing.

   (**A**) The   (**C**) It was the
   (**B**) That the   (**D**) There was a

6. Systems of phonetic writing are _____ at transcribing accurately   **A B C D**
   any sequence of speech sounds.

   (**A**) the aim   (**C**) who aims
   (**B**) aimed   (**D**) by aiming

7. In photosynthesis, _____ through which green plants manufacture   **A B C D**
   food, energy from direct sunlight is trapped by a substance called
   chlorophyll.

   (**A**) that the process   (**C**) the process
   (**B**) is a process   (**D**) in which the process

8. _____ and hard, ivory may be carved with great delicacy into   **A B C D**
   intricate patterns.

   (**A**) Because of its density   (**C**) May be dense
   (**B**) Because it is dense   (**D**) Its density

Go on to the next page ▶

9. A solar eclipse occurs when the Moon is between the Sun and Earth   **A B C D**
   _____ shadow of the Moon moves across the face of Earth.

   (**A**) and the   (**C**) that the
   (**B**) and it is the   (**D**) that it is the

10. The spectacularly beautiful and sultry voice of Lena Horne   **A B C D**
    made her _____ .

    (**A**) being a nationally celebrated vocalist   (**C**) as nationally celebrated vocalist
    (**B**) a vocalist was nationally celebrated   (**D**) a nationally celebrated vocalist

11. The existence of very long channels _____ into the deep-sea   **A B C D**
    floor of the Atlantic and Pacific oceans has been well documented.

    (**A**) are cut   (**C**) to cut
    (**B**) cuts   (**D**) cutting

12. Lillian Wald's _____ lies in the field of public health nursing.   **A B C D**

    (**A**) contribution was most distinctive   (**C**) most contributions are distinctive
    (**B**) whose most distinctive contribution   (**D**) most distinctive contribution

13. Fine rubies _____ of flaws are extremely rare and command   **A B C D**
    high prices.

    (**A**) free   (**C**) which free
    (**B**) are free   (**D**) when are they free

14. In some parts of the world, not only _____ a form of   **A B C D**
    entertainment, but it is also a means of communication.

    (**A**) whistling   (**C**) that whistling is
    (**B**) is whistling   (**D**) why is whistling

15. Invented in the 1780's, threshing machines enabled farmers to   **A B C D**
    process grain _____ they could by hand.

    (**A**) than much faster   (**C**) much faster than
    (**B**) much than faster   (**D**) faster than much

Go on to the next page ➤

PART 2

Directions: *In questions 16–40 each sentence has four underlined words or phrases. The four underlined parts of the sentence are marked (A), (B), (C), and (D). Circle the letter of the ONE underlined word or phrase that must be changed in order for the sentence to be correct.*

Example I

Guppies are sometimes <u>call</u> rainbow <u>fish</u> <u>because of</u> the   Ⓐ B C D
                   A   **B**   **C**

males' <u>bright</u> colors.
      D

The sentence should read, "Guppies are sometimes called rainbow fish because of the males' bright colors." Therefore, you should choose (**A**).

Example II

<u>Serving</u> several <u>term</u> in Congress, Shirley Chisholm became   A Ⓑ C D
   A   **B**

an <u>important</u> figure in United States <u>politics</u>.
     C   **D**

The sentence should read, "Serving several terms in Congress, Shirley Chisholm became an important figure in United States politics." Therefore, you should choose (**B**).

Now begin work on the questions.

Go on to the next page

16. Patients <u>they</u> suffer <u>from</u> common arthritis <u>can</u> be treated
            A   B   C

    using <u>heat</u>, physical therapy, and aspirin.
           D

A B C D

17. Forests contain more than merely <u>tree</u>; they <u>also</u> include
                                     A   B

    smaller plants, <u>such as</u> mosses, shrubs, and wild <u>flowers</u>.
                  C   D

A B C D

18. The <u>game of</u> marbles, <u>which</u> originated in prehistoric times,
         A   B

    <u>is</u> still played today in <u>much</u> lands.
    C   D

A B C D

19. The <u>modern</u> racing bicycle is <u>carefully</u> engineered <u>for</u> safety,
        A   B   C

    lightness, and <u>reliable</u>.
                 D

A B C D

20. <u>On</u> 1954, the United States Supreme Court ruled on <u>the case</u>
    A   B

    of *Brown v. Board of Education,* <u>declaring</u> segregated
                                        C

    <u>education</u> unconstitutional.
    D

A B C D

21. Human skin is <u>a complex</u>, sensitive organ <u>that</u> serves many
                 A   B

    <u>functions</u> necessary for the <u>maintain</u> of life.
    C   D

A B C D

22. Because <u>glass</u> objects are fragile, <u>least</u> have survived <u>from</u>
            A   B   C

    ancient <u>civilizations</u>.
             D

A B C D

23. An important <u>effect</u> that criticism <u>can have</u> on contemporary
              A   B

    poets is the assurance that <u>there is a</u> growing <u>interest their</u>
                           C   D

    work.

A B C D

24. Music festivals, which date back as far <u>as</u> the mid-seventeenth
                                       A

    century, have increased <u>significantly</u> in <u>popular</u> within the <u>past</u>
                            B   C   D

    few decades.

A B C D

Go on to the next page ➡

25. <u>Space</u> photography and advanced measurement technology,
    A

    <u>including</u> a laser reflector placed on the Moon,
    B

    <u>have possible made</u> <u>extremely</u> precise measurements of the
    C   **D**

    surfaces of Earth.

    A B C D

26. The scale of the demographic <u>change</u> that are now occurring
    A

    and that are <u>projected</u> for the near <u>future</u> is unprecedented in
    B   **C**

    <u>human</u> history.
    D

    A B C D

27. <u>The paintings</u> of artist Abraham Rattner are <u>noted for</u> their
    A   **B**

    brilliant <u>color</u>, rich texture, and <u>symbolic</u>.
    C   **D**

    A B C D

28. <u>Between</u> the high and low tidemarks of marine coasts <u>existing</u>
    A   **B**

    abundant and <u>varied</u> plant <u>and</u> animal life.
    C   **D**

    A B C D

29. The total <u>amount of water</u> in the world's <u>ecological system</u>
    A   **B**

    has remained the <u>same than</u> throughout the <u>ages</u> of human
    C   **D**

    history.

    A B C D

30. In exchange <u>for</u> requiring them <u>to disclose</u> the workings of
    A   **B**

    their inventions, patents give <u>inventors</u> temporary, <u>legally</u>
    C   **D**

    monopolies.

    A B C D

31. Butterflies and moths <u>comprise</u> the Lepidoptera order of
    A

    insects <u>find</u> <u>throughout</u> <u>most of</u> the world.
    B   **C**   **D**

    A B C D

32. The <u>planet</u> Neptune has over a dozen <u>known</u> satellites: one
    A   **B**

    <u>about</u> the size <u>with</u> Earth's Moon, the others much smaller.
    C   **D**

    A B C D

33. Harry Truman's victory <u>over</u> Thomas Dewey was one <u>of</u> the
    A   **B**

    biggest <u>surprise</u> in the <u>political</u> history of the United States.
    C   **D**

    A B C D

Go on to the next page

34. The narwhal <u>resembles like</u> other whales, but it has <u>a long</u>,
                         A   B

    spiral tusk <u>growing</u> from <u>its</u> head.
                     C   D

A B C D

35. Lillian Gish is <u>best</u> known for her <u>roles</u> in such <u>silently</u> films
                     A   B   C

    <u>as</u> *The Birth of a Nation* and *Broken Blossoms*.
    D

A B C D

36. <u>It</u> <u>may take</u> several <u>hundred years</u> to <u>build inch</u> of topsoil.
    A   B   C   D

A B C D

37. Known for power, <u>speed</u>, and maneuverability, the goshawk
                     A

    has short wings and <u>a</u> long tail, <u>enabling</u> <u>them</u> to dodge
                     B   C   D

    branches in pursuit of prey.

A B C D

38. Lubrication is essential in machinery because <u>if</u> the
                                            A

    <u>moving part</u> of a machine come into <u>direct contact</u> with
       B   C

    <u>each other</u>, friction interferes with motion.
      D

A B C D

39. One basic principle of <u>international</u> air law <u>recognize</u> a
                       A   B

    country's complete sovereignty <u>over</u> the airspace above its
                               C

    <u>territory</u>.
      D

A B C D

40. Oraibi, Arizona, <u>built by</u> the Hopi Indians during the 1100's,
                  A

    is <u>probably the</u> oldest <u>continuous</u> inhabited <u>settlement</u> in the
         B   C   D

    United States.

A B C D

ETS Grammar Proficiency Test

Form B

This test is designed to measure your ability to recognize language that is appropriate for standard written English. There are two types of questions on this test, with special directions for each type.

Directions: *Questions 1–15 are incomplete sentences. Beneath each sentence you will see four words or phrases, marked (A), (B), (C), and (D). Circle the letter of the ONE word or phrase that best completes the sentence.*

Example I

Geysers have often been compared to volcanoes _____ they both emit hot liquids from below the Earth's surface.

A Ⓑ **C D**

(**A**) due to (**C**) in spite of
(**B**) because (**D**) regardless of

The sentence should read, "Geysers have often been compared to volcanoes because they both emit hot liquids from below the Earth's surface." Therefore, you should choose (**B**).

Example II

During the early period of ocean navigation, _____ any need for sophisticated instruments and techniques.

A B C Ⓓ

(**A**) so that hardly (**C**) hardly was
(**B**) when there hardly was (**D**) there was hardly

The sentence should read, "During the early period of ocean navigation, there was hardly any need for sophisticated instruments and techniques." Therefore, you should choose (**D**).

Now begin work on the questions.

Go on to the next page ➤

1. Sage is a small shrubby plant, usually not more _____ .   **A B C D**

   (**A**) than eighteen inches high   (**C**) high than inches eighteen
   (**B**) than high eighteen inches   (**D**) than inches high eighteen

2. Graphite, which _____ , is a good conductor of electricity.   **A B C D**

   (**A**) easily not burning   (**C**) not burn easily
   (**B**) easily not to burn   (**D**) does not burn easily

3. The Ozark Mountains in Missouri consist largely of porous   **A B C D**
   limestone and dolomite overlain by stronger rock, _____
   sandstone.

   (**A**) was   (**C**) similar
   (**B**) which   (**D**) such as

4. Best known for her dazzling technique and daring   **A B C D**
   interpretations of violin music, _____ that few classical
   artists encounter.

   (**A**) was young Nadja   (**C**) the recognition that young Nadja
         Salerno-Sonnenberg recognized   Salerno-Sonnenberg got was
   (**B**) one recognized Nadja   (**D**) young Nadja Salerno-Sonnenberg
         Salerno-Sonnenberg as young   got recognition

5. _____ Emily Dickinson completed over 1,000 poems, only   **A B C D**
   seven were published during her lifetime.

   (**A**) Not only   (**C**) Despite
   (**B**) Although   (**D**) However

6. The story of the pioneers in North America is a tale of the   **A B C D**
   men and women _____ the frontier of European settlement
   from the Appalachian Mountains to the Pacific Ocean.

   (**A**) pushed   (**C**) pushed them
   (**B**) who pushed   (**D**) they pushed

7. For many years, because of the size of the batteries needed,   **A B C D**
   _____ for electric cars to compete with cars having internal
   combustion engines.

   (**A**) it had not been possible   (**C**) it possibly had not
   (**B**) the possibility had not   (**D**) there had been no possible

8. The walls of the heart are constructed _____ special kind   **A B C D**
   of muscle.

   (**A**) a   (**C**) of it
   (**B**) of a   (**D**) are of

Go on to the next page ➡

9. Fewer than 20 percent of the diamonds _____ are suitable
   for use as gems.   **A B C D**

   (**A**) mining of each year   (**C**) mined each year and
   (**B**) each year are being mined (**D**) mined each year

10. People may reject foods whose taste they dislike _____ not
    have a proper diet.   **A B C D**

    (**A**) then they   (**C**) and consequently
    (**B**) thereby   (**D**) for that

11. The grass family includes the cereal grasses that provide
    grain, _____ .   **A B C D**

    (**A**) in most countries is the staple food   (**C**) the staple food in most countries
    (**B**) is in most countries the staple food   (**D**) that the staple food in most countries

12. A mire is an area of land, such as a bog or swamp, that is
    more or less permanently waterlogged but _____ open water.   **A B C D**

    (**A**) contains no   (**C**) contains none of
    (**B**) not to contain   (**D**) not contain

13. _____ type of music known as jazz got its name remains
    obscure.   **A B C D**

    (**A**) It is how   (**C**) How the
    (**B**) That is how the   (**D**) How

14. At the center of a well-developed hurricane _____ , a
    relatively calm area surrounded by whirling winds.   **A B C D**

    (**A**) the eye lies there   (**C**) where lies the eye
    (**B**) that the eye lies   (**D**) lies the eye

15. Probably few birds can fly _____ the powerful peregrine
    falcon.   **A B C D**

    (**A**) as faster   (**C**) faster than
    (**B**) faster   (**D**) the faster of

Go on to the next page ➡

PART 2

Directions: *In questions 16–40 each sentence has four underlined words or phrases. The four underlined parts of the sentence are marked (A), (B), (C), and (D). Circle the letter of the ONE underlined word or phrase that must be changed in order for the sentence to be correct.*

Example I

Guppies are sometimes <u>call</u> rainbow <u>fish</u> <u>because of</u> the   Ⓐ B C D
                  A   **B**   **C**

males' <u>bright</u> colors.
      D

The sentence should read, "Guppies are sometimes called rainbow fish because of the males' bright colors." Therefore, you should choose (**A**).

Example II

<u>Serving</u> several <u>term</u> in Congress, Shirley Chisholm became   A Ⓑ C D
  A   **B**

an <u>important</u> figure in United States <u>politics</u>.
    C   **D**

The sentence should read, "Serving several terms in Congress, Shirley Chisholm became an important figure in United States politics." Therefore, you should choose (**B**).

Now begin work on the questions.

Go on to the next page

16. Physical therapy is often <u>employed</u> to stimulate <u>nerves</u>,
                            A   **B**

    prevent <u>muscle</u> atrophy, and <u>training</u> new muscles.
                 C   **D**

A B C D

17. In 1893, Florence Bascom, <u>a</u> geologist, was the <u>first woman</u>
                                  A   **B**

    <u>to awarded</u> a doctoral degree <u>from</u> Johns Hopkins University.
        C   **D**

A B C D

18. In the Middle Ages, <u>before</u> the <u>invent</u> of the <u>printing</u> press,
                        A   **B**   **C**

    manuscripts <u>were copied</u> by hand.
                D

A B C D

19. Transparent plastics <u>keep</u> food and other <u>products</u> fresh and
                        A   **B**

    <u>clean</u> and allow customers to see <u>that</u> they buy.
     C   **D**

A B C D

20. Most complex carbohydrates <u>provide</u> the body with <u>energetic</u>
                             A   **B**

    and fiber, a <u>good</u> source of protein, and an abundance of
             C

    vitamins and <u>minerals</u>.
             D

A B C D

21. The Fair Deal <u>was</u> the name <u>giving</u> to the <u>domestic</u> programs
             A   **B**   **C**

    <u>of</u> United States President Harry S. Truman.
    D

A B C D

22. <u>In spite of</u> great diversity among the traditional <u>cultures</u> of
    A   **B**

    Native American populations, <u>key several</u> concepts underlie
                           C

    the artistic expression of <u>most groups</u>.
                   D

A B C D

23. Political cartoons have <u>existed</u> throughout United States
                  A

    <u>history can</u> be useful tools for <u>understanding</u> the <u>social</u>
     B   **C**   **D**

    history of a given period.

A B C D

24. The cacao <u>beans</u> destined to <u>be used</u> in the <u>making</u> of
          A   **B**   **C**

    chocolate are <u>choosed</u> carefully.
            D

A B C D

Go on to the next page ➤

25. Potatoes produce <u>more food</u> per unit area <u>of land planted</u>   A B C D
                          A   B

    <u>than</u> any <u>major other</u> crop.
     C   D

26. Joe Louis, still considered by some <u>to be</u> the <u>greatest</u> boxer   A B C D
                                           A   B

    who ever lived, <u>is holding</u> the heavyweight boxing title from
                C

    1937 <u>to</u> 1949.
        D

27. The <u>first</u> odes were <u>poems written</u> to be <u>sung</u> with the   A B C D
            A   B   C

    accompaniment of a <u>musician</u> instrument.
              D

28. Baltimore has one of the world's <u>natural largest</u> harbors,   A B C D
                                       A

    <u>and its</u> port handles <u>about</u> 31 million short tons of cargo
     B   C

    <u>annually</u>.
     D

29. Basal metabolism, the <u>heat produced</u> by <u>a organism</u> at rest,   A B C D
                             A   B

    represents the minimum amount of energy that is <u>required</u> to
                      C

    maintain life at <u>normal</u> body temperature.
           D

30. The first <u>demand</u> put upon prose <u>dialogue</u> in drama is that it   A B C D
                A   B

    be an effective <u>frames</u> for everything <u>that is</u> to pass on the
            C   D

    stage.

31. The most <u>abundance</u> occurrences of calcite are in sedimentary   A B C D
                A

    rocks, <u>where</u> biogenic calcite, derived from the <u>remains</u> of
        B   C

    calcareous marine organisms, is the <u>principal</u> constituent of
                 D

    limestone.

32. The <u>rise and fall</u> of sea level <u>during</u> the Pleistocene Epoch   A B C D
            A   B

    caused <u>great changes</u> in the size of the <u>plains coastal</u> of
        C   D

    North America.

Go on to the next page ➡

Test questions are copyrighted by Educational Testing Service and used with permission. ■ FORM B

33. The history of ballet <u>is history</u> of <u>dance technique</u> <u>as well as</u>
                      A   B   C

    of its evolution as a <u>cultural institution</u>.
                             D

            A B C D

34. Coyotes are <u>so</u> widely <u>hunted</u> in the United States that <u>their</u>
               A   B   C

    survival may be <u>threaten</u>.
                       D

            A B C D

35. The thyroid gland <u>regulation</u> basal metabolism, the <u>rate</u>
                      A   B

    <u>at which</u> food and oxygen <u>are converted</u> into energy.
       C   D

            A B C D

36. Flourishing thousands <u>of years</u> ago, ferns similar to <u>that</u> of
                          A   B

    today supplied <u>some</u> of the vegetable matter that <u>later</u> formed
                   C   D

    large coal deposits.

            A B C D

37. Generally, a child who can easily <u>hold</u> a conversation about
                                  A

    things that are not <u>physical</u> present is <u>one</u> who deals <u>well</u>
                     B   C   D

    with abstraction.

            A B C D

38. <u>Many</u> of the sayings in Benjamin Franklin's *Poor Richard's*
    A

    Almanack, issued <u>yearly</u> from 1733 to 1758, preached the
                           B

    <u>virtues</u> of industry, frugality, and <u>thrifty</u>.
       C   D

            A B C D

39. <u>Desert</u> support only <u>those</u> animals and plants that have
    A   B

    adapted <u>to living</u> without <u>much water</u>.
             C   D

            A B C D

40. <u>Reliable</u> surface observation of the <u>main</u> climatic variables,
    A   B

    <u>such like</u> temperature, wind velocity, and <u>humidity</u>, began in
       C   D

    the seventeenth century.

Answer Key

Form A

1. C	11. D	21. D	31. B
2. A	12. D	22. B	32. D
3. B	13. A	23. D	33. C
4. C	14. B	24. C	34. A
5. A	15. C	25. C	35. C
6. B	16. A	26. A	36. D
7. C	17. A	27. D	37. D
8. B	18. D	28. B	38. B
9. A	19. D	29. C	39. B
10. D	20. A	30. D	40. C

Form B

1. A	11. C	21. B	31. A
2. D	12. A	22. C	32. D
3. D	13. C	23. B	33. A
4. D	14. D	24. D	34. D
5. B	15. C	25. D	35. A
6. B	16. D	26. C	36. B
7. A	17. C	27. D	37. B
8. B	18. B	28. A	38. D
9. D	19. D	29. B	39. A
10. C	20. B	30. C	40. C

Test Generating CD-ROM

General Information

The test generating CD-ROM (TestGen®) that accompanies the *Focus on Grammar Assessment Pack* provides you with the TestGen software program and a testbank of hundreds of items per level. You can use the software program to create and customize tests. With TestGen, you can:

- create tests quickly using the TestGen Wizard
- select questions by part, unit, or grammar topic
- edit questions
- add your own questions
- create multiple versions of a test

Because the items in the TestGen testbank are different from those in the printed tests, you can use TestGen to create additional tests, review quizzes, or practice exercises.

Organization of Items in the *Focus on Grammar* TestGen CD-ROM

The *Focus on Grammar* TestGen CD-ROM includes five testbanks, one for each level of *Focus on Grammar*. Within each testbank, the items are divided by part of the Student Book.

Each *Focus on Grammar* test item is labeled for easy sorting. You can sort by grammar point or unit. See "How to Create a Test" for an example of a test with items sorted by grammar point.

How to Create a Test

There are two ways to create a test using the TestGen software. You can create a test manually, or you can use the TestGen Wizard.

Using the TestGen Wizard to Create a Test The TestGen Wizard is the easiest, fastest way to create a customized test. Follow these easy steps to create a test.

STEP 1
Select a **Testbank** from the **Testbank Library** window.

STEP 2
Click on **Use the TestGen Wizard to create a new paper test** icon.

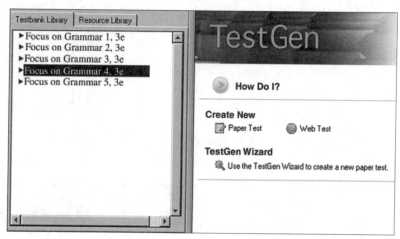

STEP 3
When the **TestGen Wizard** launches, you will be prompted to enter a name for your test. After assigning a name to your test, click the **Next** button to proceed.

STEP 4
Select the part or parts you want to include in your test.

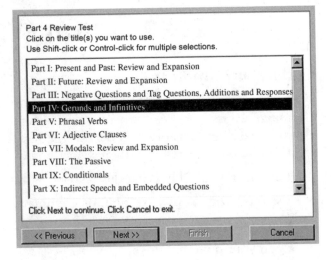

STEP 5
On the next screen, you will choose "Select questions randomly" or "Select specific questions from a list." Choose **Select questions randomly** and click the **Next** button.

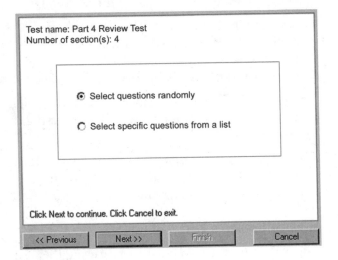

STEP 6
Use the drop-down list to choose questions randomly by Question Type, Section,* Grammar Point, or Unit.

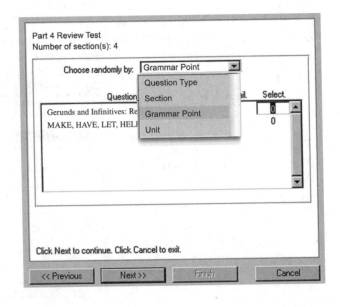

* "Section" refers to *Focus on Grammar* parts. Each level has 8 to 10 parts.

STEP 7

Under the "Select" column, choose the number of items you want in the test. Click the **Next** button to continue to the **Test Summary.**

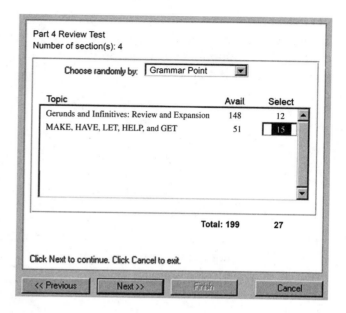

STEP 8

The **Test Summary** window will display the name of your test, the number of sections (parts) you selected, the selection method, and the total number of questions on the test. Click **Finish** to build the test.

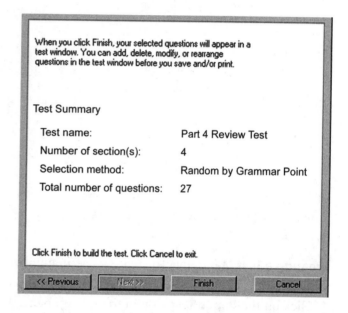

STEP 9

The **TestGen Wizard** will close, and a **Test Window** will open with your selected questions.

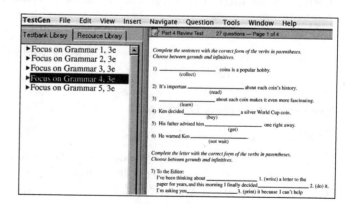

10

your questions in the correct order, on the **Question** menu at the top of the screen and select **Sort**.

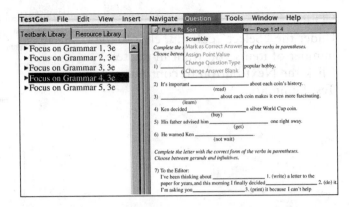

STEP 11

Next, click **Keep questions in the same order as they are in the testbank** under **SmartSort by test bank order** and click **OK**.

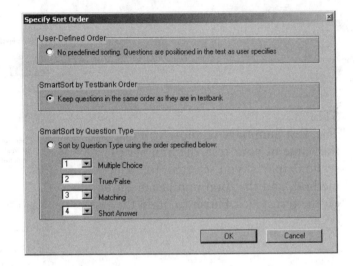

STEP 12

Finish by saving and/or printing the test.

Creating a Test Manually To create a test manually:

1. Open the TestGen software and select a **Testbank** from the **Testbank Library** window.
2. Click on the **Paper Test** icon in the startup pane. A new blank test appears.
3. Click on the arrows in the **Testbank Library** window to expand the outline and see the testbank questions.
4. Drag and drop each question you want to include into the **Test** window.

For more information, see the User's Guide located on the TestGen CD-ROM in the "Resources" folder.

How to Create New Questions

To add a new question to your test:

1. Click the place in the **Test window** where you want to add a new question.
2. In the menu bar, click **Insert > Question.**
3. Choose a **Question Type** from the drop down menu.
4. Double-click on the new question in the **Test** window.
5. Type the question and answer into the appropriate fields.

How to Edit Questions

To edit a question in your test:

1. Click on the **Tools** menu at the top of the screen and select **Preferences > Test Options.**
2. Click on the **Descriptors** tab.
3. Check **Correct Answer** to display the answers in the Test window.
4. Return to the test window and double-click on the question you want to edit.
5. Make any changes you want to both the question and answer.

How to Change the Order of Questions

If you want to move a question to a specific location in the test:

1. Click on the **Tools** menu and select **Sort.**
2. Click **User-defined order.**
3. Click **OK.**
4. Now you can drag the question to any location you want in the test.

Other TestGen Features

You can modify your TestGen test in many ways. You can change the display, create questions with graphics, edit direction lines, and much, much more. To learn more about the features that the TestGen software offers, go to the *Focus on Grammar* Companion Website (www.longman.com/focusongrammar) and click on the **TestGen** link.

TestGen 7.2 System Requirements

Windows®

Operating System:	Microsoft® Windows NT®, Windows 2000 or Windows XP	
Processor	233MHz or faster Pentium-compatible processor	
Random access memory (RAM)	128 MB	
Available hard disk space	20 MB (varies depending on testbank size)	
Web browser*	Windows NT®	Internet Explorer 5.5 or Netscape® Navigator 6.2.3
	Windows 2000	Internet Explorer 5.5, 6.0 or Netscape Navigator 6.2.3
	Windows XP	Internet Explorer 6.0 or Netscape Navigator 7.0

Macintosh®

Operating System:	Mac OS X v 10.2, 10.3, 10.4**
Processor	PowerPC G3, G4, or G5 processor
Random access memory (RAM)	128 MB
Available hard disk space	20 MB (varies depending on testbank size)
Web browser*	Internet Explorer 5.2 or Netscape Navigator 7.0

*Required only for viewing TestGen tests on the Web with TestGen Plug-in and for viewing TestGen Help.

**The TestGen application is supported on Mac OS X v 10.3 and 10.4. The TestGen Plug-in is not currently supported on this platform.

Installing TestGen

Windows Computers

- Insert the TestGen CD into your computer's CD drive.

- Open **My Computer**. Then double click on the CD drive icon.

- Double-click on "tgesetup.exe."

- Follow the directions on the screen to complete the installation. Once the installation is complete the program will begin automatically.

Macintosh Computers

- Insert the TestGen CD into your computer's CD drive.

- Double-click on "TestGen 7 Setup."

- Follow the directions on the screen to complete the installation. Once the installation is complete the program will begin automatically.

Note:

If you have existing versions of TestGen on your computer, you will receive a message providing you with the option to remove earlier versions of the program. Click *Yes* to remove the older TestGen versions and continue (recommended).

Removing older versions of the TestGen program does not delete or otherwise compromise tests and testbanks created with earlier versions of the program located on your computer. You can convert older tests and testbanks simply by opening them in the TestGen 7.2 program.

Product Support

The *User's Guide* can be found on the TestGen CD in the "Resources" folder (see TG7UserGuide.pdf). It provides detailed instructions about how to use all of TestGen's tools and features. Once TestGen has been installed, the *User's Guide* is also available by clicking "Help" in the TestGen menu at the top of the screen. To view the *User's Guide,* Adobe® Acrobat® Reader® is required. This free software can be installed from the Internet at the following address: www.adobe.com/acrobat.

For further technical assistance:

- Call Pearson's toll-free product support line: 1-800-677-6337

- Send an email to media.support@pearsoned.com

- Fill out a web form at: http://247.pearsoned.com/mediaform

Our technical staff will need to know certain things about your system in order to help us solve your problems more quickly and efficiently. If possible, please be at your computer when you call for support. You should have the following information ready:

- Product title and product ISBN

- Computer make and model

- RAM available

- Hard disk space available

- Graphics card type

- Printer make and model (if applicable)

- Detailed description of the problem, including the exact wording of any error messages.